MASTERS OF MINDFULNESS

TRANSFORMING YOUR MIND AND BODY

Shauna Shapiro, Rick Hanson,
Kristine Carlson, Juna Mustad, Mike Robbins, Amishi Jha,
Elissa Epel, Jessica Graham, Dacher Keltner,
Wallace J. Nichols, and Daniel J. Siegel

THE
GREAT
COURSES®

Published by

THE GREAT COURSES

Corporate Headquarters

4840 Westfields Boulevard | Suite 500 | Chantilly, Virginia | 20151-2299

[PHONE] 1.800.832.2412 | [FAX] 703.378.3819 | [WEB] www.thegreatcourses.com

Copyright © The Teaching Company, 2018

SHAUNA SHAPIRO

Shauna Shapiro, PhD, is a Professor of Psychology at Santa Clara University, an author, and an internationally recognized expert in mindfulness and compassion. Nearly a million people have watched her TEDx talk "The Power of Mindfulness: What You Practice Grows Stronger." Dr. Shapiro has published more than 100 journal articles and has coauthored two critically acclaimed books: *The Art and Science of Mindfulness: Integrating Mindfulness into Psychology and the Helping Professions* and *Mindful Discipline: A Loving Approach to Setting Limits and Raising an Emotionally Intelligent Child*.

Dr. Shapiro's work has been featured on *The Dr. Oz Show* and in *The Wall Street Journal*, *Mashable*, *Wired*, *USA Today*, *HuffPost*, *Yoga Journal*, and *American Psychologist*. She has been an invited speaker for the king of Thailand, the Danish government, Bhutan's Gross National Happiness Summit, and the World Council for Psychotherapy, as well as to Fortune 100 companies, including Google, Cisco Systems, Procter & Gamble, and Genentech. Dr. Shapiro is a summa cum laude graduate of Duke University and a fellow of the Mind & Life Institute, cofounded by the 14th Dalai Lama.

Learn more at
http://www.drshaunashapiro.com. ∎

RICK HANSON

Rick Hanson, PhD, is a psychologist, *New York Times* best-selling author, and senior fellow of the Greater Good Science Center at the University of California, Berkeley. His books are available in 28 languages and include *Resilient: How to Grow an Unshakable Core of Calm, Strength, and Happiness*; *Hardwiring Happiness: The New Brain Science of Contentment, Calm, and Confidence*; *Buddha's Brain: The Practical Neuroscience of Happiness, Love, and Wisdom*; *Just One Thing: Developing a Buddha Brain One Simple Practice at a Time*; and *Mother Nurture: A Mother's Guide to Health in Body, Mind, and Intimate Relationships*.

A summa cum laude graduate of the University of California, Los Angeles, and the founder of the Wellspring Institute for Neuroscience and Contemplative Wisdom, Dr. Hanson has been an invited speaker at Google and NASA as well as the University of Oxford, Stanford University, Harvard University, and other major universities. He has taught in meditation centers worldwide, and his work has been featured on CBS, Fox, NPR, and the BBC. Dr. Hanson offers the free newsletter *Just One Thing*, which has more than 135,000 subscribers, and his Foundations of Well-Being online program in positive neuroplasticity is free to anyone with financial need.

Learn more at https://www.rickhanson.net. ∎

KRISTINE CARLSON

Kristine Carlson is passionate about spreading her message of waking up to life with joy and gratitude amid the ups and downs of this earthly existence. Her life mission expands on the phenomenal success of her late husband Dr. Richard Carlson's work in the Don't Sweat the Small Stuff series. She continues his legacy of peaceful and mindful living through her own best-selling books, including *Don't Sweat the Small Stuff in Love: Simple Ways to Nurture and Strengthen Your Relationships*; *Don't Sweat the Small Stuff for Women: Simple and Practical Ways to Do What Matters Most and Find Time for You*; *Don't Sweat the Small Stuff for Moms: Simple Ways to Stress Less and Enjoy Your Family More*; *An Hour to Live, an Hour to Love: The True Story of the Best Gift Ever Given*; *Heartbroken Open: A Memoir through Loss to Self-Discovery*; and *From Heartbreak to Wholeness: The Hero's Journey to Joy*. She also leads the well-known What Now? program.

Learn more at http://kristinecarlson.com. ∎

JUNA MUSTAD

Juna Mustad is a corporate mindfulness coach, an author, and an expert in mindful anger. She works with companies, organizations, and individuals around the world, teaching and coaching emotional intelligence, mindfulness, and skills for building healthy and effective relationships. She is also a Somatic Experiencing Practitioner and has trained extensively in stress and trauma resolution. She offers an accessible, nonthreatening approach to creating a healthy relationship with the world's most stigmatized emotion. She helps people unpack their beliefs about anger and skillfully uses mindfulness techniques to help them grow a balanced and holistic relationship with their anger. She is also writing a book on mindful anger.

Learn more at https://www.junamustad.com. ∎

MIKE ROBBINS

Mike Robbins is the author of four books: *Focus on the Good Stuff: The Power of Appreciation*; *Be Yourself, Everyone Else Is Already Taken: Transform Your Life with the Power of Authenticity*; *Nothing Changes until You Do: A Guide to Self-Compassion and Getting Out of Your Own Way*; and *Bring Your Whole Self to Work: How Vulnerability Unlocks Creativity, Connection, and Performance.* As an expert in teamwork, leadership, and emotional intelligence, he delivers keynotes and seminars around the world that empower people, leaders, and teams to engage in their work, collaborate, and perform at their best. Through his speeches, seminars, consulting, and writing, he teaches important techniques that allow individuals and organizations to be more appreciative, authentic, and effective with others and themselves.

Learn more at https://mike-robbins.com. ■

AMISHI JHA

Amishi Jha, PhD, is a neuroscientist and an Associate Professor in the Department of Psychology at the University of Miami. She is also the director of Contemplative Neuroscience for the UMindfulness initiative, prior to which she was an Assistant Professor at the University of Pennsylvania's Center for Cognitive Neuroscience. She received her PhD from the University of California, Davis, and completed her postdoctoral training in functional neuroimaging at the Brain Imaging and Analysis Center at Duke University.

Dr. Jha studies the neural bases of attention and the effects of mindfulness-based training programs on cognition, emotion, and resilience. With grants from the US Department of Defense and several private foundations, she has been systematically investigating the potential applications of mindfulness training in education, sports, business, and the military. Her work has been featured in the *Journal of Cognitive Neuroscience*, *Emotion*, and *PLOS ONE*, and she serves on the editorial boards of the *Journal of Experimental Psychology: General*; *Frontiers in Cognitive Science*; and *Frontiers in Cognition*.

Learn more at http://www.amishi.com. ∎

ELISSA EPEL

Elissa Epel, PhD, is a Professor in the Department of Psychiatry at the University of California, San Francisco. She studies how chronic stress can impact biological aging, including the telomere/telomerase system, and how mindfulness interventions may buffer stress effects and promote psychological and physiological thriving. She also studies food addiction and obesity.

Dr. Epel is a member of the National Academy of Medicine, a steering council member for the Mind & Life Institute, and the president-elect of the Academy of Behavioral Medicine Research. She is the coauthor of *The Telomere Effect: A Revolutionary Approach to Living Younger, Healthier, Longer*, a *New York Times* best seller that integrates the science of cell aging with practical daily tips.

Dr. Epel has won many awards for her research. Her work has been featured in various media outlets, including *The New York Times*, *The Wall Street Journal*, NPR, *TODAY*, *CBS This Morning*, *60 Minutes*, TEDMED, Wisdom 2.0, Health 2.0, and many science documentaries. In addition to doing research, she enjoys leading meditation retreats with her colleagues.

Learn more at http://www.amecenter.ucsf.edu/elissa-epel and follow her on Twitter: @Dr_Epel. ∎

JESSICA GRAHAM

Jessica Graham is a spiritual and sexual activist, a meditation teacher, an author, a sex and intimacy guide, an actor, and a filmmaker. She is a contributing editor of the meditation blog *Deconstructing Yourself*, in which her popular series Mindful Sex appears. She cofounded The Eastside Mindfulness Collective, dedicated to exploring secular spirituality through mindful living and learning. She also created Wild Awakening to help people evolve psychospiritually through private sessions, workshops, and retreats. In her book *Good Sex: Getting Off without Checking Out*, she demonstrates that a deep spiritual life and an extraordinary sex life are not mutually exclusive. This keenly personal and unflinchingly frank guide helps readers apply mindfulness in sex without losing the fun and adventure.

Learn more at http://yourwildawakening.com and connect with her on Instagram: @jessicaclarkgraham. ■

DACHER KELTNER

Dacher Keltner, PhD, is a Professor of Psychology at the University of California, Berkeley, and the faculty director of the Greater Good Science Center. His research focuses on the biological and evolutionary origins of emotion—in particular, prosocial states, such as compassion, awe, love, and beauty—as well as power, social class, and inequality.

He is the author of *Born to Be Good: The Science of a Meaningful Life*; *The Compassionate Instinct: The Science of Human Goodness*; and *The Power Paradox: How We Gain and Lose Influence*. Dr. Keltner has published more than 200 scientific articles written for many media outlets and has consulted for the Center for Constitutional Rights (to help end solitary confinement), Google, Facebook, the Sierra Club, and Pixar's *Inside Out*.

Learn more at https://ggsc.berkeley.edu. ∎

WALLACE J. NICHOLS

Wallace J. Nichols, PhD, is an innovative and entrepreneurial scientist, a renowned marine biologist, a wild-water advocate, a bestselling author, and a sought-after lecturer. In addition to being Chief Evangelist for Water (CEH$_2$O) at Buoy Labs, he is a senior fellow at the Middlebury Institute of International Studies' Center for the Blue Economy and a research associate at the California Academy of Sciences. Dr. Nichols is a cofounder of Ocean Revolution, an international network of young ocean advocates; SEEtheWILD, a conservation travel network; Grupo Tortuguero de las Californias, an international sea turtle conservation network; and Blue Mind Works, a global campaign to tell the new story of water.

Dr. Nichols has authored more than 200 scientific papers, technical reports, book chapters, and popular publications. His national best seller—*Blue Mind: The Surprising Science That Shows How Being Near, In, On, or Under Water Can Make You Happier, Healthier, More Connected, and Better at What You Do*—has been translated into numerous languages and inspired a wave of media, new research, and practical applications across many fields, including water resources and management, health and wellness, and spirituality and mindfulness.

Learn more at http://www.wallacejnichols.org. ■

DANIEL J. SIEGEL

Daniel J. Siegel, MD, is a Clinical Professor of Psychiatry in the David Geffen School of Medicine at the University of California, Los Angeles, where he is also the founding codirector of the Mindful Awareness Research Center. In addition, he is the executive director of the Mindsight Institute, which focuses on the development of mindsight—our human capacity to perceive the mind of the self and others—in individuals, families, and communities.

Dr. Siegel has published extensively for both professional and lay audiences. He is the author or coauthor of five *New York Times* best sellers: *Aware: The Science and Practice of Presence*; *Mind: A Journey to the Heart of Being Human*; *Brainstorm: The Power and Purpose of the Teenage Brain*; *The Whole-Brain Child: 12 Revolutionary Strategies to Nurture Your Child's Developing Mind*; and *No-Drama Discipline: The Whole-Brain Way to Calm the Chaos and Nurture Your Child's Developing Mind*. His other books include *Mindsight: The New Science of Personal Transformation*; *The Mindful Brain: Reflection and Attunement in the Cultivation of Well-Being*; and *The Yes Brain: How to Cultivate Courage, Curiosity, and Resilience in Your Child*. Dr. Siegel also serves as the founding series editor for the Norton Professional Series on Interpersonal Neurobiology, which contains more than 70 textbooks.

Learn more at http://www.drdansiegel.com. ∎

TABLE OF CONTENTS

INTRODUCTION

LESSON GUIDES

SUPPLEMENTARY MATERIAL

MASTERS OF MINDFULNESS

TRANSFORMING YOUR MIND AND BODY

n this course, Dr. Shauna Shapiro and 10 of her colleagues take you on a guided tour of the many ways mindfulness can help you reduce stress and pain, improve your health, increase your happiness, and find meaning in your life. You'll explore both the modern science and the ancient wisdom behind mindfulness, and you'll learn practical techniques to integrate this powerful tool for positive change into your daily routine.

Dr. Shapiro introduces the concept of mindfulness and shows how you can begin practicing it.

Dr. Rick Hanson teaches you to use mindfulness to strengthen your inner resources while making the most of positive experiences.

Author Kristine Carlson illustrates how mindfulness can help you rediscover your passion after shattering heartache and loss.

Mindfulness coach Juna Mustad teaches you to mine stigmatized emotions like anger for the hidden gems they contain.

Author and speaker Mike Robbins illustrates how organizations, leaders, and employees can bring compassion, authenticity, and effectiveness into the workplace.

Dr. Amishi Jha takes you on a deep dive into the neuroscience of attention and presents the mounting evidence that mindfulness training is an effective type of brain training.

By sharing her cutting-edge research on telomeres, which protect our chromosomes from deterioration, Dr. Elissa Epel explains how mindfulness techniques allow you to live younger, healthier, and longer.

Author and mindfulness teacher Jessica Graham reveals how mindfulness can revitalize your sex life and deepen communication with your partner.

Dr. Dacher Keltner explains how the emotion of awe defines us as human beings and teaches you how to cultivate your own experiences of awe to find new meaning in your life.

Dr. Wallace J. Nichols introduces you to blue mind, a revolution in environmental awareness and activism.

Finally, Dr. Dan Siegel takes you on a journey of personal transformation through what he calls mindsight and the wheel of awareness.

Whether you're a beginner or a longtime practitioner of mindfulness, this course will deepen your understanding of mindfulness and help you integrate it at home and at work, in your relationships and your self-identity, and as you grow and evolve. ∎

WHAT YOU PRACTICE GROWS STRONGER

LESSON 1

Mindfulness, the art of being present, has revolutionized the lives of millions. This course will empower you with scientific knowledge and teach you valuable skills to improve your life. This lesson covers some of the research that has been conducted on the practice of mindfulness and its benefits.

BENEFITS OF MINDFULNESS

An explosion of research has demonstrated the beneficial effects of mindfulness. It strengthens our immune system, decreases stress, lowers cortisol, and improves our sleep. It also has significant cognitive effects, including increasing our focus, attention, memory, creativity, and innovation. Perhaps most importantly, mindfulness improves our ethical decision making, reduces our cultural bias, and increases our compassion. In our complex world, mindfulness is a powerful tool.

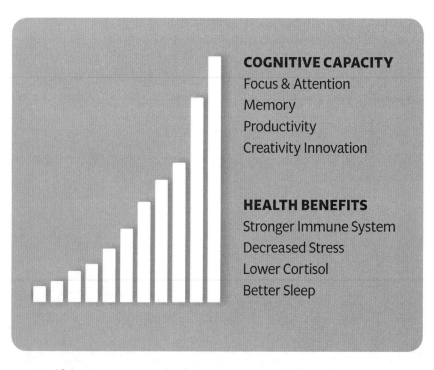

COGNITIVE CAPACITY
Focus & Attention
Memory
Productivity
Creativity Innovation

HEALTH BENEFITS
Stronger Immune System
Decreased Stress
Lower Cortisol
Better Sleep

Mindfulness means to see clearly so we can respond effectively. The way we do this involves the synergistic co-arising of three core elements: intention, attention, and attitude.

INTENTION is simply knowing why you are paying attention and what's important. We forget so easily what's most important in life, so part of mindfulness is simply remembering what's most important to you.

ATTITUDE is the element that's most often overlooked, but it's an essential part of mindfulness. What you practice grows stronger: If you're meditating with judgment or frustration, you're just growing judgment or frustration. Mindfulness isn't just about paying attention; it's about paying attention with an attitude of kindness and curiosity. Yet this attitude of kindness is often so elusive for us. More often, we experience self-judgment, shame, and self-doubt.

ATTENTION is simply learning how to pay attention in the present moment. Have you noticed that your mind has wandered since the beginning of this lesson? Everyone's mind wanders. In fact, research from Harvard shows that the mind wanders on average 47 percent of the time. That equates to about half of our waking lives that we're missing—that we're not present for. Part of mindfulness is simply training our attention to stabilize in the present moment so we can see clearly and respond effectively.

MINDFULNESS EXERCISE

Take a moment to let your eyes close and just connect with your intention. Why are you engaging on this journey of mindfulness? The reason could be to find greater ease, to reduce stress, to connect more with your children or grandchildren, or to improve your happiness. Whatever it is, just find what your intention is. Feel it in your body. Then, let your eyes open.

Physiologically, when we feel shame, the amygdala triggers a cascade of adrenaline and norepinephrine to flood our system, shutting down the learning centers of the brain and shuttling our resources to survival pathways. In other words, shame robs the brain of the energy it needs to do the work of changing.

Kindness, unlike shame, turns on the learning centers of the brain. It bathes our system with dopamine and gives us the resources we need to change. True and lasting transformation requires kind attention.

THE SCIENCE OF THE POWER OF PRACTICE

We used to think that the brain was static and fixed—that it couldn't change. This is referred to as the doctrine of the unchanging brain. However, one of the most important discoveries in the past 400 years of brain science changed everything: neuroplasticity. We learned that the brain is malleable—that it *can* change.

MINDFULNESS EXERCISE

We all have the capacity to change, so the question that really matters is this: What do you want to grow in your life?

Take a moment and just listen. What's most important to you? Try to soften your body five percent more and listen with your whole being, not with some mental idea of what you need to change in your life. What will uplift you? It could be more peace, more presence, more compassion, more joy. Find a word or phrase that feels true for you and let it seep into your body—into your cellular knowing. Then, as you're ready, take a deep breath in and let it out.

A very famous study of London taxi drivers found that the visuospatial mapping part of their brain grew bigger and stronger after practicing navigating the 25,000 streets of London all day. The same is true with meditation: When we practice, areas of the brain that have to do with creativity, attention, compassion, learning, and memory grow bigger and stronger. It's called cortical thickening—the growth of new neurons in response to repeated practice.

This means that all of us have the capacity to change. All of us can grow new neural pathways. We can even rewire our brain to be happier. This is very hopeful news.

Decades of psychological research have shown repeatedly that no matter what happens in our external life, we typically return to our baseline level of happiness. In psychological terms, we have a happiness set point.

Research has been conducted on people who won the lottery and people who were in a terrible accident and became paralyzed. Researchers discovered that when you win the lottery, you experience a blip of happiness, but then a year later you return to your baseline. Even more surprisingly, if you're in a terrible accident and become paralyzed, your happiness decreases, but then a few years later you return to your baseline.

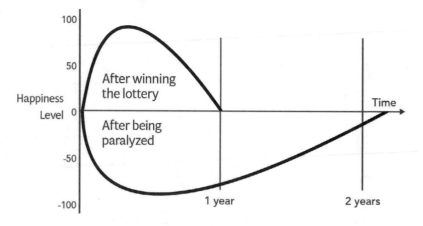

Happiness Baseline

This is great news if you're born happy: No matter what happens in your life, when you are knocked down, you pop back up. But this isn't such good news if you weren't born happy, because then no matter how great your wins are—no matter what successes you have—you always return to your baseline level of happiness.

This research shows that even though external changes won't shift your happiness level, internal changes can. According to neuroscientist Dr. Richard Davidson, "Happiness can be trained, because the very structure of our brain can be modified." In fact, anything can be trained, because the very structure of our brain can be modified.

Research by Dr. Sara Lazar at Harvard shows that mindfulness practice can grow areas of the brain associated with happiness, creativity, memory, emotional intelligence, and compassion. We can learn practices to rewire our brain and grow resources.

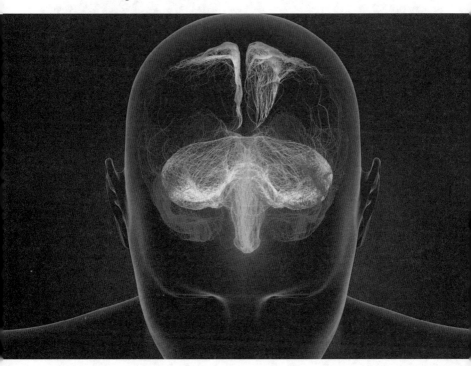

MINDFULNESS EXERCISE

Take a moment and let everything you've learned in this lecture settle in. Let your eyes close and let the information become part of your cellular memory. Perhaps focus on one point that you want to encode into your long-term memory. It could be the lesson that what you practice grows stronger. It could be the idea of having an attitude of kindness. It could be that all of us have the capacity to change. When you're ready, take a deep breath in and out, letting your eyes open.

WHAT YOU PRACTICE GROWS STRONGER

LESSON 1 TRANSCRIPT

[Introduction]

Welcome to the *Masters of Mindfulness*. In this course, Dr. Shauna Shapiro and 11 of her colleagues will take you on a guided tour of the many ways mindfulness can help you reduce stress and pain, improve your health, increase your happiness, and find meaning in your life. You'll explore both the modern science and the ancient wisdom behind mindfulness, and you'll learn practical techniques to integrate this powerful tool for positive change into your daily routine.

Dr. Shapiro introduces the concept of mindfulness and shows you how you can begin practicing it.

Dr. Rick Hanson teaches you to use mindfulness to strengthen your inner resources while making the most of positive experiences.

Through powerful stories of grief and transformation, author Kristine Carlson illustrates how mindfulness can help you rediscover your passion after shattering heartache and loss.

Mindfulness coach Juna Mustad teaches you to mine stigmatized emotions like anger for the hidden gems they contain.

Author and speaker Mike Robbins illustrates how organizations, leaders, and employees can bring compassion, authenticity, and effectiveness into the workplace.

Dr. Amishi Jha takes you on a deep dive into the neuroscience of attention, and presents the mounting evidence that mindfulness training really is an effective type of brain training.

And by sharing her research on telomeres, which protect our chromosomes from damage, Dr. Elissa Epel explains how mindfulness techniques allow you to live younger, healthier, longer.

Author and spiritual teacher Jessica Graham reveals how mindfulness can revitalize your sex life and deepen communication with your partner.

Professor Dacher Keltner shows how the emotion of awe defines us as human beings, and he teaches you to cultivate your own experiences of awe.

You'll also learn about Blue Mind, a revolution in environmental awareness and activism from marine biologist Wallace J. Nichols.

And finally, Dr. Dan Siegel will take you on a journey of personal transformation through what he calls mindsight and the wheel of awareness.

Masters of Mindfulness was shot on location at the Esalen Institute in Big Sur, California, the birthplace of the Human Potential Movement. Since 1962, Esalen has provided a unique and beautiful sanctuary for anyone interested in exploring human consciousness and finding new connections between the self, society, and the universe.

Whether you're a beginner or a longtime practitioner of mindfulness this course will deepen your understanding and help you to integrate mindfulness at home and at work, in your relationships, and your self-identity and as you grow and evolve.

And now, please welcome Dr. Shauna Shapiro.

[End of introduction]

Welcome. So, let's begin by just arriving here together. Take a moment to let your eyes close. And just gather your attention in your body. Maybe feel your feet wiggle your toes. Just arriving. Take a moment to feel your breath. And as you're ready, letting your eyes open.

Welcome I'm Dr. Shauna Shapiro, and I'm delighted to be sharing this course with you. Mindfulness, the art of being present, has revolutionized the lives of millions. And I'm delighted to welcome you to this journey. One that will empower you with scientific knowledge and teach you valuable skills to improve your life. The beauty of mindfulness is that you can begin in any moment. No matter what your circumstances, it is never too late. As Kabir beautifully says, "Wherever you are is the entry point." So, let's begin.

The word mindfulness means to see clearly. We want to see clearly so we can respond effectively. There's been an explosion of research demonstrating the beneficial effects of mindfulness. It's good for us. It strengthens our immune system, it decreases stress, lowers cortisol, improves our sleep.

It also has significant cognitive capacities increasing our focus, our attention, our memory, our creativity and innovation. And perhaps, most importantly, mindfulness improves our ethical decision making, it reduces our cultural bias, and it increases our compassion. In this world of increasing complexity, mindfulness is a powerful tool.

So again, mindfulness means to see clearly so we can respond effectively. The way we do this involves three core elements: intention, attention, and attitude. I want to speak about each of these three elements and show how they work together synergistically.

The first is intention; simply knowing why are you paying attention? What's important? One of my favorite sayings is, "The most important thing is simply to remember the most important thing." Just remembering what's important to you.

So, I want to share a story about my son Jackson. A couple of years ago when he was nine years old, I was away teaching in Europe, and we were apart for two weeks which was the longest we'd ever been apart. And on the flight home from Copenhagen I started getting really anxious. I'd missed him terribly and I was worried that I'd been away too long or I had ruined our attachment bond. And so instead of starting to shame myself and judge myself, I set a really clear intention. When I get home I just want to let Jackson know I love him. Mama's home. You're safe.

So, I arrived home on a Saturday. It was this beautiful day and we decided to go to the beach together. And I start packing up our picnic and packing his favorite foods and gathering all his toys and I walk out to my car and I'm waving to the neighbors. I'm like look I'm home. See what a good mom I am. (You know this isn't going to end well.) So, I go back inside say, "Jackson let's go." And he's like, "Nah I don't feel like it."

I'm like what? We're going to go to the beach and I'm going to show you how much I love you, damn it. So, he gets on his swim trunks and we start walking out the door and I'm already at the car ready to go. And he sits down on our front porch. And I say, "Hey, Jackson! Let's go!" He doesn't even look up. And I notice I start getting impatient. And then luckily I remembered my intention. What's the most important thing? I don't care if we go to the beach, I just want to spend time with my son.

So, I walked back over to where he's sitting and he was actually watching these ants. And I sit down next to him and we're kind of sitting there for a few moments, and then all of a sudden I feel his little body begin to soften. And I feel his shoulder lean into my shoulder. I feel the sun on our backs. And that was it. That was the most important thing. But we forget. We forget so easily. So, part of mindfulness is simply remembering what's most important.

I want to invite you right now to take a moment, let your eyes close and just connect with your intention. Why are you here? Why are you engaging on this journey of mindfulness? Perhaps it's to find greater ease, to reduce stress. Maybe it's to connect more with your children, your grandchildren. Maybe it's simply to improve your happiness. Whatever it is just finding what your intention is. Feel it in your body. Good. You can let your eyes open.

The second element of mindfulness is our attention: simply learning how to pay attention in the present moment. So, I've been talking for about six or seven minutes. I'm wondering if you noticed that your mind has wandered. Don't worry, everyone's mind wanders. In fact, research from Harvard shows the mind wanders on average 47 percent of the time. 47 percent! So, that's about half of our waking lives that we're missing. That we're not here. So, part of mindfulness is simply training our attention, stabilizing our attention in the present moment so we can see clearly and respond effectively.

The third element of mindfulness is our attitude, and this is the element that's most often overlooked. And I want to share with you why this is essential, why it's such an important part of mindfulness.

When I was first learning about mindfulness I went to Thailand and I did a meditation retreat at one of the monasteries there. I didn't know much about mindfulness, but I kind of understood it had to do with paying attention in the present moment. So, when I got to the monastery the monks didn't speak much English and I didn't speak any Thai. My only instruction was to feel my breath going in and out of my nose. So, I began. One breath, two breaths, my mind wandered off, I'd bring it back. One breath, two, it wandered again. I'd get swept into the future and what I was scared about or what I hoped to do or I'd get lost in the past. I wish I hadn't have done that or if only I had done this. And no matter how hard I tried I just couldn't stay in the present moment.

Now this was really frustrating because I had this romantic idea that I'd go to Thailand and I'd sit and meditate and all of a sudden I'd be at peace and enlightened. And instead my mind was crazy. And so, I started to try harder and I started to judge myself. What's wrong with you? You're terrible at this. Why are you even here? You're a fake! And then not only was I judging myself, I started judging all the monks around me. Why are they just sitting here shouldn't they be doing something?

Luckily a monk from London arrived who spoke English and as I shared with him my struggles, he looked at me and he said "Oh dear, you're not practicing mindfulness. You're practicing judgment, impatience, frustration." And then he said five forwards which I've never forgotten: What you practice grows stronger. What you practice grows stronger.

We know this now with neuroplasticity, and I'll be speaking about this later. But what he was teaching is that if I'm meditating with judgment, I'm just growing judgment. If I'm meditating with frustration, I'm growing frustration. He helped me understand that mindfulness isn't just about paying attention. It's about how we pay attention— our attitude. Paying attention with an attitude of kindness and curiosity. He said mindfulness is like these loving arms and they welcome everything, even the messy imperfect parts of ourselves. And yet this attitude of kindness is often so elusive for us.

In my work with thousands of people—from stressed out college students to women with breast cancer to high level CEOs—what I've been most struck by is the enormous sense of self-judgment, of shame, of self-doubt, of this "I'm not doing it right, I'm not good enough, I'm not okay." And my sense is you know what they're talking about, just as I do, because all of us have experienced this shame, this self-doubt, this judgment. What I want to share with you is that shame doesn't work. Shame literally can't work. Physiologically, when we feel shame, the centers of the brain that have to do with learning shut down. What happens is the amygdala triggers a cascade of adrenalin and norepinephrine to flood our system. It shuts down the learning centers of the brain and shuttles our resources to survival pathways. She literally robs the brain of the energy it needs to do the work of changing.

So, what's the alternative? We've made a mistake we've said something we shouldn't of. We don't want to do it again. I want to be clear that this isn't about letting ourselves off the hook, and yet shame doesn't work.

If it worked, maybe I'd say go ahead beat yourself up, but it doesn't work. So, what's the alternative? An attitude of kindness. Kindness, unlike shame, turns on the learning centers of the brain. It bathes our system with dopamine and gives us the resources we need to change. True and lasting transformation requires kind attention. Mindfulness then is this synergistic co-arising of all three elements: intention, attention, and attitude.

I want to share a story about mindfulness in action. So, as many of you know mindfulness has become quite popular in the United States, and it's even made its way into the military. And I want to share a story about a lieutenant who was referred to a mindfulness program for his severe anger management issues. At first he was very resistant and didn't really want to engage, but eventually he started practicing. About a month into the course he shared this story.

He's at the grocery store and he has a cart full of groceries. And in front of him is an elderly woman with a young baby girl, and she only has one single item. And he looks to the right and the express lane is completely empty and he starts getting frustrated. Why isn't she in that lane? She's supposed to be in the correct lane. You know he's in the military, he likes people to follow orders. But he remembers his mindfulness and he takes a breath, and then as he's standing there he notices that the woman and the checkout clerk start cooing over the baby. And then all of a sudden the woman hands the young cashier the baby girl for a hug and he nearly explodes in anger. Are you kidding? Is this a nursery? What are they thinking?

But again, he remembers his mindfulness and he brings his kind attitude to the situation, into his anger. And as his anger begins to subside, he looks up and he notices the baby girl is actually quite cute. A moment later the little girl is back in the arms of the woman and they walk out the door. And as the young cashier is checking out his groceries he says, "That little girl was quite cute." She looks up and she says, "Really? You think so? That's my daughter." And then she says, "My husband died in combat last year and I had to go back to work full time, so my mother brings her through my line every day so I can give her a hug."

Can you feel in that moment how everything changes? Can you imagine how grateful he was that he was able to see clearly in that moment and respond wisely? That's really the heart of mindfulness: bringing us into the present moment. Paying attention with this attitude of kindness and curiosity so we don't automatically react; so, we can actually respond to each moment with wisdom and compassion. And yet everything I've shared with you about mindfulness doesn't matter unless we put it into practice. I want to share with you the science of the power of practice.

As recently as the 1990s, we thought the brain was static and fixed that it couldn't change: it's referred to as the doctrine of the unchanging brain. However, one of the most important discoveries in the past 400 years of brain science changed everything: neuroplasticity. We learned that the brain is malleable. That it can change. In fact, there's a very famous study of London taxi drivers that shows the visual spatial mapping part of their brain grew bigger and stronger after practicing navigating the 25,000 streets of London all day long.

The same is true with meditation. When we practice meditation, what happens is that areas of the brain that have to do with creativity, attention, compassion, learning, memory grow bigger and stronger. It's called cortical thickening: the growth of new neurons in response to repeated practice. What you practice grows stronger. The monk shared this with me 20 years ago. He had probably never taken a course on neuroscience, but he understood this fundamental teaching. What we practice grows stronger. What this means is that all of us have the capacity to change. All of us can grow new neural pathways. We can even rewire our brain to be happier.

This is very hopeful news and I want to explain why. There's something in psychology called the happiness set point, and basically what decades of research has shown, over and over again, is that no matter what happens in our external life, we typically return to our baseline level of happiness. So, they've done research on people who won the lottery and people who were in a terrible accident and became paralyzed. What happened is when you win the lottery you have this blip of happiness, but then one year later you go back to your baseline. Even more surprising if you're in a terrible accident, your happiness decreases. One year later you're back to your baseline. This is great news if you're born happy, right? No matter what happens in your life, it knocks you down, you pop back up. But this isn't such good news if you weren't born happy, because then no matter how great your wins, no matter what successes you have, you always return to your baseline level of happiness.

What is so hopeful about this new research is what it's showing is that even though external changes won't shift your happiness level, internal changes can. Happiness can be trained because the very structure of our brain can be modified, says neuroscientist Richie Davidson. What I like to say is anything can be trained because the very structure of our brain can be modified. Research by Dr. Sara Lazar at Harvard shows that mindfulness practice can grow areas of the brain associated with happiness. It can grow areas of the brain associated with creativity, with memory, with emotional intelligence, with compassion. We can learn practices to rewire our brain and grow resources.

If there's one thing that I want you to take with you, it's this: What you practice grows stronger. All of us have the capacity to change. So, the question that really matters is: What do you want to grow? What do you want to grow in your life?

So again, I want to invite you to take a moment and just listen. What do you want to grow? What's important in your life? See if you can soften your body five percent more and listen with your whole being, not with some mental idea of what you need a change in your life. What do you want to grow? What will uplift you? It could be more peace in your life, more presence more compassion, more joy. Just finding a word or phrase that feels true for you. Letting it seep into your body, into your cellular knowing. And then as you're ready taking a deeper breath in and out. Good.

So, we've covered the research, we've covered the practice of mindfulness, and I want to invite us to just take a moment and let everything I've shared settle in. So, let your eyes close and just let this information, and these teachings, really become part of your cellular memory. And perhaps focusing on one point that you want to remember; one I call them gold nugget—one gold nugget that you really want to encode into your long-term memory. It could be what you practice grows stronger. It could be an attitude of kindness. It could be that all of us have the capacity to change. And as you're ready, taking a deeper breath in and out, letting your eyes open. Good.

So, next we'll be talking about essential themes of mindfulness and how to integrate them into your daily life.

ESSENTIAL THEMES OF MINDFULNESS

LESSON 2

This lesson covers the essential themes of mindfulness and how to integrate them into your daily life.

MINDFULNESS EXERCISE

Settle into a comfortable position. Allow your eyes to close and just focus on your intention. Why are you practicing? It could be to cultivate greater presence, attention, ease and relaxation, or compassion. Whatever it is for you in this moment, find a word or phrase that reminds you of what's important.

Then, when you're ready, begin to focus your attention in the present moment on your body. Feel your feet on the floor. Wiggle your toes. Become aware of both of your ankles, calves, and shins. Feel your knees and thighs. Feel your buttocks, your hips, your whole pelvic floor. Then, begin to draw your awareness up the spine. Feel your awareness move up the spine and spread out over the shoulder blades and shoulders, softening them. Let the awareness pour down both arms into the palms of your hands and let your awareness rest here. Try to feel the pulse of your heart in the palms of your hands. This energy is your aliveness.

Next, shift your attention into your stomach, softening it, and notice that you're breathing. Feel that practice as it naturally flows into the body and out of the body. Feel that natural rise of each inhale and that natural release of each exhale. Your body knows exactly what to do, oxygenating with each inhale and releasing any stress and toxins with each exhale.

Allow this awareness of the breath to move up into the chest, feeling the chest expand with each inhale and fall with each exhale. As you attend to your chest, try to sense or feel your heartbeat. Place one hand on your heart. Just like the breath, the heart knows exactly how to take care of you, sending oxygen and nutrients to all the trillions of cells in your body right now. And you don't have to do anything. Try to just rest and let the heart take care of you. When you're ready, put your hand back in your lap.

Continue moving your awareness up into the throat and face, softening your jaw and letting it rest. Soften the eyes in the forehead and temples. Tilt your chin down a tiny bit and let the back of the neck lengthen and open. Feel the back and sides and top of your head.

Then, just get a sense of your whole body resting here. Feel the front, right, left, and back of your body, focusing a little bit more of your attention into the back of your body and down. Try to soften five percent more and at the same time heighten your attention.

Invite in the attitude of kindness and curiosity. Be interested in what your experience is like right now. Can you bring five percent more kindness to yourself? Whatever you're feeling is okay; it's just what you're feeling right now. Mindfulness isn't about changing our experience. It's about relating to it differently—relating to whatever is here with kindness with curiosity. And if at any point the mind wanders, which it will, gently bring it back to this moment and to your breathing. The breath is a wonderful anchor to keep us in the present moment. Try to stay focused on one breath at a time, or maybe just half a breath. Inhale and then exhale.

As you practice, your pathways of presence and kindness are growing stronger. When you're ready, take a deeper breath in and out, letting some light come back in through the eyes and moving the body in any way that feels comfortable.

COMMON QUESTIONS ABOUT MEDIATION

At the end of a meditation practice, many questions may arise. What follows are some of the most common ones.

"I'm terrible at this. My mind wandered all the time. What can I do?"

The mind wanders; it's what it means to be human. Meditation is not about shutting down your thoughts or stopping your mind. It's about noticing the mind wandering and bringing it back into the present moment without judgment—without condemning yourself and without feeling like you're doing it wrong. You're learning how to focus and stabilize the attention in the present moment, and every time it wanders off, you bring it back. That's called shifting and switching attentional focus, and you're cultivating that pathway.

"Every time I meditate, I get so tired. Am I doing it wrong?"

Generally, the reason you get so tired is because you're tired. Mindfulness is about seeing clearly what's true, and most of us are sleep deprived. So, when we actually sit to meditate, we start to notice how tired we are. Don't worry about doing anything wrong when you notice the tiredness. Just try to bring some kindness and compassion to it. And if it really becomes difficult, try practicing mindfulness with your eyes open.

"How do I handle physical or emotional pain? I'm sitting and practicing my mindfulness, and either a pain in my back or some sadness or anger or confusion arises. How do I bring my mindfulness to pain?"

The first thing to do is simply to acknowledge that you're in pain right now and to bring your curious attitude to the pain. Then, begin to really attend to it. For example, if you notice sadness arise in your meditation, ask yourself what sadness feels like. Do you feel a tightness in your throat or tingling or tears in your eyes? Can you bring this loving awareness to be with whatever is here?

"How much meditation do I need to do to get the benefits?"

This isn't an exact science, but research shows that 12 minutes of meditation is the threshold where we start to see benefits, both physiologically and emotionally. But the more you practice, the more benefits you receive.

Meditation is just a way to practice mindfulness. Mindfulness—paying attention intentionally with an attitude of kindness and curiosity—can be practiced in every moment.

HOW TO BEGIN A PRACTICE

There are three key steps to focus on when beginning a practice.

Have a clear intention for why you're practicing. You want to use your intention to motivate you to practice. You don't want meditation practice to be one more thing on your to-do list. You want it to be something that really inspires you and connects you with what you truly value.

Write down what your intention is for learning the practice of meditation. What is most important to you? Write down a simple word or phrase and review it each day that you practice.

Our intentions shift and evolve; they're dynamic, not static. So, really listen each day and ask yourself these questions: Why am I practicing today? What's motivating me now?

Set extremely low goals. Don't start out with "I'm going to practice one hour every day for the next 10 years." Start small and take gentle baby steps. Choose a commitment that you can actually follow through on. You want to be able to trust yourself and trust your word and your commitments. You can even start with just one minute a day to create the habit of practice; as you begin your practice, it's important to be consistent.

Make your practice a routine part of your daily life. You need to schedule meditation into your day, just like you would if you wanted to start exercising. It's important with mindfulness practice to find a time that you put into your calendar and a place to meditate. You might also find it helpful to meditate with a group or a friend; like a running buddy, you can have a meditation buddy.

Be kind. Don't think about meditating "correctly" or perfectly. Think about taking baby steps—about having five percent more mindfulness. A small change can have a big impact. As you begin your mindfulness practice, invite a curious attitude, knowing that it's not about doing it right. It's not a self-improvement project; it's not about beating yourself up. Meditation is really about self-liberation. It's about having greater degrees of freedom, joy, ease, compassion, and clarity in your life.

THEMES OF MINDFULNESS

There are several specific themes of mindfulness that are essential.

Slowing down. Often in life we are in autopilot mode as we're rushing around doing things and moving from one thing to another. Mindfulness invites us to slow down so that we can stay connected to our true values and deepest compassion.

Acceptance. This is not about passive resignation, tolerating social injustice, or wrongs that need to be righted. Acceptance means that we acknowledge what's happening in the present moment—not because we like it, but because it's already happening.

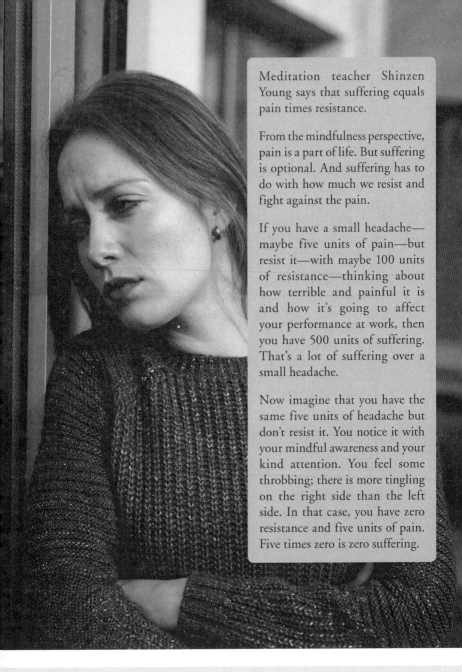

Meditation teacher Shinzen Young says that suffering equals pain times resistance.

From the mindfulness perspective, pain is a part of life. But suffering is optional. And suffering has to do with how much we resist and fight against the pain.

If you have a small headache—maybe five units of pain—but resist it—with maybe 100 units of resistance—thinking about how terrible and painful it is and how it's going to affect your performance at work, then you have 500 units of suffering. That's a lot of suffering over a small headache.

Now imagine that you have the same five units of headache but don't resist it. You notice it with your mindful awareness and your kind attention. You feel some throbbing; there is more tingling on the right side than the left side. In that case, you have zero resistance and five units of pain. Five times zero is zero suffering.

Response flexibility. This is the capacity to respond with agility and grace to what's happening instead of automatically reacting. Typically, when something stressful or unexpected occurs in our life, the amygdala hijack happens. This is when the amygdala gets triggered and releases stress hormones so that we can't think clearly and we automatically react. Mindfulness allows a pause between the stimulus and response, and into that space we can see clearly and then respond effectively. Mindfulness allows us to get out of the autopilot mode of doing and actually rest into a mode of being— where there's infinite possibility and potential. We have choices and can make changes.

Suspending judgment. Mindfulness offers an attitude of kindness and curiosity and invites us to hold off on judgment. It doesn't mean that we don't see clearly or with discernment—judgment is different. Mindfulness is about suspending judgment of right and wrong and allows us to see a situation more clearly so that we can respond with our natural wisdom and compassion.

Self-kindness. This seems to be one of the most elusive aspects of mindfulness. Kindness is what allows us to transform. Kindness turns on the learning centers of the brain. It gives us the resources we need to face difficulty in life and make change.

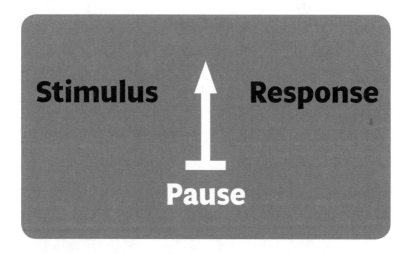

MINDFULNESS EXERCISE

Let your eyes close and put your hand on your heart. Take a moment to feel that kind touch, where you're bringing your own kindness to yourself.

It's okay to feel whatever you're feeling right now. For some people, this feels really soothing and good, and for other people, it can be challenging to bring kindness to themselves. Use your mindful awareness to welcome whatever you're feeling. Feel your breath. Invite in five percent more kindness and compassion for yourself. Notice how this feels. Soften the body five percent more.

You are practicing the pathway of self-kindness. Notice if you have thoughts about doing this "right" and just let them go. You are doing it right—simply practicing your kind attention.

When you're ready, take a deep breath in and out. Let your eyes open and move your body in any way that feels good.

ESSENTIAL THEMES OF MINDFULNESS

Now that we know the power of practice I want us to practice together. So, take a moment and just settle into a comfortable position. Allow your eyes to close, and just focus on your intention. Why are you practicing? It could be to cultivate greater presence, greater attention, greater ease and relaxation, greater compassion. Whatever it is for you in this moment, just finding a word or phrase that reminds you of what's important.

And then as you're ready, begin to gather your attention in the present moment. Right here into the body. Go ahead and feel your feet on the floor, wiggle your toes. Aware of both ankles and calves and chins. Feel your knees and thighs. Feel your seat, your hips, the whole pelvic floor. And then begin to draw your awareness up the spine. Feel your awareness move up the spine and spread out over the shoulder blades and shoulders. And just softening your shoulders. Let the awareness pour down both arms into the palms of the hands. And then just resting the awareness here in the palms of the hands. Maybe see if you can feel the pulse of your heart in the palms of the hands. This is your aliveness, this energy. Don't worry if you can't feel it. It's definitely happening.

And then shifting your attention into your belly, just softening the belly, and notice that you're breathing. Feeling the breath as it naturally flows into the body and out of the body. Feeling that natural rise of each inhale, the natural release of each exhale. Body knows exactly what to do. Oxygenating with each inhale, releasing any stress and toxins with each exhale.

And just allow this awareness of the breath to move up into the chest, feeling the chest expand with each inhale, feel it fall with each exhale. And as you attend to your chest see if you can feel your heartbeat. In fact, just put one hand on your heart. Just see if you can sense or feel the beating of your own heart. Just like the breath, the heart knows exactly how to take care of you. The heart's sending oxygen and nutrients to all the trillions of cells in your body right now. And you don't have to do anything.

You don't have to remember or make it happen or control it. The heart knows exactly what to do. So, see if you can just rest and let the heart take care of you.

As you're ready you can put your hand back in your lap and just continuing up into the throat. Up into the face, softening the jaw, really unhinge the jaw, let it rest. Soften the eyes in the forehead, temples. Maybe just tilt your chin down a millimeter and let the back of the neck lengthen and open. Feel the back and sides and top of the head.

And then just get a sense of the whole body resting here. Feel the front, right, left, back of the body; maybe just leaning a little bit more of your attention into the back body and down. We tend to lean forward into the future. Resting back into the volume of the body. And then see if you can soften five percent more, and at the same time heighten your attention. We can actually be physiologically at ease and yet laser like in our attention. So, softening, opening.

And now, inviting in the attitude of kindness, of curiosity, really being interested in what your experience is like, right now. Can you bring five percent more kindness to yourself? Whatever your feeling is okay. It's just what you're feeling right now. Mindfulness isn't about changing our experience. It's about relating to it differently. Relating to whatever is here with kindness, with curiosity.

And if at any point the mind wanders—which as we've learned, it will—just bringing it back to this moment and to your breathing. The breath is a wonderful anchor to keep us in the present moment. So, when the mind wanders off we just gently bring it back. It's like a little puppy dog. It wanders off and you say, "Stay. Stay." Wanders again you say, "Come back." Right here. Just this breathe. See if you can stay with one breath at a time. Or maybe just half a breath, just this inhale, this exhale.

What you're practicing is growing stronger. Practicing pathways of presence and kindness. Good. So, as you're ready, taking a deeper breath in and out, letting some light come back into through the eyes and just moving the body in any way that feels comfortable.

So often, when we finish a meditation practice, many questions arise. And I want to see if I can answer some of the most common ones. One of the first things I hear from people is, I'm terrible at this. My mind wandered all the time, what can I do?

So, first I want to reassure you, as we've learned, the mind wanders. It's what it means to be human. It wanders 47 percent of the time on average. So, meditation is not about shutting down your thoughts or stopping your mind, it's about noticing the mind wander and bringing it back into the present moment without judgment, without condemning yourself and without feeling like you're doing it wrong. What you're doing is you're learning how to focus and stabilize the attention in the present moment and every time it wanders off you bring it back. That's called shifting and switching attentional focus, and you're cultivating that pathway.

The second common question I get a lot is people sit and meditate and they say, every time I meditate I get so tired. Am I doing it wrong?

So, the reason you get so tired—and this is true pretty much across the board—it's because you're tired. Right? Mindfulness is about seeing clearly what's true and most of us are sleep deprived. And so, when we actually sit to meditate we start to notice how tired we are. So, don't worry about doing anything wrong when you notice the tiredness. See if you can bring some kindness and compassion to it. And if it really gets difficult, I often invite people to just open their eyes, just open their eyes and practice the mindfulness with eyes open. Because remember, meditation is just a way to practice mindfulness—mindfulness we can practice in every moment. We're simply paying attention, intentionally, with an attitude of kindness and curiosity.

The third question I often receive is, how do I handle physical or emotional pain? I'm sitting and I'm practicing my mindfulness and either I'll have a pain in my back or some sadness or anger or confusion arise. So how do we bring our mindfulness to pain?

The first thing to do is just simply acknowledge, I'm in pain right now, and to bring your kind, curious attitude to the pain. And then begin to really attend to it. For example, if I notice sadness arise in my meditation, to enquire why does sadness feel like? Do I feel a tightness in my throat or do

I feel tingling or tears in my eyes? Can I bring this loving awareness to be with whatever is here? So, you're almost like a parent who says to her child, I'm here, I care, tell me what happened. In this way meditation practice is learning to re-parent ourselves, to welcome whatever is here.

Final question I get is, how much do I need to practice? How much do I need a practice to get the benefits? What I'd say is this isn't an exact science but we have done some research which shows that 12 minutes is the threshold where we start to see benefits both physiologically and emotionally. Now that doesn't mean 12 minutes is all you should meditate, but 12 minutes is kind of the minimum. And then after that we see that the more you practice the greater the benefit. Again, what you practice grows stronger.

What I'd like to do now is talk a bit about how to begin a practice, and there are three key steps that I want to focus on. The first is having a clear intention for why you're practicing—really knowing why this is important. You want to use your intention to motivate you, to really inspire you to practice. You don't want meditation practice to be one more thing on your to-do list, one more thing you have to do. You want it to be something that really inspires you and connects you with what you truly value.

So, I want to invite you right now to take a moment and write down what your intention is for learning this practice. What is most important? Write down a simple word or a simple phrase. And then I'm going to encourage you to review this each day that you practice. And what's interesting is that our intentions shift, they evolve, they're dynamic, they're not static. So really listening each day. Why am I practicing today? What's motivating me now?

Good. The second step is to set ridiculously low goals. Don't start out with, "I'm going to practice one hour every day for the next 10 years." Start small, stay gentle, baby steps. Choose a commitment that you can actually follow through on. You want to be able to trust yourself and trust your word and your commitments. I even recommend that people start with one minute a day; just one minute to start to create the habit of practice. Now I know I just told you that it takes 12 minutes to really see the benefits of mindfulness, but as you begin your practice it's important to be consistent.

So, I remember my dentist once said to me, he said start by flossing one tooth, one tooth a day and once you're already flossing when you kind of get into the habit and you do a few more. So, if you start with a commitment to one minute a day you're certainly welcome to do more, but always know that as a baseline as a minimum you're going to pause and meditate for one minute a day.

The third step to beginning a practice is to make it a routine part of your daily life. Just like if you want to start exercising you need to schedule it in. It's important with mindfulness practice to find a time to meditate that you put into your calendar and a place to meditate. I also find it very helpful to find a group to meditate with or even just a friend—like a running buddy, you have a meditation buddy, and we have resources for you that we'll be sharing in this course.

One final note is, be kind. This is not about doing it right. It's not about doing it perfectly. Maybe think practice, not perfect. This is about baby steps. It's about five percent more mindfulness. Even a few degrees changes everything. For example, think about the last time you had a fever. You have 102 fever, you're feeling chills, you're feeling terrible and then you take a Tylenol and you bring it down to 99, 98, just a few degrees, right? But it's a huge change. So, little change has big impact.

As you began your mindfulness practice, really invite this kind, curious attitude knowing that it's not about doing it right. It's not a self-improvement project. It's not about kind of beating yourself up so now there's one more thing to do. It's really about self-liberation. It's about greater degrees of freedom in your life, greater degrees of joy, of ease, of compassion, of clarity.

So now that we've learned about the research behind mindfulness and about how to practice it, I want to focus on some specific essential themes of mindfulness. The first theme of mindfulness is slowing down. So often in our life we're rushing, we're hurrying, we're moving from one thing to another, and we got on this kind of automatic pilot mode of doing. What mindfulness invites us to do is to slow down so that we can stay connected to what we truly value.

I want to share one of my favorite studies. This was done back in the 1970s at Princeton University. It's called the Good Samaritans study. And what they did is they looked at seminary students who were becoming ministers. And one of their first assignments was to write a sermon about what it means to be a good person, a good Samaritan. So, the students went home and they diligently prepared their sermon and they came back to the university. And half the students when they came back their instructor said, "Oh dear, you're a little bit late and your lecture's all the way across campus and you better hurry because they're going to start without you." So, those students started running across campus, really anxious that they were going to miss their first lecture. And as they're running across campus they had a confederate, someone who was part of the study, fall down and say "Oh, I'm hurt. Can you stop? Can you help me?" One hundred percent of the students ran right by this person on their way to give a lecture about what it means to be a good person.

Luckily there's a second part to this study. So, the second half of students when they came in their instructor said, "Oh dear, you're a little bit late, but don't worry they're not going to start without you. Take your time." So, they start walking across campus, still going at a good pace. The same confederate falls in front of them and says "I'm hurt, please help me." They stopped. They helped him. So, part of mindfulness is about slowing down so we can stay connected to our true values, to our deepest compassion.

A second theme of mindfulness is acceptance. I want to be really clear that acceptance is not about passive resignation. This is not about tolerating social injustice or wrongs that need to be righted. What acceptance means is that we acknowledge what's happening in the present moment, not because we like it, but because it's already happening.

One of the most extraordinary mathematical equations I've learned is from one of my teachers Shinzen Young. And what he says is that suffering equals pain times resistance. Suffering equals pain times resistance. So, from the mindfulness perspective pain is a part of life. Pain is constant. All of us are going to get sick. All of us are going to grow old. All of us are going to die and so are the people that we love. Pain is a part of life. But suffering is optional. And suffering has to do with how much we resist and fight against the pain.

For example, let's say that I have a little headache. Let's say I have five units of pain. If I start resisting the headache and I say "Oh God, this is terrible, this is so painful and I'm trying to do this course right now and I really want to do a good job." And I'm resisting it let's say about 100 units of resistance. I have 500 units of suffering. That's a lot of suffering over just a little headache. So now imagine I have the same five units of headache, but I don't resist it. I notice it with my mindful awareness, my kind attention. So, a little bit of throbbing, tingling, it's more on the right side than the left side. I had zero resistance, five units a pain. Five times zero is zero suffering.

Now remember when I was learning this I was at a meditation retreat in Arizona and it was a week-long silent meditation retreat. We were meditating every day, practicing. And when I heard this teaching it felt a little too good to be true. Like, oh, if I just don't resist I'm never going to suffer again. So, I kind of tucked it away and went about my practice. And at the end of the retreat I was heading home to California and I stopped by the grocery store just to get a quick snack for the airplane.

And I was running a little bit late and I ran through the express lane. And right before I got there a woman pulled in front of me with a cart full of groceries; 23 items (not that I counted). There was a clear sign that said "10 Items or Less." And so, I noticed I started getting impatient and I started to judge her. Why is she in this lane? And then I noticed I was judging her. And I started judging myself, "Oh my god! What kind of meditator are you? You've just been like meditating for peace for all beings and now you're judging this poor woman who's just trying to get her groceries?" And I really start judging myself like, you're a fake, you're not real, you're pretending to be a good meditator.

But then I realized I actually was sincerely practicing every day for a week. And all of a sudden I had this thought: Oh, my god! It's the meditation that doesn't work and I've devoted my entire life to something that's a total farce." And then luckily this equation came into my mind. Suffering equals pain times resistance. And I realized I had this little pain of waiting in line, maybe two units of pain, but I was resisting it by like a million. I was questioning my entire life, which was two million units of suffering. And so right in that moment I dropped the resistance and just accepted I'm going to be waiting in line for another minute. Took a breath. Practiced my mindfulness. And right in that moment the woman looks back at me and smiles and says, "Oops, I'm so sorry." I said, "No problem." And it wasn't.

The third theme of mindfulness is response flexibility: the capacity to respond with agility and grace to what's happening, instead of automatically reacting. What typically happens is, when something stressful or unexpected occurs in our life, what's known as the amygdala hijack occurs. Which is the amygdala gets completely triggered and releases all of these stress hormones so that we can't think clearly and we automatically react. What mindfulness allows is a pause between the stimulus and response. And into that space we can see clearly and then respond effectively. What mindfulness allows is for us to get out of that automatic pilot mode of doing and actually rest into a mode of being. In this space, there's infinite possibility, there is infinite potential. And so, what mindfulness begins to offer us is more degrees of freedom in our life. Where we don't have to automatically react, where we don't have to keep doing the same things over and over again. Where we have choice and we can make change.

A fourth theme of mindfulness is suspending judgment. As I mentioned before, mindfulness has this attitude of kindness and curiosity and what it really invites is that we hold off on judgment. It doesn't mean that we don't see clearly or see with discernment, but judgment is different. For example, let's take poison. A judgmental view of poison is this is bad, this is evil, it'll kill you. A discerning view of poison is if you ingest it in this way it will kill you, if you use it in this way, it could be a vaccination. So, mindfulness is about suspending that judgment of right and wrong.

And I want to share a story with you that I heard from Stephen Covey. He said he's in New York on a subway. And for those of you who've lived in New York, there's a certain protocol for being on a subway in New York. You mind your own business, you don't look up, you don't make conversation. So, he's minding his own business and he's sitting there when a young father with three young children gets on the subway and the young children start wreaking havoc, they're running around, they're yelling, being totally inappropriate.

And Stephen Covey says, "Why isn't this father disciplining them?" He starts really judging the situation, and after a couple of more moments the eight-year-old boy knocks over the cane of this elderly woman, and Stephen Covey says, that's it. I have to say something. And he leans over to the father and he says, "Excuse me, are these your children?" And the father looks up a little bit dazed and says, "Yes. Can I help you?" He says, "Why aren't you disciplining them?" And the father says, "I'm so sorry we just left the hospital where my wife—their mother— died and I don't know what to do." And you can feel how in that moment everything changes. And Stephen Covey responds, "Can I help? How can I help?" What mindfulness does is it allows us to see the situation more clearly where we suspend the judgment to respond with all of our natural wisdom and compassion.

The final theme I want to talk about is self-kindness. This seems to be one of the most elusive aspects of mindfulness and really deserves some focused attention. As I mentioned earlier, kindness is what allows us to transform. It's what allows us to change. Kindness turns on the learning centers of the brain. It gives us the resources we need to face difficulty in life and make change.

So, I want to share a story about how self-kindness has been so important in my own life. Some years ago, I was going through a very difficult divorce and I'd wake up every morning with this pit of shame and fear in my stomach. My meditation teacher saw how much judgment, how much anxiety, how much fear I was practicing and she invited me to begin a practice of self-kindness. She said how about saying, "I love you, Shauna" every day? And I looked at her and I said, no way. It felt so New Agey or hippie. And so, she said how about just saying, "Good morning Shauna?" And try putting your hand on your heart when you say it. It releases oxytocin. It's good for you, you know.

She knew the science would win me over, so the next morning I woke, up put my hand on my heart. Good morning Shauna. And it was kind of nice. Right? Instead of that avalanche of self-judgment and shame, I woke up and just greeted myself with my own presence. After a few months, it became a really wonderful practice and when I went back to see her I said, "Thank you. That's been really helpful." Wonderful, you've graduated. Now the advanced practice: Good morning, I love you Shauna.

So, the next morning I went home put my hand on my heart, took a breath. Good morning, I love you Shauna. I felt nothing. Definitely not love. Maybe a little ridiculous, but definitely not love. But I kept practicing because as we know, what you practice grows stronger. And then one day I woke, up put my hand on my heart, took a breath. Good morning, I love you Shauna, and I felt it. I felt my grandmother's love. I felt my mother's love. I felt my own self-love. And I wish I could tell you that every day since then has been this bubble of self-love and I've never felt judgment or shame again. And that's not true. But what is true is this pathway of kindness has been established in me and it's growing stronger every day.

So, I want to invite you to take a moment. Let your eyes close and just put your hand on your heart. And just take a moment to feel that kind touch, where you're bringing your own kindness to yourself. And it's okay to feel whatever you're feeling right now. For some people this feels really soothing and good, and for other people it can be challenging to bring kindness to themselves.

So, using your mindful awareness to welcome whatever you're feeling. Feeling your breath. Maybe just inviting in five percent more kindness, five percent more compassion for yourself. Noticing how this feels. Softening the body five percent more. And just practicing this pathway of self-kindness. Notice if you have thoughts about doing it right and just let those go. You are doing it right. Simply practicing. Practicing your kind attention.

So, as you're ready, taking a deeper breath in and out. Letting your eyes open and just moving your body in any way that feels good. Good. So, I offer you this practice that's been so powerful in my life. And I want to invite you tomorrow morning when you wake up, put your hand on your heart. Say good morning. And if you feel really brave, good morning, I love you.

Thank you.

USING MINDFULNESS TO GROW INNER RESOURCES
LESSON 3

This lesson is about how to use mindfulness to grow inner resources—such as resilience, motivation, determination, confidence, self-worth, compassion, and happiness—using the power of positive neuroplasticity, which is the fundamental capacity of the nervous system to be changed for the better.

THE VALUE OF INNER RESOURCES

Routinely used in health care and psychology, the diathesis-stress model explains mental disorders as the interaction between genetics and stressors. According to this model, the course of a person's life is the result of three factors: challenges, vulnerabilities, and resources.

As challenges and vulnerabilities grow, we need to increase resources as well. The world, the body, and the mind are important places to look for resources. Some fundamental inner resources are as follows.

Mindfulness. This is foundational for growing the rest of the resources, because if we're not mindful of our situations, we won't know which resources to develop. We need to sustain mindfulness to help our experiences leave lasting traces as durable changes in neural structure or function.

Character virtues. This includes know-how— knowing to lean into an interaction and when to lean back; knowing how to get something done; knowing how to deal with your own thoughts and feelings; and knowing skills of various kinds. This also includes certain motivations and positive intentions as well as values, aims, and dreams that are wholesome and useful.

Positive emotions. Happiness is itself a fundamental psychological resource. Research shows that happiness—an authentic happiness, not a fake-it-till-you-make-it happiness—is very helpful for dealing with difficult conditions in life.

Compassion and **love** for other people.

Patience, determination, and **grit** from inside yourself.

The harder a person's life—the more challenges a person has—the less the outer world is helping and the more important it is for that person to develop inner resources.

ENGAGING THE MIND

The methods for engaging the mind fall into three basic categories.

Be with what is there. Feel the feelings. Experience the experiences. And do so usefully. Step back from the movie that is your life. Even if it looks horrible, still experience whatever there is to experience. Sometimes it's helpful to investigate what is underneath the surface of an experience, such as the hurt that often lies beneath anger. As you discover what's there, don't make deliberate efforts in your mind to nudge it one way or another. This way of relating to the mind is fundamental, even though it's often the last resort.

Decrease the negative. Prevent, release, or reduce what is negative, painful, or harmful for ourselves and other people. For example, you might let go of tension in your body, vent feelings, or listen to some of the thoughts that make you crazy or make other people crazy and disengage from them. Let them go. Instead, you might release, decrease, or even abandon problematic desires. These are natural and important forms of letting go.

Increase the positive. Encourage, protect, or create what is positive or beneficial for ourselves and other people. Let in. Grow inner fortitude, strength, determination, skillfulness, and compassion and empathy for others.

All three of these methods work together. For example, to simply be with the mind, it's necessary to grow resources inside so that we can tolerate what we're being with. We need to develop resources such as steadiness of mind, or distress tolerance, which entails being able to manage feelings without being flooded by them.

Mindfulness has to be present in all three ways to engage the mind. There's a misunderstanding that mindfulness means only a passive witnessing of the stream of consciousness, such that any form of wise effort with the mind is somehow in conflict with mindfulness. Mindfulness has to be present as we have opportunities for gratitude, awe, or self-compassion so that we can incorporate these experiences into our inner selves.

As the focus has emerged in positive psychology on character strengths and other forms of resourcing oneself, there has been a lot of attention on identifying and using key resources inside yourself. But what about developing them in the first place? Where do they come from, and how can we get more of them?

If we're going to develop any change that lasts, it requires some kind of physical change in the body, particularly in the nervous system, whose headquarters is the brain. In other words, if we are going to change, we have to engage the brain.

> Roughly a third of the variation in human inner resources is based on innate, heritable factors. The other two-thirds is acquired through motional, somatic, and motivational learning—which is fundamentally hopeful.

CHANGING THE BRAIN FOR THE BETTER

There is great evidence that mental practices of various kinds, such as mindfulness training, produce lasting benefits in human beings psychologically, presumably via some kind of change in the brain.

Studies of nonhuman animals have repeatedly shown—down to the cellular and even molecular level—that the experiences they are having lead to lasting physical changes in their brains.

Research commonly shows that people who routinely practice mindfulness—especially in the formal setting of meditation—exhibit measurable, lasting changes in the brain, such as a thickening of the cortex, the front part of the brain that's involved in executive control.

There is some evidence that psychological practices, such as meditation, mindfulness training, and other forms of psychological interventions, can change people's brains. But because neuroscience is in its infancy and our technology is still quite rudimentary, the evidence here is partial.

There is only a small amount of evidence scattered among various kinds of studies that there are deliberate internal learning factors—such as extending the duration of an experience or focusing on what is personally meaningful about it—that can produce a lasting change in the brain. But the absence of evidence is not evidence of absence, and more research is needed.

We have about as many neurons in our brain as there are stars in the Milky Way Galaxy.

The brain is considered by scientists to be the most complex physical object currently known to humankind. The brain contains roughly 1.1 trillion cells, about 100 billion of which are neurons. A typical neuron makes several thousand connections—called synapses—with other neurons, giving us an internal network of several hundred trillion neurons.

A typical neuron fires 5 to 50 times a second. Large-scale patterns of synchronized activity sweep through the brain many times a second. Over the course of a single minute, quadrillions of synaptic events occur in the brain.

How can we help this amazing organ be as effective as possible to help us deal with life and grow resources we can draw on? This is the fundamental process of what neuroscientist Jeffrey Schwartz calls self-directed neuroplasticity. How can the brain change for the better? And in the process, how can we become happier, stronger, wiser, and more loving?

The neuropsychology of learning—including emotional, somatic, social, attitudinal, motivational, and spiritual learning—has two necessary and sufficient stages.

> The first stage is to have the experience, such as an experience of mindfulness, gratitude, or self-worth. There's a little bit of learning that occurs through unconscious processes, but most of the processes of helping ourselves heal, grow, and strengthen occurs through conscious experiences.

> But for there to be any kind of lasting change for the better, by definition there must be a physical change as a result. Otherwise, the experience might be pleasant and useful in the moment, but it is a passing moment that leaves no lasting value.

This two-stage process of change is simplified in a saying from the work of Canadian psychologist Donald Hebb: "Neurons that fire together wire together."

There are a variety of mechanisms of experience-dependent neuroplasticity, which is neuroplasticity that depends on the experiences we have. These mechanisms include the following:

> Existing synapses can become stronger or weaker.

> New connections between neurons can form.

> Changes in neurochemicals inside the brain, such as dopamine or serotonin, can produce lasting changes.

> The expression of genes inside neurons can cause changes.

Experientially, this translates to the notion that if we want to become more compassionate, we need to experience compassion and then internalize it. If we want to be more mindful, we need to have experiences of mindfulness that we receive and that sink in, leading to increased trait mindfulness over time. Similarly, if we want to be more determined—more committed to exercise or to social justice—we need to have experiences of determination or related factors that are internalized in the second stage.

But experiencing doesn't equal learning. Experiences in the moment can be useful and enjoyable, but most experiences that people have leave no lasting traces behind.

THE NEGATIVITY BIAS

Over the 600-million-year evolutionary time scale of the human nervous system, it was really important for our ancestors to do two things: get "carrots," such as food or mating opportunities, but avoid "sticks," such as predators, natural hazards, or aggression.

Both carrots and sticks are important, but there's a fundamental difference: In the wild, if you fail to get a carrot today, then you probably have a chance to win tomorrow. But if you fail to avoid that stick today, then there are no more carrots for you forever.

As a result, we have a brain that's hardwired to do five things.

Scan for bad news in the world, in the body, and in the mind.

Overfocus on it.

> People react more to pain than to pleasure. Research has shown that people react more to losing something than to gaining the same thing. In relationships, people are much more affected by negative experiences with other people than they are by positive ones.

Overreact to it.

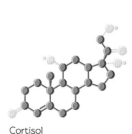

Cortisol
$C_{21}H_{30}O_5$

The hormone cortisol is released in stressful situations. When it's released, it goes to the brain, where it sensitizes the alarm bell of the brain, the amygdala. Cortisol overstimulates and eventually kills neurons and then gradually weakens a nearby part of the brain called the hippocampus, which puts things in context, inhibits the amygdala, and signals the hypothalamus (another nearby part of the brain) that there are enough stress hormones and that no more are needed.

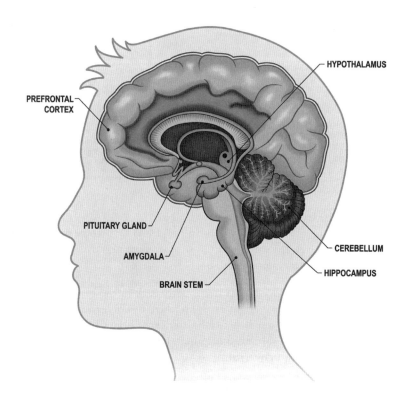

HYPOTHALAMUS

PREFRONTAL CORTEX

PITUITARY GLAND

AMYGDALA

BRAIN STEM

CEREBELLUM

HIPPOCAMPUS

Turn it quickly into memory.

Sensitize the brain to the negative.

> As we have emotionally positive experiences, our field of awareness and perception tends to widen. On the other hand, as we become more anxious, irritated, or frustrated, our attention tends to narrow.

This creates a vicious cycle. As we sensitize the alarm bell and weaken the regulation of it, we become just a little more vulnerable to stress tomorrow based on the stressful experiences we have today. This releases just a little more cortisol, which makes us even more vulnerable the day after—and so on.

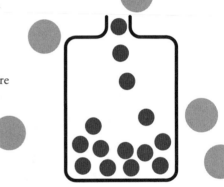

These hardwired tendencies were useful for our ancestors living in the wild, but today they create a lot of unnecessary suffering—including unnecessary worry, self-criticism, and conflict with others—under most conditions.

As the negativity bias wears on us, we tend to get involved in vicious cycles with other people. As we become more negative ourselves, the world tends to treat us more negatively, which confirms our expectations, and so on.

In effect, the negativity bias is like a bottleneck in the brain. It allows negative experiences to go right in, fast-tracked for storage and usage later. Meanwhile, most of our beneficial experiences bounce off the bottle. That's why it's so important to help ourselves get the benefits from key experiences we want to internalize.

USING MINDFULNESS
TO GROW INNER RESOURCES

[Introduction by Shauna Shapiro]

Dr. Rick Hanson is a psychologist and *New York Times* best-selling author. His work focuses on the need for mental resources: such as mindfulness, self-compassion and positive emotions; resources that we can acquire through learning. He explores how we can grow inner strengths. His breadth of knowledge is matched only by his dedicated and generous heart.

[End of introduction]

Hi, I'm Rick Hanson. And I'd like to talk with you about how to use mindfulness to grow inner resources of various kinds: like resilience, motivation, determination, confidence, self-worth, compassion, and happiness altogether, using the power of what's called positive neuroplasticity—the fundamental capacity of the nervous system to be changed. That's its plastic nature. And then positively changing it, helping it become better and better for your own sake, from the inside out. And along the way, growing strengths and other resources inside that you can offer to other people.

I'd like to begin by talking with you about the value of inner resources and framing it in terms of a model that's used routinely in healthcare and medicine and psychology. Its origin is in the term stress diathesis—the notion that stressors land on us and our impact is the result of the diathesis they make with other factors such as vulnerabilities and resources.

So, in this model there is a notion that the course of a person's life over a day, a month, a year, or the lifespan altogether, is really the result of just three factors, three kinds of causes: the challenges that wear upon a person, the vulnerabilities that penetrate through, and the resources that the person draws upon to deal with those challenges and to shore up vulnerabilities.

A kind of silly but simple example of this is imagine that you're doing the dishes and you've got your hands deep into a soapy water, it's full of germs and other crud. That's a challenge. And then let's also suppose that there's a little cut in your skin. That would be a vulnerability through which the germs could penetrate. But then to deal with it you tap into the resource of nice big yellow rubber gloves. You put them on and then you can keep on going. So, it's in this way that we cope, we adapt with changing conditions in life and find ways to maintain a lasting wellbeing in a changing world.

The takeaway point here is that as challenges grow and as vulnerabilities grow we need to increase resources as well. And as a clinician, a parent, an educator, a coach, a business consultant, and a mindfulness teacher, I've seen many situations in which the challenges and the vulnerabilities were high and the person was under-resourced.

So, that's what I want to focus with you on here, how to grow resources. Not to grow resources from a practical standpoint; like challenges and vulnerabilities, we might find resources out in the world in the body and in the mind.

All are important places to intervene. But if you think about it the mind has a special advantage in that we're able to influence it routinely and we take the benefits with us wherever we go.

So, I'm going to focus here on the fundamental process of growing resources, inner strengths, capabilities, knowhow, positive mood, and the healing of earlier life experiences. I'm going to talk with you about how to do that, how to grow those resources hardwired into your own nervous system.

Before I dive into the details though, I just like to mention some well-known fundamental resources. Mindfulness, which is foundational for growing the rest of them, because if we're not mindful of our situations we won't know which resources to develop. And you'll see we need to sustain mindfulness to the experiences that we're having to help them leave lasting traces behind as a durable change in neural structure or function.

So additionally, we have classic character virtues. As a Boy Scout, and I learned to be thrifty, brave, clean, and reverent, and I think eight other virtues. Knowhow—knowing how to lean into an interaction and knowing when to lean back; knowing how to get something done to manage a meeting, to work with the team of other people; knowing how to deal with your own thoughts and feelings skills of various kinds—those are inner resources. Certain motivations, positive intentions, values, aims, dreams that are wholesome and useful, those also are inner resources.

And then certainly positive mood. Happiness is itself a fundamental psychological resource. There is a lot of research that shows that happiness is very helpful for dealing with really hard conditions in life—an authentic happiness not a "fake it till you make it" happiness. And so, we're going to explore how to grow a positive mood and positive emotions in general. And certainly, key resources include things like compassion and caring and love for other people as well as resilience, grit, and determination, from the inside, for yourself.

It's interesting to think about these topics in terms of who needs them the most. I've found as someone who's presented this material for many years now that it's easy to reduce it to something as simple, and in a way, trivial as, well, "smell the flowers along the way." And I want to be clear here, I'm talking about something that is a foundation of self-reliance, a foundation of personal autonomy, as we deal with the world around us.

The harder a person's life, the more that that person is challenged, the more that that person is living in settings that have many vulnerabilities, the less that that person is being supported by the outer world, including that person's relationships, the more important it is for that person to look for opportunities to have beneficial experiences of various kinds in the flow of daily life. And then, critically important—and I'll talk about how to do this—help those experiences land inside as the seeds which then grow over time inside the person's nervous system of a fundamentally resilient wellbeing.

As a framing comment here, I want to talk about three ways to engage the mind because as I focus here on one of those three ways I want to put it in context. My own background includes many years of mindfulness training.

I started meditating in 1974. I'm also a clinical psychologist. I'm grounded in those methods. I've also been involved in the human potential movement, self-help territory and I've been a parent and educator and I've worked in business.

When I think back on all the methods, all the useful ideas and tools for engaging our feelings, our sensations, our desires, our mind altogether, I think they fall into three basic categories. The first category is simply to be with what's there—feel the feelings, experience the experience, do so usefully. Stepping back from the movie to witness it 20 rows back, eating some popcorn, whoa, that looks horrible! But still experiencing whatever there is to experience.

Hopefully there are other things happening as well as we'd be with what's there such as self-compassion, or self-acceptance, curiosity, investigation. Sometimes it's helpful to investigate what is more fundamental or soft or vulnerable underneath the surface, such as the hurt that often lies beneath anger. As we be with what's there, it might change but we're not making deliberate efforts in our minds to nudge it one way or another. I think this way of relating to the mind is fundamental. It's often the last resort because that's all we can do. All we can do is just ride out the storm, hopefully not making things worse. And also, as practice matures, as people develop over their lifespan, more and more they often find themselves simply being with the moment, hanging out, present at the front edge of now, continuously letting go.

But this is not the only way to practice with the mind. And I think in some quarters it's become overvalued, that the only way to relate to the mind is a kind of choice-less awareness, a sort of inert witnessing of the streaming of consciousness. It's also very important, in addition to being with the mind, to work with the mind. And there are two aspects of working with the mind in which we prevent or release or decrease what is negative, what is painful or harmful for ourselves and other people, and we encourage, protect, or create that which is positive, that which is beneficial for ourselves and other people.

So, for example in that second way to engage the mind, reducing or preventing or abandoning the negative, you might let go of tension in your body or vent feelings or listen to some of those thoughts that make you crazy or make other people crazy and disengage from them. Let them go. Or maybe release or decrease or even abandon problematic desires. Those are natural and important forms of letting go. And then of course it's important to let in, to grow inner fortitude inner strength, determination, skillfulness, compassion for others, empathy for others, compassion for yourself, the kind of inner resources that I'm going to focus on here.

All three of these are important. All three of them work together. For example, to simply be with the mind, it's necessary to grow resources inside so we can tolerate sometimes what we're being with. Otherwise opening to experience can sometimes feel like opening a trap door to hell. So, we need to develop resources such as steadiness of mind or as psychologists call it distress tolerance. Being able to manage our feelings without being flooded by them. So, by growing the resource, we are more able to be with the mind. Alternately we draw upon being with the mind to let go because we need to be with the results and see what they turn out to be. All three of these work together.

So, if you were to think of your mind as kind of like a garden, a simple metaphor here, we can witness it, we can pull weeds and we can plant flowers. I'm going to focus on the planting flowers in the garden of the mind and therefore the brain, but it's in this larger context.

The second point I like to make about all of this as a frame is that mindfulness is to be present in all three ways to relate to the mind. There's a misunderstanding that's developed that mindfulness means only a passive witnessing of the stream of consciousness. So, that any form of wise effort with the mind is somehow at odds with or in conflict with mindfulness. And I've heard people say sometimes, that's not mindfulness. I say, Oh that's not a correct understanding of mindfulness. Because mindfulness has to be present while we're walking, while we're talking with our teenager, while we're trying to get a toddler into a car seat—one of the most stressful things known to humankind.

Mindfulness is to be present as we have opportunities for gratitude or awe or self-compassion, and we take these experiences into our selves. So, mindfulness is to be present in all three ways to engage the mind.

I'm going to focus here, as I said, on the third of these: cultivating with the beneficial. But it's in this larger context. So, with that as a context then, I want to talk about something really interesting, which is that as the focus has emerged in positive psychology these days on character strengths and other forms of resourcing oneself, there's been a lot of attention on identifying key resources inside yourself and using them. Well that's great but what about growing them in the first place? What about acquiring them? Where do they come from and how can we get more of them?

It's interesting that roughly a third of the variation in human attributes, psychological characteristics including inner resources, is based on heritable factors essentially woven into our DNA. Innate. The other two thirds on average are the variation in human attributes, including our resources, are based on what is acquired as a result of the way the world treats us and what we do about it and how we engage our own minds.

This two-thirds fundamentally is under human influence, which is both hopeful and takes us to a fundamental kind of responsibility. And to bottom-line all this, if we are to heavily influence ourselves over this fundamental process of development of healing, of change for the better, that means we have to engage the brain. Because if we're going to develop anything that lasts, that requires some kind of physical change in the body, particularly in its nervous system, whose headquarters is the brain. The fundamental acquiring here then is how do we change the brain for the better? And that's what I want to talk with you about now.

So, to change the brain for the better involves many different kinds of methods and before I dive into them, I want to sort of level with you here and give you an overview of the current research on this topic. First of all, there is great evidence that mental practices of various kinds in human beings, such as mindfulness training, produce lasting benefits psychologically, presumably via some kind of change in the brain. In effect, mental practice A through something changing in the black box of the brain B produces mental results C, such as greater trait mindfulness. There's tremendous evidence for that.

Second, in studies that are invasive—acknowledging and then moving on from the ethical considerations here—invasive studies of non-human animals have shown again and again and again including down at the cellular, even molecular level, that the apparent experiences that the cat, the rat, the monkey is having are leading to lasting physical changes in their nervous systems. There's a great deal of evidence for that.

There's some evidence that psychological practices of various kinds, including meditation, mindfulness training, or other forms of psychological interventions can leave lasting changes in the brain. For example, common research findings include the fact that as people routinely practice mindfulness, especially in the formal setting of meditation and they do that as the years go by, even over actually shorter periods of time like eight weeks, there can be measurable lasting changes in the brain as a result, such as a thickening of cortex in the front part of the brain behind the forehead that's involved in executive control. Or changes elsewhere in the brain. There's some evidence for this but since neuroscience is a baby science and since our technology is still quite rudimentary the evidence here is partial. But it's already suggesting that our mental practices of various kinds can leave lasting changes in our brain.

There is only a little bit of evidence scattered in various kinds of studies, including on non-human animals, that there are internal deliberate things that people can do. Learning factors that could be described broadly, such as extending the duration of an experience or intensifying it for oneself, or focusing on what is personally meaningful about it. There's a little bit of evidence that the engagement of those learning factors—which is what I'm going to focus on here—can produce a lasting change in the brain.

So, I want to be honest with you and humble about what is currently known. It's really interesting that even as so many people are involved in broadly defined "the growth business," there is very little of the general theory of growth applied to social emotional learning and very, very little focus on what people can do from the inside out to steepen their growth curve. I think that's a missing opportunity, and I really hope that more research is being done in this area.

That said, in deeply scientific saying, the absence of evidence is not evidence of absence. And particularly if the risks or costs of an intervention are relatively low, such for example you in this program trying inside your mind some of the methods I'm describing to you. If something is plausible, and what I'm saying here is certainly plausible, it can be useful to run the experiment, run a little experiment inside the laboratory of your own mind, which means inside the laboratory of your own brain and see what the internal evidence is for you.

So, continuing here then, if you just kind of imagine the brain, it's quite an extraordinary organ. It looks like rotten cauliflower kind of from the outside. It's judged actually by scientists, even though it's a very modest looking, to be arguably the most complex physical object currently known to humankind. It contains roughly 1.1 trillion cells about 100-billion of which are neurons. We have as many neurons in our in our head as are stars in the Milky Way galaxy. Typical neuron is making several thousand connections with other neurons, little connections called synapses, giving us—and each one of them is like a little microprocessor—an internal network of several hundred trillion microprocessors sparkling away, even as I speak with you here, and even as you listen to this or watch it along the way. Wow.

Typical neuron is firing five to 50 times a second. Large scale patterns of synchronized activity sweep through the brain many times a second. Over the course of a single minute quadrillions of synoptic events have preceded, have occurred, right between our ears. Wow. So how can we help this amazing organ be as effective as possible to help us deal with our day or our life and grow things inside that we can draw upon for other people?

Now I would like to talk with you about the fundamental process of what Jeffrey Schwartz at UCLA has called self-directed neuroplasticity. How? How can the brain change for the better? And in the process of it changing for the better, how can we change for the better and become happier and stronger, wiser, and more loving along the way?

The fundamental neuropsychology of learning has two necessary and sufficient stages. And by the way, when I talk about learning I'm using that term broadly like psychologists do to include emotional learning, somatic learning, social learning, attitudinal learning, motivational learning, even spiritual learning. Really compared to the multiplication tables, probably the kind of learning that we care about actually the most. So, in terms of this process of development, which includes healing, another form of learning, it occurs in two unnecessary stages.

The first stage is to have the experience. There's a little bit of learning that occurs through unconscious processes, but most of the processes of helping ourselves heal and grow and strengthen occurs through conscious experiences. We don't yet have the kind of technology that they had in the movie *The Matrix*—and frankly hope we never do—in which we could jack a cable into the back of the head and transfer the file and suddenly somebody knows how to fly a helicopter. We don't have that. We need to begin with the experience such as an experience of mindfulness or an experience of gratitude or an experience of self-worth. That's where we start. But for there to be any kind of lasting change for the better, besides a passing experience, by definition there must be a physical change as a result. Otherwise the experience might be pleasant in the moment, might be useful in the moment, but it by definition leaves no lasting value behind.

There are different ways of talking about these two stages. One way I think of it frankly as you get the song playing in the inner iPod, or because I'm older I might think about the inner jukebox. Get that song playing. And then critically important in the second stage, turn on the inner recorder. There are different ways of talking about these stages in neurological language. We would speak of encoding and then consolidation or I might say more broadly activation installation or really, really simply the movement from state to trade. And I'm using the term trade here a little more broadly than is sometimes used to describe any kind of lasting or durable personal characteristic. This process of change, the two-stage process, is well summarized these days in a saying from the work of the Canadian psychologist Donald Hebb: Neurons that fire together wire together. It's a two-stage process here.

Now actually that process of change occurs through mechanisms deep down in the hardware of the brain that go well beyond simply wiring together. There are a variety of mechanisms of what's called experience dependent neuroplasticity—neuroplasticity that depends upon the experiences were having. Existing synapses can become stronger or weaker as a result of our experiences. New connections do form. That's the wiring together. There are also changes and ebbs and flows of neurochemicals inside the brain based on the experiences we're having that produce lasting changes inside such as changes of neurotransmitters like dopamine or serotonin or oxytocin.

Another mechanism of lasting change involves literally changes in the expression of genes. Tiny little strips of atoms inside the twisted-up molecules of DNA in the chromosomes and the nuclei of individual neurons. These are epigenetic changes. There are other mechanisms of change as well. I'll spare you a lot of the details. What's exciting is that with modern science we are now understanding what was known over a century ago, that something had to change in the brain. The basic idea of neuroplasticity is not breaking news but what is breaking news is the depth and variety and rapidity the speed of the various mechanisms that can be used to change the brain for the better.

Experientially this translates to if we want to become more compassionate we need to experience compassion and then internalize it. If we want to be more mindful we need to have experiences of mindfulness that we receive inside, that sink in some way that increase trait mindfulness over time. Similarly, if we want to be more determined, more committed to exercise, more committed to sobriety, more committed to social justice, we need to have experience of determination or related factors that are in the second necessary stage internalized.

The takeaway here, for me, as a longtime psychologist, parent, educator, and so forth, is actually a really humbling one. Experiences in the moment can be useful. They can be enjoyable, but do they leave any lasting value? Do we gain from them in any way? Is there any kind of healing, growth, or development or position of inner strengths, inner resources? And it's for me humbling, even haunting, to appreciate that most of the experiences that people have, even hard won, well-earned experiences, leave no lasting traces behind. They wash through the brain like water through a sieve.

And it's remarkable to appreciate that we have this phenomenal opportunity right under our noses to get better at helping the experiences that we're having leave some kind of lasting value inside us, hardwired into our nervous system. And of course, I'm going to be talking with you about how to do this.

And this general point about the low conversion rate from experiences we're having into any kind of lasting change is sharpened when you consider what scientists call the brain's evolved negativity bias. I think of it as we have a brain like Velcro for bad experiences, but Teflon for good ones. And that's because as we evolved, as our ancestors evolved over the 600-million-year evolutionary time scale of the human nervous system, it was really important to do two things. To kind of simplify it to "get carrots" like food or mating opportunities, but avoid "sticks" like predators or natural hazards or aggression between bands or inside bands. Both are important—carrots and sticks—but there's a fundamental difference in the wild. If you fail to get a carrot today, you probably have a chance at one tomorrow. But if you fail to avoid that stick today, whack! No more carrots forever.

As a result, we have a brain that's designed to do five things. It's hardwired into it. First we tend to scan for bad news out in the world, in the body, in the mind. What could go wrong? What's coming around the horizon? What do I need to deal with?

Second, soon as we find that one tile in the mosaic of reality that's blinking red, whoosh, the brain zooms in and hyper focuses upon it. That's one reason why in Barbara Fredrickson's wonderful theory of the effects of positive emotions is described as broaden and build. Because as we're experiencing emotionally positive things, our field of awareness and perceptual field tends to widen. On the other hand, as we become more anxious, more irritated, more frustrated, our attention tends to close down on that one tile, as I said, in the mosaic of our experience, that's flashing red.

The third thing that happens by design is that we overreact to the negative. People react more to pain than to pleasure. People will react more to losing something than to gaining the same thing. That's the basis for Daniel Kahneman, the psychologist who won a Nobel Prize in Economics, for what's called loss aversion or prospect theory.

Another example of this overreaction to things is that we are much more affected by negative experiences with other people than we are by positive ones. Negative interactions in a relationship have much more impact than positive ones, and need therefore to be offset by a lot of positive interactions. When I came across that finding a grad school I immediately rewound the tape of the last two days with my wife and thought, "Mmm, I need to raise my game."

And then the brain has this fourth fundamental characteristic as an aspect of the negativity bias in which it fast tracks the experience into memory, especially emotional memory, somatic memory, body memory. Once burned twice shy. For example, we're very effected, we're designed to be effected quickly by experiences of helplessness, defeat and entrapment, futility, and very rapidly acquire was called learned helplessness. And it takes many times, as many counter experiences, to acquire over time of what's called learned optimism.

The fifth evolved feature of the negativity bias hardwired into the brain—thanks, Mother Nature—is the ways in which our painful, irritating, frustrating, stressful experiences sensitize us to negative experiences and that happens with the hormone cortisol. It is released when we are feeling pressured or irritated or driving. It's certainly released in moderate to severe, even traumatic stressful conditions. And cortisol, as it's released, goes up into the brain where it has a kind of one-two punch. The first thing it does is that it's sensitizes the alarm bell of the brain, the amygdala, these two little regions about the size of almonds in the center of the brain that are like threat detectors. So now the threat detector is a little more on a hair trigger and it's going to ring a little more loudly.

The second thing the cortisol does in the brain is that it overstimulates and eventually kills neurons and then gradually weakens a nearby part of the brain called the hippocampus—a little seahorse shaped region in the brain which is the basis of its name that's close to the amygdala. And this is important because the hippocampus helps us in three ways. First it puts things in context. This is now that was then. Second the hippocampus inhibits—it calms down the alarm bell, the amygdala. And the third thing that the hippocampus does for us is that it signals another nearby and really important part of the brain, the hypothalamus, that there are enough stress hormones already. No more.

Well this creates a vicious cycle. As we sensitize the alarm bell and weaken the regulation of it, we become just a little more vulnerable to stress tomorrow based on the stressful experiences we have today. And as we become a little more vulnerable tomorrow to exacerbation, anxiety, hurt, drivenness—as we become a little more vulnerable to that tomorrow—that releases just a little more cortisol which makes us even more vulnerable the day after, in a vicious cycle. And it's important to appreciate that these are deliberate. These are useful for ancestors living in Jurassic Park or back in the Stone Age on the Serengeti plains. But today these hardwired tendencies in us create a lot of unnecessary suffering under most conditions. A lot of unnecessary worry, unnecessary self-criticism, and unnecessary conflicts with others.

Because as the negativity bias wears on us, it has a sixth feature which is that we tend to get involved in vicious cycles with other people as we become more negative ourselves, the world tends to treat us more negatively which confirms our expectations and round and round and round we go. In effect, the negativity bias functions as a kind of universal well intended learning disability. In effect, the negativity bias is like a bottleneck in the brain. It allows negative experiences to go right in, fast tracked for storage and for usage and influence later. And meanwhile most of our beneficial experiences sort of just bounce right off. And that's why it's so important to help ourselves a handful of times every day, and maybe in particular with key experiences we want to internalize.

It's so important to help ourselves get the benefit from the useful experiences we're having. Not to cling to them, not to crave them. In fact, actually as we fill ourselves up increasingly over time we become less hungry. We become less driven to grab for the next shiny object down the road. And then my next talk I'll tell you how to do this, step by step, grounded in the science of positive neuroplasticity and in the flow of everyday life.

HARDWIRING INNER RESOURCES: HEAL

LESSON 4

This lesson teaches you how to have lasting gains from passing experiences. In effect, how can you increase the conversion rate of beneficial states to beneficial traits?

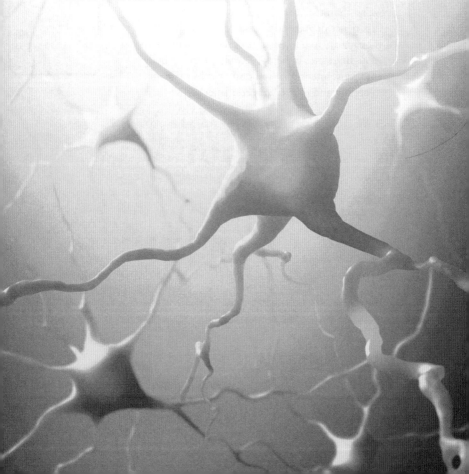

HEAL

The framework known as HEAL speaks to the fundamental process of self-directed neuroplasticity, including the two necessary and sufficient stages in this process.

Have a beneficial experience. Usually, this is an experience we're already having—such as a sense of accomplishment or a moment of connection with another person—and all we need to do is notice it and then take it into ourselves. The other way to have a beneficial experience is to deliberately create one, such as calling up things we're thankful for to help ourselves have an experience of gratitude. Research has shown that the capacity to self-generate or self-activate useful thoughts, states of being, sensations in the body, emotions, intentions, and desires is fundamental to coping and to everyday resilience.

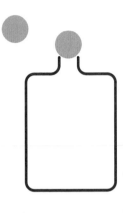

Once we have a beneficial experience, how can we internalize it?

Internalization has two fundamentally distinct aspects, subjectively and objectively: enriching and absorbing. Subjectively, the enriching aspect is a sense of the experience being big, intense, and lasting in the mind. Absorbing subjectively feels like really receiving it into oneself and giving over to it experientially. Objectively, enriching is a matter of a sustained, intense, pervading pattern of neural activation. Absorbing objectively is a matter of sensitizing, priming, and making more efficient the memory-making machinery of the nervous system.

Enrich the experience. Enriching is a matter of popping open the bottleneck in the brain to help the good experiences—which can be metaphorically described as balls—come in. There are five different ways you can help yourself enrich your experiences so that the installation of them in your nervous system is increased.

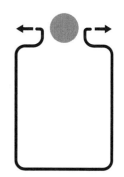

Duration. Keep those neurons firing together so they have a chance to wire together.

Intensity. Intensify the experience. Help it pervade your mind, even if it's a purely subtle experience, such as awe or tranquility. Sometimes gratitude can feel fairly subtle, but if it's all that fills your mind, it's effectively intense.

Multimodality. Help the experience be multisensory, or multimodal, bringing to bear thoughts, feelings, sensations, intentions, actions, and desires. The richer the experience, the more it's enriched.

Novelty. The brain is a big novelty detector. As our ancestors moved around in the wild, they needed to know what new thing they had to pay attention to. If we bring a sense of childlike interest or curiosity to the experiences we're having, then that will naturally intensify them in terms of their internalization.

Salience. Focus on what's relevant or meaningful to you in the experience you're having. The brain is designed to learn from the experiences that the animal—in this case, a human being—considers to be relevant. Focusing on the personal relevance of an experience will really help it land.

Absorb the experience. It's as if the experience, or ball, has moved to the bottleneck of the brain and is now coming in, sinking, and staying put. There are three ways you can help an experience be absorbed—in other words, ways you can sensitize and turbocharge the memory-making machinery of the brain.

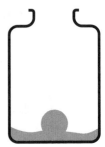

> **Intend to receive the experience into yourself**. For many people, this is a critical first step because there's something that makes them uncomfortable about actually sustaining an experience of gratitude or of feeling close to or affectionate with another person. We can be with our beneficial experiences, and we can intend to receive them in ways that are private and, in the process, grow strengths inside for dealing with challenges.
>
> **Sense the experience sinking into you**. This tends to engage a part of the brain on the inside of the temporal lobes called the insula, which is involved in interoception (the sense that includes gut feelings) and with the sense of who we are becoming. Engaging the insula tends to increase the memory and neural traces that are left behind.
>
> **Be aware of ways the experience is rewarding**. This tends to increase the activity of dopamine and norepinephrine, two important neurotransmitter systems that are involved with the tracking of reward. As dopamine and norepinephrine activity increases in the hippocampus—which is the front end of the internalization of beneficial experiences—that flags the experience we're having at the time as a keeper and prioritizes it for protection during processes of long-term storage.

Link positive and negative material. Linking is the process in which we are aware of something beneficial—something positive— alongside some matched negative material. For example, we could be aware of a worry while simultaneously drawing our attention to the resources we have to deal with that issue, such as allies who will help or a sense of calm strength. And because neurons that fire together wire together, through association—especially if the positive experience is stronger—the positive experience will gradually ease, calm, bring wisdom to, contextualize, and even eventually replace the negative material. Linking is natural and routine, and we can do it deliberately and effectively in the flow of everyday life. One of the most powerful ways to do this is to know what the negative material is that you're grappling with, such as a generally anxious mood or the residues of childhood feelings of inadequacy. If you know what the negative material is, then everyday life gives you many opportunities to be mindful of ways in which you could have beneficial experiences that are usefully matched to that negative material.

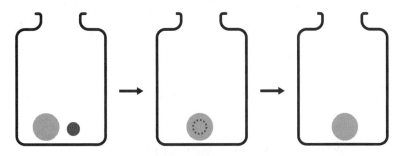

Most beneficial experiences are enjoyable. Occasionally, there are beneficial experiences that are unpleasant or painful, such as healthy remorse. It's unpleasant, but it's important to take in. And some pleasant experiences are not so good for us, such as that first rush of anger or eating too many cookies.

To summarize all of this in four direct and simple words: Have it, enjoy it. In other words, have the beneficial experience and then enjoy it—receive it into yourself. Help the beneficial experience enter into the bottleneck and stay in the bottle.

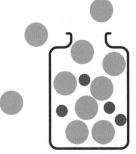

MINDFULNESS EXERCISES

The following are three different ways to take in the good and engage the HEAL framework, focusing on the first three steps (the linking step is optional).

NOTICING RELAXING AS YOU EXHALE

Notice the fact that as you exhale, you naturally relax. This is because as you exhale, part of the nervous system—the parasympathetic wing of the autonomic nervous system—engages exhalation and naturally slows the rate of your heart beating. On the other hand, when you inhale, the sympathetic wing of the nervous system gets involved, accelerating the rate of your heart beating.

Start foregrounding an awareness, meaning start noticing what's already happening in the back of your awareness: that as you exhale, you slow down and naturally relax.

Naturally extend the length of your exhalation to give you more opportunities to be aware of the relaxation that comes with it. As you start to have an experience of relaxing, move into installing this experience in your nervous system by enriching and absorbing it.

> Stay with the feeling of relaxing and bring awareness to it in your body as you relax. Here, the sense of relaxing is being used as the object of attention upon which you are meditating.

> You can also have a sense of absorbing, often mixed with enriching. You can explore the sense of the relaxation spreading in your body, making room for it. And you can be aware of what feels good and is rewarding about it as you focus on absorbing relaxation into yourself.

CREATING GRATITUDE/GLADNESS

Bring to mind one or more things that you naturally and easily feel thankful for. This could be other people. It could be simple, such as thankfulness for chocolate, or vast, such as thankfulness for life altogether. As you start to recognize things to be thankful for, help that recognition become an experience of gratitude, perhaps along with other related experiences, such as gladness or happiness.

Then, as you start to have an experience of gratitude, move into enriching and absorbing it so it can increase its likelihood of leaving a lasting trace behind.

> With regard to enriching the experience of gratitude, keep it going. Try to get a sense in your own body of what it's like to be grateful. Stay with it. And if you want, you can be aware of how gratitude is relevant to you or why it's important to you. This, too, is a factor of enriching.

> You can also absorb this experience with the sense of giving over to it, letting it land in you and sinking into gratitude as it sinks into you. You might have a sense of this experience landing inside you to help you develop an attitude of gratitude—in other words, to establish more trait gratitude inside you.

CREATING WARM FEELINGS FOR SOMEONE

Bring to mind one or more beings that you care about, such as a pet, friend, partner, child, or group of friends. As you bring them to mind, help the knowing of them become an experience of warm caring—perhaps compassion, kindness, friendliness, or love. Help yourself create an experience of warm feelings for someone.

Then, as you start to have some sense of warmth and caring, move into installation and internalize this experience.

> You can enrich this experience through multimodality, which means to have it be more experiential with an action, such as putting your hand on your heart or getting a sense of what happens in your face as you bring to mind someone you care about. This involves taking warm feelings as your object of meditation—in effect, marinating in a warmth like caring or lovingness.

> You can also absorb this experience into yourself, letting it really spread inside and letting yourself have it.

As you do this, other thoughts might arise or your mind might wander. This is normal. Sometimes the opposite feeling arises, such as not feeling so caring or so cared about. That's okay, too. Just come back to placing your attention on the primary experience you're wanting to take in—in this case, warm feelings for someone. You can also be aware of what feels good about warmheartedness, which will help the experience sink in even more.

BENEFITS OF ENGAGING POSITIVE NEUROPLASTICITY

Several benefits are available to us when we engage positive neuroplasticity in a deliberate way.

Inside, we grow particular resources, such as relaxation and calm, trait gratitude, or trait warmheartedness, and related qualities, such as compassion, kindness, or loyalty to other people. We can also grow specific resources that are particularly matched to the issues that we have. For example, if we tend toward anxiety, we can deliberately grow resources such as calm strength.

Built into this process are implicit benefits. For example, there's some mindfulness training. In meditative language, it's a kind of mini concentration practice in which we sustain attention to something useful to draw it into ourselves. In addition, implicit in taking in the good is a sense of being on your own side, or trying to help yourself.

You could be sensitizing your brain to the positive. In effect, if the brain has a negativity bias, we can gradually potentially train it into more of a positivity bias. By sensitizing the brain to the positive, it becomes faster, more efficient, and better at turning passing beneficial states into lasting beneficial traits.

As we grow resources inside ourselves, we often become more effective and capable in the world and with other people. The world starts treating us better, doors start opening, and we start seeing opportunities. Positive cycles with others can develop as well.

HARDWIRING INNER RESOURCES: HEAL

So, now let's explore how to have lasting gains from passing experiences. In effect, how can we increase the conversion rate, the return on investment, from the experiences we're having, the beneficial states, how can we increase their conversion rate into beneficial traits? And to frame this topic I'd like to share with you a story that I heard in a particular frame. You may have heard this story as well. Essentially the way I heard it was that a woman was asked toward the end of her life, "Grandmother, how did you become so happy? What did you do? How did you become so strong, so capable, so effective? What did you do? How did you become so wise? How did you become so loved? What did you do? How did you do it?"

She paused. She reflected and then she said, "You know, when I was young like you I realized that in my heart were two wolves, one of love and one of hate. And I realized that everything depended upon which one I fed each day."

That's a profound teaching story. It speaks of course to the presence, metaphorically, of the wolf of hate, and most beings—certainly myself—the capacity of and inclination toward resentment, envy, aggression, even violence and war. If we hate the wolf of hate, we just feed the wolf of hate. And what the story speaks to in its second aspect is the vital importance of the one we feed. Do we feed the wolf of hate or the wolf of love? Do we feed the wolf of self-criticism that's destructive and tears us down? Do we feed the wolf of needless worry, anxious rumination, getting involved in our case against other people that's resentful and aggrieved? Do we feed those tendencies in us? And in the process of feeding them—since neurons that fire together wire together—stimulate and therefore strengthen the neural substrates of those unhelpful, unskillful, even unwholesome states of mind? Or alternately do we feed the wolf of love? Or the wolf of mindfulness or gratitude or grit or motivation or happiness altogether? That's our opportunity. Day after day, as we make those choices to withdraw food from the problematic tendencies in us or the inclinations of our own mind and heart, and instead feed that which is helpful, that which is happy and wholesome and beneficial for ourselves and often for others as well.

So now I'd like to talk with you about how to actually do that in your own brain. And I'm going to use a framework that I've developed summarized in the acronym HEAL—H-E-A-L. It speaks to the fundamental process of self-directed neuroplasticity, including the necessary and sufficient two stages in this process. To begin with we first must have a beneficial experience. Like I said we can't just jack cable into the back of the head and suddenly become more confident. We need to begin with some kind of an experience. Usually it's an experience we're already having and all we need to do is notice it.

There are we are moving through our day. There's a moment of friendly ness with the hot dog vendor. There's a moment of relief that things turned out well. There's a moment of connection with another person, and maybe a sense of accomplishment that we got something done. Or maybe there's a sense of our own good intentions or our own durability, our own capacity to endure and keep on going. Whatever it might be, the song is already playing as it were in the inner iPod, why not turn on the recorder? Notice it and then take it into ourselves.

The other way to have a beneficial experience is to deliberately create it, such as calling up things that we're thankful for to help ourselves have an experience of gratitude. Or in my case, as a longtime rock climber, calling up the body memory of pulling over an overhang to have a sense of strength when I have to really deal with someone who's coming at me. There is a place for creating experiences.

Sometimes people think that that's overly manipulative. I say so what? Our mind our brains are being manipulated all day long by other people, forces of media, including alarm bells that are ringing out there in the world. And we're being manipulated by the reactions arising inside ourselves. So, why not manipulate ourselves skillfully? And has a lot of research shows the capacity to self-generate, self-activate useful states of being useful thoughts, useful sensations in the body, useful emotions, useful intentions and desires is very fundamental to coping and to everyday resilience.

All right now we have that beneficial experience. It's happening. How can we take it on? How can we internalize it? I think internalization has two fundamentally distinct aspects: a subjectively and objectively. I call them enriching and absorbing. The enriching aspect, subjectively, is a sense of the experience being big, intense, lasting in the mind. The song is playing loudly. Absorbing subjectively feels like really receiving it into one's self, making room for one's self, giving over to it experientially. Maybe with a sense, even literally, of something sinking in like water into a sponge or light moving inside into shadows or a kind of soothing balm coming down into oneself. That's the experience of absorbing.

Objectively, in terms of what's happening in the in the neurology, enriching is essentially as a matter of a sustained, intense, pervading pattern of neural activation. And absorbing objectively is a matter of sensitizing, priming and making more efficient the memory making machinery of the nervous system. It's in effect like helping that recorder be better at registering the music that's playing in your mind.

So, just to talk about each one of them in particular, enriching is kind of a matter of popping open the bottleneck in the brain to help the good experiences, maybe metaphorically described as green balls, to really come on in. And there are five different ways you can help yourself enrich your experiences so that the installation of them in your nervous system is increased. You don't need to do all these five techniques, just one of them is fine. But I like to know that there are different things I can do. If you think about it, a lot of the essence of what I'm talking about here is self-reliance and resourcefulness. So, it's nice to know, resourcefully, that there are multiple things we can do inside our own mind, authentically, to help learning land inside us, in the broadest sense of that word learning.

So, the first way to enrich an experience is to keep it going. Keep that song playing, keep those neurons firing together so they have a chance to wire together. A second way to increase the enrichment of an experience is to intensify the experience. Turn up the music. Help it pervade your mind, even if it's a purely subtle experience like awe or tranquility. Sometimes gratitude can feel fairly subtle, but if it's all that fills your mind, it's effectively intense.

A third aspect of enriching, as every kindergarten teacher knows, is to help the experience be multisensory, multi-modal I say. Bringing to bear thoughts, feelings, sensations, intentions, actions, desires. The richer the experience the more it's enriched.

A fourth factor of enriching is novelty. The brain is a big novelty detector. As our ancestors moved around back in the Stone Age, what's the news? What's the new thing I need to pay attention to? So, if we bring a sense of childlike interest or curiosity, or as the saying has it "Zen mind, Beginner's mind," or quality of beginner's mind, to the experiences we're having, then that will naturally intensify them in terms of their internalization.

And then the fifth factor of enriching, one that I find personally really useful, is to focus on what's relevant. What's meaningful for you or salient in the experience or having? The brain is designed to learn from the experiences that the animal, in this case us, considers to be relevant. So, for example why might it be particularly relevant today to really register that it goes better with your partner if you lean into a tricky interaction than lean away and search for the remote control for the television? Or why might it be meaningful or relevant for you today to really pay attention to an opportunity to feel seen or respected by another person? Particularly given a childhood, perhaps, or earlier in adulthood, in which you were left out dismissed or devalued. Focusing on the personal relevance of an experience will really help it land.

And then moving on to absorbing. It's like that green ball, as it were, or the experience as it were that's moved to the bottleneck of the brain and coming into us, is now coming in and sinking and sticking to our mental ribs.

There are three ways you can help and experience be absorbed—in other words three ways you can sensitize and turbocharge the memory making machinery of the brain. The first is simple: intend to receive it into yourself. For many people that's a critical first step because there's something that makes them uncomfortable about actually sustaining an experience of gratitude or sustaining an experience of feeling close to or affectionate with another person. There is something hard about that. Maybe they feel they don't deserve it. Maybe they're worried that if they pay attention to, and experience is beneficial, over the course of a single breath, they'll lower their guard and that's when the world will get them. Understandable, and still not really true.

We can stay with, we can be with, our beneficial experiences and we can intend to receive them in ways that are private. The world doesn't need to know we're doing it. And in the process of doing this, grow strengths inside for dealing with the bad things. We can be both vigilant and aware of what's happening around us while, simultaneously on the inside out, receiving into ourselves whatever is beneficial that we judge is beneficial in the present moment. So, that's intending.

A second factor that turbochargers the memory making machinery of the brain is to sense in the body that the experience is sinking in. Technically, that tends to engage a part of the brain called the insula on the inside of the temporal lobes. Two of them, like most of us in the brain, kind of like Noah's Ark, there's two of almost everything in the brain. And if there's only one of something in the brain that means that it's really old and really fundamental in terms of the evolution of the brain; such as there's only one hypothalamus.

So, if we tune into or sense into the experience, we engage the insula. The insula is very involved in what's called interoception, including gut feelings. And it's very involved with the sense of who we are becoming. So, engaging the insula by sensing the experience coming in gets it involved, and that tends to increase the memory traces, the neural traces, that are left behind.

And a third way, last, to increase absorbing is to focus on what's rewarding about the experience. What's enjoyable about it or meaningful about it? In so doing that will tend to increase the activity of dopamine and norepinephrine, two important neurotransmitter systems that are involved with the tracking of reward. And as dopamine and norepinephrine activity increase in the hippocampus—which is the front end of a lot of internalization of beneficial experiences—as dopamine and norepinephrine activity increase in the hippocampus, that flags the experience we're having at the time as a keeper for, and prioritizes it for protection, during processes of long term storage that can last hours and days and even weeks.

So, in these three different kinds of ways—and any one of them is good, the more the better—you can increase the sensitivity of the memory making machinery of your brain. In effect, you can increase its capacity to absorb the experience in ways that leave lasting physical changes behind. This is the fundamental process of self-directed helping yourself to grow and learn and develop.

I think of it a little bit like a fire. I've done a lot of camping, and step one: have the experience, have fire. Often, usually, because you notice it's already burning or if need be, create the experience like the fire. Step two enriching. Protect the fire. Don't let other people rain on your parade. Watch that tendency in the mind to just click on to the next shiny object or chase the next word. Stay with the beneficial experience. There's no exact right number. Probably at least a few seconds in a row are really important. I use the sense of staying with an experience over the duration of a breath or two or three, half a dozen, a dozen, several dozen seconds. Just the more the better. But with the fire as it were, watch the tendency to move away from the fire or let other people put it out, and even add fuel to the fire, enrich it further, so it burns even more brightly.

And then in the third step, absorb, Ahhh! We take the warmth of the fire into ourselves and receive it. That's the fundamental necessary and sufficient process of the neuropsychology of personal growth, personal healing, and change for the better.

Additionally, in the HEAL acronym, there's a fourth step. I call it linking. This is the process in which we are aware of two things at once. Previously I was only talking about beneficial experiences, most of which are enjoyable. Occasionally there are beneficial experiences that are unpleasant or painful, such as healthy remorse or the sense of disenchantment—healthy disenchantment, where you realize that a particular job or a particular relationship is just not really going to work out. It's unpleasant but it's important to take in. It's also true that some pleasant experiences are not so good for us, such as that first rush of anger, or you know eating way too many cookies, or having way too many drinks.

That said, most beneficial experiences are actually enjoyable. They have a positive reward value. And that's because as our ancestors evolved, they evolved with Mother Nature's help, reward systems to mark and motivate those experiences, those states of being, that were most useful for themselves, and others of their kind, for survival purposes, and which helped grow resources over time also for survival purposes. So, the enjoyability of an experience actually is typically a marker of its value.

By the way, it's interesting that I think maybe in reaction to the field of positive psychology, we have these professional Grinches around who are saying, "Oh, happiness is fooling you and so forth." No, happiness is skillful means. The positive experiential quality, emotionally positive quality, of the experiences is a marker, in most cases, that they're useful for us. They don't just feel good; they are good for us.

So, in that context then, I want to talk about linking, in which we are aware of something beneficial, something positive, quote unquote, alongside, at the same time as some matched negative material. For example, we could be aware of an anxiety, a worry, while simultaneously drawing our attention to the resources we have to deal with that issue, drawing our attention to allies and others who are on our side and will help, maybe drawing our attention to a sense of calming in the body and the centering in a place of calm strength, alongside that negative experience. And since neurons that fire together wire together, through association, especially if the positive experience is bigger, it will gradually associate with and ease and calm and bring wisdom to and contextualize, and even eventually replace that negative material. In effect, using my metaphor of the garden of the mind brain system, we can use flowers to compensate for, crowd out, and even actually over time replace the weeds.

This is the fundamental process of linking. It's natural to do it. Mindful awareness is itself a process of linking. If what we're aware of is, quote unquote, negative, painful, or difficult, or challenging, the spaciousness of open awareness is itself inherently untroubled. Trouble may pass through it, but awareness itself is never damaged or tainted or harmed by what it represents. In effect, awareness is like the sky, and the sky is never damaged or changed by the storm clouds passing through it. That right there is a kind of linking.

Linking might sound fancy, but it's really natural, it's routine. If we talk ourselves off the ledge when we're getting really cranked up about something that's a form of linking. Our daughter, when she was in middle school, who had a friend who said to her "Laurel remember your happy place," that is a form of linking. And we can do linking deliberately and effectively in the flow of everyday life.

And one of the most powerful ways to do linking is to know what the red ball is. Know what your negative material is that you're grappling with. Maybe, generally, an anxious mood, or a mildly depressed mood, or the residues of childhood and old feelings of inadequacy, or being left out, or not worth as much as other people, being less than other people. And then if you know what that negative material is then everyday life gives you lots of wonderful opportunities to be mindful of ways in which you could have beneficial experiences that are usefully matched to the negative material. Such as in my example of feeling left out and inadequate, based on previous life experiences, looking for opportunities that are authentic, typically mild but real. Not more than what they are, but not less than what they are. Looking for opportunities to have beneficial experiences, let's say of worth. Being seen by others, being appreciated by others, others who are grateful, others who care about you, and also opportunities to feel and recognize your own good qualities, your own good intentions, your capabilities, and your own good heart.

In effect, I'm talking here about really three things. See the good facts. The opportunities to have some kind of useful experience. But don't just see them, feel something. Often we see this someone who smiled, we see that we got something done, but it doesn't move the needle. We don't feel anything. See the good fact and let it become a good experience. I don't mean this morally, I mean it pragmatically—a beneficial experience. See the good fact, help it become a good experience, and then take that good into yourself. That's the fundamental process. And we can apply it to looking for the beneficial experiences that can help with our anxieties, our losses, our physical pains, the challenges around us and the residues of our childhood.

To summarize all this stuff in four direct and simple words: Have it, enjoy it. In other words, have the beneficial experience, help that song play inside the inner iPod, and then enjoy it, receive it into yourself. Turn on the recorder. Help the green balls—metaphorically of beneficial experiences—enter into the bottleneck and lodge in and stay in and last in your own nervous system. This is the essence of the process.

And now if you're up for it, I'd like to do something experiential with you. And you could think of this as a little kind of experiment inside the inner laboratory of your mind, which means inside the laboratory of your own brain. So, I'll talk you through three different ways to take in the good here and engage the HEAL framework with three different kinds of experiences. I'll only focus on the first three steps, because they're necessary and sufficient steps. And I won't get into the linking step here. By the way the linking step is optional because, first, it's not necessary for change. And second, sometimes those negative experiences have a surprising power. They are like black holes inside our own mind and they can just really suck us in.

So, if you do linking, it's really important to not be hijacked by the negative and to make sure that the positive experience is larger and more lasting. And if you do start getting sucked into the negative, if you try linking, just disengage from it. Re-establish the resource of the matched positive experience, and then if you want, go back to the linking. And in this experiential practice I won't do linking at all.

Always know, as with anything I'm saying, including in this practice, feel free to ignore it. Go your own way. Adapt my suggestions for your own use. And if you'd like to stay with something a little longer than I'm doing here you can do that or if you want to scoot ahead, you can do that as well. Here we go.

So, first notice the fact that as you exhale you naturally relax. That's because as we exhale a part of the nervous system called the parasympathetic wing of the autonomic nervous system engages exhalation and naturally slows the rate of the heart beating. On the other hand, when we inhale, the sympathetic wing of the nervous system gets involved which accelerates the rate of the heart beating. So, there's a natural relaxation that occurs as we exhale. So, I'll be quiet for a few moments here as I encourage you to start foregrounding an awareness. Start noticing what's already happening in the back of your awareness. That as you exhale you slow down and calm and naturally relax.

If you like, you could play with this a bit and naturally extend the length of the exhalation to give you more opportunities to be aware of the relaxation that comes with that. And as you start to have an experience of relaxing, let's move into installing this experience a little bit in your nervous system through enriching and absorbing it. Staying with the feeling of relaxing, and let's say bringing awareness to it in your body as you relax here. As a kind of meditative practice, we're using the sense of relaxing as the object of attention upon which you are meditating.

Also, often sort of mixed together with enriching, you can have a sense of absorbing. You can explore the sense of the relaxation kind of spreading in your body making room for it. And you can be aware of some of what feels good about it, what's rewarding about it, as you focus now on absorbing relaxation into yourself.

Okay, that was the first experiment: relaxation. In the flow of everyday life, most of the time when we take in the good, when we register beneficial experiences, it's quick. It's 10 seconds here, half a minute there. It's on the fly. All these different ways to turbocharge the growth process inside your own brain kind of mush together. But here, in this more formal teaching environment, I'm going to unpack these various methods and we're going to focus on them in a slightly longer and more deliberate way. But just because that's how I'm doing it here doesn't mean that this is how to do it in the flow of everyday life.

Okay, let's try the second little experiment here, experientially, and create a sense of gratitude or maybe gladness. So, if you will bring to mind one or more things that you naturally and easily feel thankful for. Could be other people. Could be a simple thing like thankfulness for chocolate. It could be vast such as thankfulness for life altogether. And as you start to recognize things to be thankful for, help that recognition become an experience of gratitude. Perhaps along with other related experiences, such as gladness or happiness.

And then as you start to have an experience of gratitude—which might have a mainly conceptual dimension to it and that's perfectly fine, the knowledge of things you've received, the things you've been given, that you're thankful for—as you have this experience let's move into enriching and absorbing it so it can increase its likelihood of leaving a lasting trace behind. So, with regard to enriching the experience of gratitude, keep it going. Try to get a sense in your own body of what it's like to be grateful. Stay with it.

And if you want you can be aware of how gratitude is relevant to you. It's important to you for whatever reasons. This too is a factor of enriching. You can also absorb this experience with the sense of giving over to it, letting it land in you, sinking into gratitude as it sinks into you. You might have a sense of this experience really landing inside to help you develop what's called an attitude of gratitude, or more of an attitude of gratitude, to establish more trait gratitude inside you. Letting it really land as you absorb it.

Okay, that's the second experiment. And by the way it's perfectly fine to continue to feel a little more relaxed or a little more grateful as we continue.

And now I like to talk about the third experiment, third little practice here, of creating warm feelings for someone and then receiving these warm feelings and related feelings of caring or feeling liked yourself by this other person. Letting them sink in. So, bring to mind one or more beings that you care about: can be a pet, can be a friend, a partner, a child, someone who's helped you, could be a group of friends. Bringing these beings to mind. And as you bring them to mine help the knowing of them become an experience of warm caring: perhaps compassion, perhaps kindness, perhaps friendliness, perhaps love altogether. Helping yourself create an experience of warm feelings for someone here.

And then as you start to have some sense here of warmth and caring, let's move into installation and internalize this experience. For example, if you want you might enrich this experience in a factor I call multi-modality—it just means to have it be more experiential within action— such as putting your hand on your heart. Or getting a sense of what happens in your face as you bring to mind someone you care about. Taking warm feelings as your object of meditation. In effect, sort of marinating in a warmth like caring, perhaps a lovingness. And you can also absorb this experience into yourself, letting it really spread inside, letting yourself have it.

As you do this, other thoughts might arise, your mind might wander, that's really normal. Sometimes the opposite arises, like not feeling so caring or so cared about. That's okay too. Just come back to, rest attention on, the primary thing, the primary experience you're wanting to take in. In this case, warm feelings for someone. You can also be aware of what feels good about warm heartedness which will help us experience sink in even more.

That completes the third little practice here, and this experiential portion. It's okay to continue feeling if you like, a little relaxed, a little grateful, and a little warm hearted as we keep on going.

And now I'd like to step back, if we can, and talk about the benefits that are available to us when we engage positive neuroplasticity in a deliberate way. The first kind of benefit is that we grow particular resources inside— resources such as relaxation and calm or trait gratitude or trait warm heartedness and related qualities such as compassion or kindness or loyalty to other people. We can also grow specific resources, as I mentioned a little bit earlier, that are particularly matched to the issues that we've got. For example, if we tend toward anxiety we can grow inner resources inside deliberately, such as calm strength, or the recognition that in most moments we're actually basically alright. We may not have been basically alright in the past, we may not be basically alright in the future, but in this moment, at least we're basically alright. And we can also grow resources, let's say for anxiety, such as clarity about how big the threats actually are. So, we don't overestimate them or underestimate them, and clarity about the kind of resources we have for dealing with them.

That's the first major benefit of routinely taking in the good, growing resources in particular. Second, built into this process, are implicit benefits. For example, there's some mindfulness training. In meditative language, it's a kind of mini-concentration practice in which we sustain attention to something useful to draw it into ourselves. It's really quite powerful to appreciate the quotation from the godfather of psychology in America, William James, who said "The education of attention would be the education par excellence." Where we rest our attention, and what we do with what our attention rests upon, is the front end of who we are becoming.

There's an old saying, you are what you eat. Actually, more fundamentally you are what you pay attention to and what you do with what you pay attention to. So implicitly in taking the good, in addition to mindfulness training, is a sense of being on your own side, of being for yourself. You're trying to help yourself. You're treating yourself like you matter, which is especially important if you haven't felt like you've mattered enough to other people.

A third kind of benefit from repeatedly and deliberately internalizing beneficial experiences—which is my core definition of taking in the good, deliberately internalizing beneficial experiences—the third benefit of that plausibly is that you could be sensitizing your brain to the positive. In effect, if the brain has a negativity bias, we can gradually potentially train it into more of a positivity bias. We'll still see the red lights, we'll still see that strange expression on the face of that other person we've got to deal with, but we'll be more resourced inside for dealing with it and will actually be more effective with those other people when we shift out of the negativity bias. Because less and less and less of the negative experiences of life will be sticking to us like Velcro, and instead we'll be more able to see real threats, real issues, rather than being distracted by little ones and little preoccupations and we'll have more resources for dealing with these challenges. So, that's the third kind of benefit: the actual sensitization of the brain to the positive, so it becomes quicker and more efficient and better at turning passing beneficial states into lasting beneficial traits.

And then the fourth benefit of doing this is that as we grow resources inside ourselves we become more effective and capable in the world and with other people. Not always, but it's a good odds strategy. The world starts treating us better, doors start opening, we start seeing opportunities and positive cycles with others can develop as well.

As I finish here I'd like to step back and really summarize where we've been. I think that it's so important in life to grow strengths inside, to grow resources of various kinds. It's easy to dismiss this process as some kind of "La Di Da" luxury item. No. This is the essence of self-reliance, including the self-reliance we need to draw upon and develop inside for the challenges all around us. We need to develop these strengths.

Well, how do we develop these strengths? One of the great strengths is learning: knowing how to learn. And it's the strength that grows the other strengths. As a kid, I read a lot of comic books, I think about superpowers. Learning is the super power of superpowers because it's a one we draw upon to grow the rest of them. So, learning how to learn the things that are important to you could be the greatest strength of all.

I hope this program has been useful to you. This is the fundamental how of self-help. This is the fundamental how of moving through your day in ways that no one can defeat, to grow the good bit by bit, synapse by synapse, drop by drop inside you. No one can stop you from doing this, in the experiences that you're having over the course of your day in the inner sanctuary of your own mind, no one can stop you from learning and growing, healing and developing bit by bit, step by step. And no one can do it for you. This is what makes it authentic and real and legitimate. And as we've explored, even in the context of the baby science that is neuroscience, everything we've explored here is completely plausible, based on research evidence.

So, to finish here I'd like to offer a quotation that has been personally very meaningful to me and I think really summarizes everything we've explored here. And it comes to us from the *Dhammapada*, a text written over 2,000 years ago. Here's the quotation: "Think not lightly of good saying it will not come to me. Drop by drop is the water pot filled. Likewise, the wise one, gathering it little by little, fills oneself with good."

As you fill yourself with good, drop by drop, bit by bit, synapse by synapse, hour by hour, and day by day that you can grow more of the good inside yourself for your own sake, and in ways that can ripple out and help other people.

Thank you very much.

MINDFULNESS IN HEARTBREAK

LESSON 5

People face hardship, heartbreak, and loss for many different reasons and in many different ways. Can you prepare for a loss? Yes, you can prepare—in the way you practice life. Understanding and practicing mindfulness will not only help you in your everyday life, but it will help you immensely as you heal from heartbreak of all kinds.

MINDFULNESS EXERCISE: A GOLDEN PAUSE

Begin by sitting comfortably. If you're sitting in a chair, make sure your legs are uncrossed. If you're sitting on the floor, lean back against something, keeping your shoulders back and arms on your lap with palms open.

Close your eyes and breathe through your nose, allowing your chest and belly to fully expand and taking in the fullness of your breath. As you exhale, relax. Sink into your body; sink into your breath.

The next time you breathe in, breathe in pure, golden sunlight from the top of your head to the tips of your fingers and toes—to every cell of your being. And as you exhale, relax and sink a little deeper into your body.

Then, as you breathe in pure, golden sunlight again, place your hand on your heart, activating and opening it. Spend the moment thinking of one thing you feel incredibly grateful for. It could be a person, place, or thing, such as something somebody recently said to you. Breathe in that gratitude, filling your whole being with it. Then, exhale and open your eyes.

FIVE PRINCIPLES OF AWARENESS

There are five principles of mental health and well-being that are the foundation of the *Don't Sweat the Small Stuff* book series, which has impacted millions of people around the globe. These principles of awareness teach us how to practice accessing our mental health and well-being in all situations—including during heartbreak and loss.

There is no doubt that we are going to endure both physical and emotional pain in life, but suffering is optional. It's in your mental reactions and emotions and your ability to return to a gentle and loving awareness of them that will help you recover from loss in a healthy way. Once you understand these principles, you'll free yourself from the mental dynamics that can keep you stuck and suffering.

The five principles of awareness are thoughts, moods, feelings, your agreement with reality, and present moment living.

Thoughts. There are two important things to understand about thoughts. First, thinking is automatic to you. Think of your thinking as being as automatic to you as breathing; we have 60,000 to 80,000 thoughts a day, and we are not really aware of many of them. Second, you are the thinker. You're just making up thoughts in your own head all day. They're coming from you, not from outside of you. You are your own thinker. Also be aware that we have repetitive thought patterns—sometimes called thought attacks—which are characterized by getting on a cycle of circular thinking that is difficult to stop.

Moods. We all have moods—specifically high moods and low moods. Life looks different in a low mood versus a high mood. In a low mood, everything could be annoying. The same thing your spouse or partner says to you that doesn't even hit your radar when you're in a high mood might really bother you in a low mood. It behooves you, in all of your relationships, to consider what kind of mood the other person is in as well as what kind of mood you are in. The ideal is to become graceful when low and grateful when high.

Feelings. We all have feelings, but often we can't have feelings before we think a thought. Most of the time, you can ask yourself, what am I thinking right now? And in this way, feelings become a guidepost and a barometer to helping you understand and become more aware of your thoughts, which can be invisible to you.

Agreement with reality. We all have separate realities. We all view the world through our own lens, our own unique filter. And every experience we have affects our filter. Along with this comes the notion of what kind of agreement with reality you have. You can choose to be the victim of your circumstances or the victor over your circumstances—the hero of your own story. And you can choose to change your agreement with reality at any time.

Present moment living. This is the highest level of awareness and engagement that you can have in your life. Research shows that people are most engaged in their lives while they're having sex, because they're not likely to be concerned about anything else in that moment. People are also highly engaged in dangerous situations; you might notice life slowing down, which is what happens when you're super present. Present moment living is the safest place to land as you're going through any kind of heartbreak or loss. This is because as you think about your past, you might dwell on your regrets, and as you think about your future, you might experience fear, but when you land in the center—in the moment—you don't have anything filling you up in the present and your awareness is what is right now.

PREPARING FOR GRIEF

Life can change on a dime. And sometimes it does. The event that causes life to change is called the initiation by crisis event. In Joseph Campbell's work *The Hero's Journey*, he talks about the initiation section of the hero's journey, in which the hero eventually faces a crisis event that shatters the hero's world, causing the hero to head on a new trajectory in life.

We can always tell when we're experiencing an initiation by crisis event because it represents a loss of identity. This can come in many different forms and in different times in our lives. The event could be the loss of a loved one through death or divorce or the loss of your health. And in this loss of identity, you can either shut down and become bitter, or you can be heartbroken open—waking up to feeling more alive.

Often grief comes over us like a wave. But these waves come and go. And if you resist, you will feel it in your body. And your body will begin to inform you when you need to grieve more deeply. If you allow your body to feel whatever is present, then whatever you need will come. Just express out what's there, and then your body will reward you with feeling good.

In times of grief, what you need is crystal clear if you take the time to reflect on it.

THE STARR MANTRA

I surrender
I trust
I accept
I release
I receive

Note that surrender doesn't mean giving up or giving in. It means allowing yourself to be broken open—to be open to what is, to be present for what is. There is only one question that you need to ask yourself to know if surrender is what you need: Can I change this?

It's okay for you to design this time of grief however you need it to be, not how anybody else wants you to have it. The world will tell you to stay busy when you're going through grief. Instead, consider this a time for you to create time for stillness and spaciousness—a time to heal and to weed out anything you don't need to do. Spend time just sitting in silence when you can.

Supreme self-care is very important when you're going through heartbreak and loss of all kinds. Think of the ways in which you can care for yourself that will be gentle and nurturing. Consider spending more time in nature, taking long baths, spending time with good friends, or spending time on your own. But most importantly, be gentle with yourself. Be self-compassionate.

Don't numb out. Don't use any substance or do anything to feel numb, because your grief is not going to go anywhere. It's going to land in your body until you feel it to heal it.

MINDFULNESS EXERCISE: SURRENDER AND TRUST

Wherever you are, sit comfortably. You can also lay on the floor in a spread-eagle position with your palms upright.

Close your eyes and breathe in through your nose, allowing your chest and belly to expand, taking in the fullness of your breath. As you exhale, allow yourself to relax and sink into your chair or into the floor.

Where do you feel tension in your body? If you're experiencing loss or heartbreak, this becomes a very important question. Your body will tell you through your symptoms. What do you need to do to move that energy out? You might feel your stomach hurt if you're not crying enough. Whatever your symptom is, it's telling you that you're not feeling your feelings deep enough. You're not expressing them outwardly.

As you start to identify where there is tension in your body, breathe and let yourself shake and move. Wiggle your legs and move your arms. Try to shake a sound or a tear loose. Try to let go of what you're holding onto and let your tears come if they come. Let them empty out of you. Let them carve out a place in you for more joy and peace to come in. Sometimes joy isn't present when going through a loss, but peace can be.

As you make this part of your process of surrender and trust, you'll notice that it becomes less and less scary and that you feel more and more peace.

Notice how you feel afterward. Most likely, you're going to feel much better after you go through this process. And you'll rinse and repeat several times—maybe even several times a day. Do it as often as you need in order to empty out all of the emotions and feelings you have. Feel to heal.

MINDFULNESS IN HEARTBREAK

LESSON 5 TRANSCRIPT

[Introduction by Shauna Shapiro]

Kristine Carlson is a passionate messenger for joyful and peaceful living, mindfulness, and self-rediscovery. Her mission expands on the phenomenal success of her late husband Dr. Richard Carlson's work on the *Don't Sweat the Small Stuff* series. Kristine is one of the most generous, compassionate and wise women I know, and it is an honor to have her join this course, *Masters of Mindfulness*

[End of introduction]

Hello, I'm Kristin Carlson. It is my honor to be a teacher in this series as I share this hour with you. But first let's take a pause together, something I call a golden pause. That just gets you listening in your heart and get you grounded and centered for this hour. So, let's begin by sitting comfortably with our legs uncrossed if you're sitting in a chair. And if you're sitting Indian style on the floor, just lean back against something and keep your shoulders back and arms on your lap and palms open and let's just begin to breathe together.

So, go ahead and close your eyes and breathe with me. As you breathe in, breath in through your nose, allowing your chest and your belly to fully expand, taking in the fullness of your breath. And as you exhale just go ahead and relax and sink into your body, sink into your breath. This time as you breathe in, breathe in golden sunlight, pure golden sunlight to the top of your head to the tips of your fingers and toes to every cell of your being, pure, golden sunlight. And as you exhale, just go ahead and relax and sink a little bit deeper.

And this time as you breathe in golden sunlight—pure golden sunlight— place your hand on your heart, activating your heart, opening your heart, and just spend the moment with me thinking of one thing you feel incredibly grateful for.

It could be a person, a place, a thing, something somebody recently said to you. And just breathe in that gratitude. And as you breathe in that gratitude, taking it in, soaking it in, filling your whole being with gratitude, go ahead and exhale and open your eyes.

That golden pause is just an amazing thing to put into practice. No matter what you're doing throughout your busy day, it doesn't matter where you are, you can always take a pause and it just helps you become more responsive more grounded in your body and much more responsive to life.

So, there are so many reasons and so many different ways that we face hardship and heartbreak and loss. And people have asked me many times can we prepare for loss? And the answer is yes, we can prepare for a loss. We prepare for a loss and how we live—it's how we practice life that prepares us. And understanding and practicing mindfulness will not only help you in your everyday life, but will help you immensely as you heal from heartbreak of all kinds.

There are five principles of mental health and well-being I'd like to share with you today. These principles are the foundation of the *Don't Sweat the Small Stuff* book series; a series that has impacted millions of people around the globe. These principles of awareness teach us how to practice accessing our mental health and wellbeing in all situations and including heartbreak and loss.

There is no doubt that we are going to endure both physical and emotional pain in life, but here's how suffering becomes optional. It's in your mental reactions and your emotions and your ability to return to a gentle and loving awareness of them that will help you recover from loss in a healthy way. As you understand these principles, you'll free yourself from the mental dynamics that can keep you stuck and suffering.

Five principles of awareness are: thoughts, moods, feelings, your agreement with reality, and present moment living. So, I'm going to share with you a little bit about each one of these principles, and throughout this session today I'll be referring to them. So, here's what I have to say about thought.

You know I want you to think of thinking, your thinking, as being as automatic to you as your breathing. You just don't think about every breath until you sit down to meditate, right? Well thinking it's the same way—thinking is very automatic to us. And we have so many thousands of thoughts, 60,000 to 80,000 thoughts a day. And how many of those thoughts are we really aware of? Not very many of them. But one really interesting thing about thought is that so many of those thoughts are repetitive as well.

But there's two things. That's the first that I'd love you to understand about thought is that it's automatic to you, and that the other thing is that you are the thinker. Just repeat that to yourself for a moment: You are the thinker. You're literally just making up these thoughts in your own head all day long. It's coming from you; it's not coming from something outside of you. You are your own thinker. Just understanding those two things about thought are profound.

But the other thing I want you to be aware of about thought is that we have repetitive thinking, repetitive thought patterns that we get into. In our work in the *Don't Sweat the Small Stuff* book series, and in my late husband Dr. Richard Carlson's work, he called them thought attacks. When you get on this circular thinking and you just can't stop it. Do you know what I'm talking about? You know that thing that bugged you, that happened yesterday, but today you're still thinking about it and you can't get off of it? Or it's that conversation that you're repeating over and over and over in your head as if you need some sort of dress rehearsal? Yeah, I know you're looking at me going, uh-huh, I get it. So, you are the thinker and thinking is automatic to you.

The second principle of moods is that we all have them, don't we? You have moods? I'm sure you're saying yes, you have moods. Doesn't your toddler have moods? Don't you know even your dog has moods? We all go up and down with our moods, and our moods move up and down like the weather. And we have high moods and we have low moods. So, let me just ask you this. If you've ever been in a relationship or in a current relationship, when do you, most people and relationship talk about their problems? Do they talk about their problems in a high mood or do they talk about their problems in a low mood? Yeah I know you're laughing at that, right? Yep.

Most couples will talk about their problems in a low mood. But what would happen if you waited to talk about your problems until your mood got higher?

In a low mood, everything could be annoying. Even your dog wagging his tail because he wants something from you can be annoying. You know the same thing that your spouse or partner says to you when you're in a high mood might really bother you in a low mood. And ladies, if you're watching, if you've got PMS, you know what I'm talking about when I'm talking about low moods. Life just looks different in a low mood than it does in a high mood. And that's the same for all of us. So, doesn't it behoove us as a culture to think about, in all of our relationships, when we're in conflict with somebody, to ask the question, what kind of mood is this person in? Or what kind of mood am I in? Should I really be talking to this person now when I'm in a low mood or when they're in a low mood?

I used to ask my husband before I asked him for something that I really wanted, I used to ask him and he knew exactly where I was going with this. Because of course we learned these principles together a long time ago. I used to say, "Hey honey, are you in a high mood or a low mood?" And he would say, "Yeah, why are you asking?" But the reason why I would ask is because knowing that life looks different in a higher mood, I'm much more likely to receive, you know what I'm looking for if I ask it a high mood, right? It's just smart. But it's also smart in all of your relationships to think of that concept of moods. Is somebody in a high mood or a low mood? And the ideal is when you can become graceful when low and grateful when high.

So, I'm going to talk about feelings as a principle of awareness. Feelings can become a guidepost and a barometer of your thinking. We all have feelings. But a lot of times we can't have feelings before we think a thought first. I'm not saying it's impossible to have a feeling without a thought, but I'm just saying that most of the time you can ask yourself if you're feeling low. You can ask yourself to look to your thinking and ask yourself, what am I thinking right now? And in this way feelings become an amazing barometer to helping you understand and become more aware of all of those thoughts that we talked about earlier which become invisible to you.

So now we'll talk about what is your agreement with reality. First of all, I want to talk about separate realities and the fact that we all view the world through our own lens, our own unique filter. And this filter is made up from our belief system, from our childhoods, from actually every experience that we have. This affects the filter by which we view the world.

Now every person has their own filter very unique to them. They see the world through their own unique lens. But along with this is, what kind of agreement with reality do we have? And what I mean by that is many people—I'm to talk throughout this session about what it means to choose to be the victim or the victor over your circumstances or the victim or the hero. And when I do, I'm talking about what kind of agreement with reality do you have.

Sometimes unknowingly, we have an agreement with reality that we're living at the affect of our circumstances, and that means that in a way we have a victim mentality. What I'm going to hope to do is show you that you can choose and change your agreement with reality at any time. And at any time, you can choose to be the victor over your circumstances or the hero of your own story. And that's all I'm going to say about agreement with reality for right now, because there's more to come.

The last principle, which is probably the most profoundly important principle, is present moment living. It's the highest level of awareness and engagement that you can have in your life, is present moment living. Now it's really funny to think of it this way, but when do you think people are most engaged in their lives? I'll tell you research shows that people are most engaged in their lives while they're having sex. That's right. Because they're not likely to look down at their cell phone, and they're not likely to you know be concerned about anything else in that moment. Now if they are, well, maybe you've got some problems there. But the truth is people are super highly engaged. People are also really highly engaged in a dangerous situation too. You know, when you're hiking and you have to scale rocks or you have to watch your footing. You know these are times when you might notice life really slowing down. And life does slow down when you're super present.

But also—where I'm going to talk about present moment living in this session—is that present moment living is the safest place to land as you're going through any kind of heartbreak or loss. It's because as we think about our past and we're thinking and our regrets about what we'd like to change about what happened to us, about any kind of situation, we're not living presently and what we're thinking in our future, generally we could be super afraid, we could be having a lot of fear. And that's not being present moment oriented either. But when you land in the center, right in the center, in the moment, it truly is the safest place because you don't have anything filling you up at this present moment and the awareness of what is right now.

So, to share my personal story with you now. Just start back in college when I met my late husband Richard Carlson. We were very young and we had kind of a fairytale romance to be sure. It was one of those meet, fall in love and almost at first meeting—I won't say first sight but first meeting. Anyways, fast forward. We got married a few a few years later and we co-authored our first daughter about four years into our marriage—Jasmine— and then a couple of years later we had Kenna. And our lives were really humming along, were very much on a spiritual path together. Richard was getting his master's and his PhD in psychology. I was running a business. We were practicing meditation every day. We had this, we were just building our lives.

So, I liked to say that *Don't Sweat the Small Stuff* was an overnight success story because it took 10 years and it took 10 books. And after Richard's 10th book he had been saying the same things in his work and his early work— *You Can Be Happy No Matter What, You Can Feel Good Again, Stop Thinking Start Living*— all of those books. And yet *Don't Sweat the Small Stuff* resonated with millions of people around the globe. We had no idea that was going to happen—of course we hoped it would, but we had no idea that that would happen.

So, speed forward again on the 10th anniversary of *Don't Sweat the Small Stuff*. And by this time there were about seven or eight books in the series at this point. Richard had invited me to write with him in the series in *Don't Sweat the Small Stuff in Love*, and also I had written my first solo book *Don't Sweat the Small Stuff for Women*.

At the 10th anniversary Richard was departing his *Don't Sweat the Small Stuff* series and working on other works. And he was on a book tour—going on a book tour. And one ordinary day just like any other, he was headed out to New York on a flight. And on that day, I woke up and did my breakfast dishes, you know got my kids off to school. This was back in 2006. And I got a phone call. And I looked down at my phone and it was the New York area code. And Richard always called me when he landed safely, so I assumed it was that he was calling me. And I opened up the phone call, you know started talking on the phone. And there was a nurse and a doctor on the phone and they were firing questions at me—very urgently firing questions at me. And it became concerning to me, you know, why they were asking me so many questions. And then they told me that something had happened on Richard's flight into New York. And I said, "What do you mean something happened?" And they said "We're sorry to inform you Mrs. Carlson, Mr. Carlson has expired."

And you can imagine how that word didn't land with me very well. How I became very— I couldn't comprehend what that word meant. I couldn't comprehend what these people were telling me. I'm not sure I would have been able to comprehend it anyways. In a few minutes later, I realized that the love of my life had died from a pulmonary embolism on that flight, and it was really sudden. And in one phone call it completely shattered my life and the life of my daughters, Richard's parents, his sisters, my parents, and everyone who knew him. We were completely heartbroken at this news.

Now just take a deep breath with me. I know that's a hard story to sit and hear, and it touches everyone because we all know that life can change on a dime. And sometimes it does. And it did for me. I call this the initiation by crisis event. And the reason why I call it that is I follow along in Joseph Campbell's work a little bit here where he talks about on the hero's journey the initiation, and that a crisis event shatters our world, causing us to head on a new trajectory of life. We can always tell when we're having an initiation by crisis event because it represents a loss of identity.

Now this loss of identity can come so many different ways to all of us, in different ways and different times in our lives. It could be the loss of a loved one through death or divorce as I experienced, it could be the loss of your health. You know one day you're humming along you're thinking you're this healthy person. You go to the doctor and find out otherwise. You could lose your home. You could have a 40-year career and it's suddenly over. You can have all sorts of different losses that represent this loss of identity. But I'm going to share with you that there's just really two ways that this can land for you. In this heartbreak, in this loss, you can either be heartbroken open or you can become shut down and bitter. But if you become heartbroken open as I did in your loss, you'll wake up to feeling more alive.

You know, just before Richard died, I remember hiking on our hill and I remember feeling very passionless in my life at that point. In fact, I had a conversation with a friend too and he asked me, "Kris, what are you feeling really passionate about?" And I remember saying to him "I don't know, I don't feel very much passion right now. Why do I need passion?" And I think that's really funny now but that's really how I felt at that at the time and just right before Richard died. It was like I got that news in a pressurized water hose hit me square in the face and it woke me up. Really, really woke me up. Woke me up to feeling life, feeling all of it.

But it also woke me up to a mantra, a way to heal that I hadn't thought of and a lot of years. And you know when you go through such a sudden loss—and I didn't have a lot of experience with grief—my parents were alive; Richard's parents were alive. I didn't really know how I was going to go through this loss. But I did know that I had to surrender to what was coming. I did know based on all my years in the personal growth world and my own personal study that this was not something I was going to be able to fight or resist. This was something I was going to have to open to. And I was going to have to feel my feelings to heal. I was going to have to go through a process of healing, a process of grieving.

So, this mantra, this mantra I now call the star mantra, because it goes, "I surrender, I trust, I accept, I release, I receive." I'm going to talk more about this mantra throughout this session, so I'm not going to talk as much about it right here. But what I want you to really understand about surrender is this: surrender doesn't mean giving up. It doesn't mean giving in. Surrender means allowing, surrender means allowing yourself to be broken open, allowing yourself to open to what is, allowing yourself to be present for what is.

Now there is only one question that any of us need to ask in order to know if surrender is what we need, and that is can I change this? Can I change this?

So, as I said I didn't really know that much about grieving, but I'll tell you what, when that first wave of grief hit me I knew what it was. I remember I was walking up our driveway and I was headed up to our water softener. I had to get a bag of a 50-pound bag of salt out of our car and I had to carry it to the water softener and put it in. It was three weeks after Richard had died and my kids were getting ready for school and I pulled this bag of salt out of my car. And I remember thinking, "Wow, I have to do this now too." You know how guys always carry out the garbage? Well, Richard carried out the garbage and it carried the salt up to the water softener, so that it really hit me hard, that I was doing something that he'd be doing that day. And it really hit me hard. I had a big wave of grief come over to me over me, knocked me to my knees, clear to my knees, knocked the wind out of me it was so big.

But what that really taught me was that I knew in that moment I was giving birth to something. I knew because the only pain I'd ever felt that severe was when I was birthing my children and it felt like the same kind of contractions. I thought "By God I feel like I'm in labor." Wow. I had no idea that I was going to be birthing a new life.

But here's the other thing I learned through grief: that these waves would come and go, but if I did resist, I would feel it in my body. And my body began to inform me when I needed to grieve more deeply. My body began to talk to me. And I became very aware that I had this healer inside.

How did I learn this? Well, in my process of surrender, I would lay down on the floor and I would lay down in a spread-eagle position. And I knew that my stomach would hurt when I wasn't crying enough. And I knew that if I just allowed my body to shake and I allowed myself to feel whatever was present that that would come, my tears would come, my screams would come, whatever I would need would come. And I would just express—you know that's what I always tell people, you know just express out what's there. And then when you do your body then rewards you with feeling good.

So just—I want to touch a little bit on this time of grieving and how you can almost prepare for your journey of grief in a way. What you need is always really crystal clear in these situations, if you take the time to reflect on that. I know that when I was in labor I was really crystal clear about what I needed then too. And most women will tell you that they are. They know exactly what they need and when they need it. Well this time period is also like that. It's okay for you to completely design this time period how you need it, not how anybody else wants you to have it.

So, the first thing I would say is the world's going to tell you to stay really busy when you're going through grief and going through a loss. But I'm going to tell you the opposite. I'm going to say consider this time is a time for you to create time for stillness, to create spaciousness, to heal, to weed out anything you don't need to do, and spend time just sitting in silence when you can.

You know supreme self-care is really important when you're going through heartbreak and loss too, of all kinds. And what I mean by that is you have to think of the ways in which you can care for yourself that will be gentle and nurturing. You might want to think of spending more time in nature, taking long Epsom salts baths. Spend time with good friends if you want to, or spend time on your own too—a lot of time on your own if that's what you wish to do. But most importantly be gentle with yourself. Be gentle, be self-compassionate. These are the things that are really going to help you as you go through loss.

Oh, and one other thing: Don't numb out. Don't numb out. Don't use any substance, don't do anything to numb out, because your grief, you're in loss is not going to go anywhere it's going to land in your body until you feel it to heal it. So be gentle with yourself. Make spaciousness and do what you need to do.

You know how this really close girlfriend, and she had the news last year that she had breast cancer, that she got breast cancer. And I watched her immediately just do all the right things in my mind. You know, she immediately created spaciousness for herself. She pared back her schedule so that she would have time on her own to heal. She did what she needed to do for herself even though sometimes it was an opposition of what the people around her wanted. For example, you know people oftentimes they want to show up for you when you're going through something. This is a woman that was has always been so caring of others, always the first person you would call if you needed something, and she'd be there. So, people wanted to do that for her, but you knew what she needed? She didn't want to be around people. She needed time on her own and she knew that. So, at the risk of disappointing others, she told people that she needed time on her own. She needed time just to be in her own healing cocoon.

So right now, I thought we'd practice what surrender and trust looks like in the early stages of healing. So, wherever you are just sit comfortably, and you can lay on the floor as I said earlier, and you can lay and you know a spread-eagle position and just comfortably, your palms upright. And just close your eyes with me and breathe. And as you breathe, and you breathe in through your nose, allow your chest and your belly to expand, taking in the fullness of you breathe. And as you exhale, just to allow yourself to sink into the floor or sink into your chair. As you breathe, you can sit comfortably and relaxed. You can ask yourself where do you feel tension in your body?

If you're in loss or you're in heartbreak, this becomes very important question. Again, your bodies going to tell you through your symptoms.

What you need to do in order to move that energy out? You might cough, you might feel your tummy hurts. Whatever your symptom is, it's telling you that you're not feeling your feelings deep enough. You're not expressing them out.

So, as you they're comfortable and you start to identify where is there tension in your body, just begin to breathe and just let yourself shake. Let yourself move. Let yourself wiggle your legs, let yourself move your arms, just breathe and let go and see if you can't shake a tear loose. See if you can't shake a sound loose. See if you can't just let go of what you're holding onto and let your tears come if they come. Let them empty out of you. Let them carve out a place in you for more joy to come, for more peace to come. Sometimes joy isn't present when we're going through a loss, but peace can be.

So, as you go through this process and you make it a part of your own process of surrender and trust, you'll notice that it gets less and less scary, and you feel more and more peace and you just feel better. The last thing I want you to notice is how are you feeling afterwards? My guess is if you're anything like I am, or I was, you're going to feel a whole lot better after you go through this process. And you'll rinse and repeat several times, maybe even several times a day. Just do it as much as you need to, to empty out all of those emotions, those feelings that you have. Feel to heal.

And remember that your breath, it's in the breath. This is the single most important practice that you can ever do, is just to be in your breath, feel your feelings, and know that in time it will dissipate just like dew does with the sunshine. And you're going to feel better.

EMBRACING CHANGE AND CHOOSING GROWTH

LESSON 6

Healing is all about embracing the journey ahead. When you're going through heartbreak and loss, you are standing on fertile ground for your growth. But your journey depends on what kind of agreement with reality you have. Could you see this as a time of richness in your life, a time when your soul is calling you to grow? This understanding of your agreement with reality is your pivot into growth and healing.

HELPING OTHERS IN LOSS

Transformation means that life is not perfect, but everyone can transform. Yet it can be messy.

Probably the easiest way to help ourselves is to help somebody else. We all need the support of the right people—those who can hold us without fixing us and who can see our brokenness as temporary.

Mindfulness can be helpful as you decide you want to help others in loss. And this is how you can be mindful as you help others:

> You can think in terms of holding space with empty presence. This means you listen with an emptiness inside, where you're holding the person. You need to provide a container for the person, a safe place for him or her to land so that he or she can talk with you, cry with you, and be with you.
>
> You can't possibly know exactly what somebody is feeling when he or she is feeling it, and you don't know where somebody is in his or her grief. That's why the best strategy in this situation is fewer words and more love.
>
> It's important to allow people to experience their grief—to allow them to cry when they need to cry, to be angry when they need to be angry, to feel all of the emotions that come with heartbreak and loss. You don't need to fix the person; there's nothing to fix.

The beauty of *kintsugi*, the ancient Japanese art of repairing pottery with gold, is that a thing is more beautiful in its character after it's been broken and repaired—not hiding its cracks and imperfections but instead highlighting how beautiful the object has become by filling the imperfections with gold. This represents the alchemy of change.

In the same way, our character can heal and grow, and we can become more beautiful in our loss, too.

EMBRACING CHANGE AND CHOOSING GROWTH

The largest pivot you'll make is understanding that life is happening for you. Even this loss—even this thing that has shattered your life—is happening for you. And you might lever back and forth between all kinds of feelings, such as anger, sadness, or self-pity. And you might feel victimized by what's happened and ask yourself, Why did this happen to me?

At this point, you can shift and change your agreement with reality. When you can shift from asking yourself, Why did this happen *to* me? to Why did this happen *for* me?, that's when your agreement with reality has shifted from being a victim of your circumstances to being the hero of your own story.

There is a profound gift that you're going to receive in this shift: a message in the mess. The circumstances of your life don't make or break you, but they do reveal who you are. We don't always get to choose the circumstances we are in, but we do get to choose how we think and how we move forward.

You have begun to accept what is when you can ask and answer, What's the message in the mess? At this point, you have made a pivot toward true growth and transformation, and you are on your way to embracing this change.

Our relationship to our experience is important. When our thoughts converge with our agreement with reality, we create a story. And it's the stories that we tell ourselves about our experiences that matter most. This is supported by the fact that two people can have the same circumstances and tell completely different stories. They have separate realities; they're viewing the world through their own lenses. Our lens is the story that we tell ourselves about what happens to us, and we can create a new story if we want.

From Heartbreak to Wholeness: The Hero's Journey to Joy uses a soul mantra, a soul inquiry, and journaling to show you how to go inward, because it is in the questions you ask yourself that you will receive answers.

A soul mantra becomes a guidepost—something to put your attention on. There is also an intention in the mantra: "I surrender, trust, and accept. I feel to heal."

A soul inquiry follows the soul mantra. You do a meditation to put yourself in a grounded, aware state and open to your own inquiry. Then, you ask the questions. You then journal the answers, uncensored; just allow yourself to journal. Your soul inquiry could be, What's the message in the mess?

MOVING FORWARD AND LEANING IN

Embracing the unknown with gentleness and self-compassion is the result of practicing "surrender, trust, and accept" as a mantra for living and healing. But first, you have to address your fears. It's normal to feel fear during change. Few people automatically embrace huge life change immediately; most people must address their fears first.

You can think of your fear as a hoop of fire in front of you. Your hoop of fire is created by your ego, which screams in the loss of identity you're going through. Your ego wants to put fear in front of you because it's saying that it's not safe to go beyond and into your authentic self, your true nature, your highest expression of who you are.

In this way, you can view emotional fear as a guide. If you start to think of your fears as just something to move through, lean into, and be your guide, you'll start to feel almost excited when you feel that sense of fear. You won't be scared anymore, because that feeling is telling you that you're out of your comfort zone. This is a good thing, because it means you're stretching yourself.

Your greatest fear might be being alone. But you don't have to be alone in loss. You can lean into loving again after heartbreak—or not. This is your choice.

Many people will immediately try to fill the gaping hole of loss of any kind with something else. Instead, think of filling that hole with nothing but the present moment. Spend some time with yourself and in reflection.

If we don't address our fears, they can create a barrier that can put us in a place of waiting, which can stop our healing. We feel stuck and in a place of not here, not there.

When you've leaned into your fears and healed, one question can be your guide to a new dream. Something new may emerge from you as you open. Your adventure begins and you get to choose to have a great love affair with your life. This one question is, What is your deepest desire and passion? Follow that.

In the STARR mantra, the other side of "release" and letting go is "receive." It's rebirthing a new life and a new dream. There is a time when you feel better. And it's different for everyone. There's no real timeline.

You don't know when you're going to suddenly be out of deep grief and feel better. But once you have accepted the change—when you have released a lot of emotions and feelings—you receive this new life. And there's a delightful sense of awareness that comes in this awakened heart state that you have well earned. You feel so much more alive. You are awake to life.

The profound awakening you feel in the present moment allows you to deepen your engagement with life. You are living much more presently than you ever have. And that's what loss or heartbreak can teach us: It can bring us into mindfulness, into the present moment, and the result is seeing the ordinary as extraordinary.

RECOVERY, REDISCOVERY, AND DISCOVERY

As you heal and begin to see that a new life is coming, this is a great opportunity to discover who you are now. Your identity is shattered, but you can take a look back to see where you left behind aspects, passions, and self-expression to live the life you've lived. An identity "crisis" can be an opportunity to reclaim and rediscover those passions or innate qualities that have lain dormant in your career, or your relationship—or whatever you've identified with so strongly that has overshadowed something else that has kept you from feeling whole.

What you have lost actually helps you discover what you value presently and see the world through a new agreement with reality—a new lens.

Who are you after this career, or this breakup, or this loss?

What did you leave behind in the past to live the life you've lived? Your dream shattered; now is the time to dream again.

Look to your passion. What excites you? What excites you ignites you.

What gives your life meaning now?

Perhaps the greatest adventure of all is living in and open to the mystery of the unknown and allowing it to unfold. Being present is the key that puts you in the flow.

EMBRACING
CHANGE AND CHOOSING GROWTH

So, this stuff of healing is really all about embracing the journey ahead. And what I want you to know is that when you're going through heartbreak and loss, you are standing on fertile ground, really fertile ground for your growth. This really depends on what is your agreement with reality. Could you see this as a time of richness in your life, a time where your soul is calling you to grow? This loss is actually possibly something that has shown up to transform you, to change your life for the better, but you have to be really open to that. This understanding of your agreement with reality is your pivot into growth and healing.

So, transformation means that life is not perfect, but everyone can transform. Everyone heals. Yet it can be messy. Childbirth is really messy too, but on the other side is an incredible gift. And on the other side of transformation, there's an incredible gift waiting for you too. I'm going to share with you a story of the very first woman that I ever helped through her grief. Really I call it more like being a doula—really is, because we just can, if we reach out we help somebody else, it's probably the easiest way to help ourselves as to help somebody else. And that's certainly what I've found.

I had just finished the book *Heartbroken Open: A Memoir Through Loss to Self-Discovery*, and some friends of mine told me about a woman who had just lost her husband, a friend of theirs. And they asked me what I meet with her? So, I met Mary at a restaurant and I remember just looking at her, just two weeks after her husband died. And how just completely heartbroken she was, how completely shattered she was. And I remember thinking, "Oh my gosh, this is like looking in a mirror of me two years earlier." I knew how she felt. I put my hand across the table and I looked in her eyes and I said "Mary, look into my eyes. I want you to see hope. I want you to see that you are going to heal. And I'm going to tell you now you've got to trust someone, and I hope that you trust me."

So, we all need the support of the right people. We all need to be held in our loss, in our grief. And we want to be with people who can hold us without fixing us, who see our brokenness as completely temporary. Believe me, in my own loss I realized that our earthly angel show up. They really do, and they showed up for me.

Now me a touch on how mindfulness can be extremely helpful as you decide you want to help others in loss. And this is how you can be mindful as you help others. You can think in terms of holding space with what I like to call empty presence. And what that means is that you listen with an emptiness inside, where you're holding the person. You know that you don't need to fix them. There's nothing to fix. You need to provide a container for them, a safe place for them to land so that they can talk with you, cry with you, be with you.

Next thing I'm going to say can sting a little bit. I'm going to say that we can't possibly necessarily know what somebody is feeling when they're feeling it, and we don't know where they are in their grief. So, I'm going to say that fewer words and more love are the best strategy in this situation. I remember when I was in loss, the last thing I wanted to hear was some trite phrase from somebody, even though people mean well, they want to say something. But I'm just going to say it again: Fewer words and more love.

The times some people would come up to me and say, I know I don't know what you're feeling but I want you to know I'm praying for you and you have my love, that really made me feel like they had my back. And no, they didn't know what I was feeling and I just want you to be aware that you might not know what somebody is feeling either. So fewer words and more love. And remember you don't need to fix them. It's really important to allow people to do their grief, to allow themselves to cry when they need to cry, to be angry when they need to be angry, to feel all of the emotions that come in heartbreak and loss.

I love this Japanese art of tradition which is called *kintsugi*. The reason I love it is that kintsugi takes a broken piece of pottery, and kintsugi artist looks at that object in its brokenness and they put gold—they repair that object with gold. And the beauty of this is that the kintsugi artist doesn't see the object as broken, the kintsugi artist sees that its character is enlivened, its character is enhanced by filling these imperfections with gold. So instead of seeing them as imperfections, they are actually highlighted as part of their character. And we in the same way can grow and heal and experience that same alchemy of change. That can happen for us too, and our character can grow and we can become more beautiful in our loss, too.

So, let's go ahead and take another golden pause. The reason why is I think it's so valuable for you to learn how to do this so that you can practice this day to day in your daily life, no matter what you're going through. So, let's go ahead and try again and do another one. So, wherever you are, sit comfortably, and if you're seated on the floor in your Indian style, place your palms open on your lap. If you're seated in a chair, please uncross your legs and sit upright and close your eyes and begin to breathe with me.

As you breathe in through your nose, allow your chest and your belly to fully expand, taking in the maximum of your breath, the fullness of your breath. And as you exhale, just go ahead and let go. You can let out a sigh. Feel the tension leave your body. This time as you breathe in, breathe in golden sunlight, pure golden sunlight, the tips of your fingers and toes. To your core, to your head, pure, golden sunlight. And as you exhale just sink in a little bit deeper, relax a little bit more. This time as you breathe in golden sunlight, breathing it in to every cell of your being, place your hand on your heart, activating your heart, opening your heart. Just spend a moment thinking of one thing that you feel incredibly grateful for. It could be something as simple as this breath right here, right now. And as you continue to breathe, breathing in that gratitude, filling your heart with gratitude, go ahead and exhale and open your eyes.

So, I'm going to talk about what it really means to embrace change and how you can choose growth and that how you choose growth is really choosing transformation. Choosing a transformation that is going to transform you into something better, not bitter. But it does require you making a choice. And this means right now we're going to talk about how you can choose your agreement with reality.

Now this is the largest pivot that you'll make, is your understanding of this. And that is, that life is happening for you. Even this loss, even this change, even this thing that has shattered your life, is happening for you. And I just want you to know that you might lever back and forth between all sorts of feelings, whether you might feel angry, you might feel sad, you might feel self-pity. I know I did. And you might lever her back and forth between feeling victimized by what's happened. And believe me everyone asks the question when they're going through huge change and adversity and loss. Why did this happen to me?

But here's where you know you've really shifted. Here's where you know you can shift and change your agreement with reality. When you can shift from saying "Why did this happen to me?" to "Why did this happen for me?" That's when you know your agreement with reality has shifted from being a victim of your circumstances to being the hero of your own story.

Now there is a profound gift that you're going to receive in this shift, if you can shift to why has this happened for me? That is going to be your message in the mess. The circumstances of your life really don't make or break you, but they do reveal who you are. We don't always get to choose the hand we're dealt in life, but how we play the hand and how we think, those are our choices and that's how we move forward. We get to choose how to move forward.

Alright. So, I just want to share with you for a moment that my message in the mess happened when I was sitting onstage with Oprah. Just 11 months after Richard's death, I went to Oprah, she asked me to come and we paid tribute to him. And she asks me on camera, "Kris, do you think that Richard's death has given you the gift of feeling your life?"

And then, in front of about 20 million viewers, I had a golf ball size—you know tear the size of a golf ball in my throat—and I gulped and I let those tears fall. And I said "Absolutely." And I was crystal clear that she was right about that. That that whole passionless time that I was feeling before Richard passed, before he died, I was really clear that I was one passion-filled woman now. And I was really clear that this was going to be part of what my message in the mess was. And, boy, I'll tell you, I was like this I was like "Gee if I got wake up this way, everyone has to wake up." Everyone that I need, anyways.

So, when you began to accept what is, and you can ask and answer what's your message in the mess, you have made a pivot toward true growth and true transformation, and you are really on your way to embracing this change.

Now, our relationship to our experience and our thoughts is really what matters most. And when your thoughts converge with your agreement with reality, you create a story. So, what's your story? It's the stories that we tell ourselves and the quietness of our own thoughts that matter most. Now you can tell this is true by—you know look at people and families. They have the same mom, the same dad. One person in that family will tell the story that their mom was hard on them, she was a taskmaster. The person the same family will say, no my mom was gentle and kind. Right? Because again it goes back to that separate reality that we're viewing the world through our own lens, which is the story that we tell ourselves about what happens to us that matters most. It really is. This life is always happening, and we can create a new story that we want.

In my work, I, you know, don't just tell people to go inward, that this is an inward journey. I actually show you how. And in my latest book, *From Heartbreak to Wholeness: The Hero's Journey to Joy*, I use what I call the soul mantra and soul inquiry and journaling, a transformational writing process, to show you how to go inward. Because it is in the questions that you ask that you will receive the answers.

Now the sole mantra becomes a guidepost, something to put your attention on, but it also has an intention. And the mantra that I spoke of earlier— surrender, trust, accept, release, and receive—we're going to start to break that down a little here.

So, surrender, trust, and accept. I feel to heal. Let's try it. Let's do a soul mantra. So, this isn't a lot different than what we've been doing, but we're going to repeat the mantra about 10 times silently to ourselves. And I'll just chime in now and then see you don't get bored. So, let's go and try it. Go ahead and close your eyes and sit comfortably. And just begin to breathe with me. Take a few deep breaths in, through your chest, allow your belly to expand, and exhale, sink in, and relax.

And as you breathe, just repeat to yourself, I surrender, trust, and accept. I feel to heal. I surrender, trust, except. I feel to heal. I surrender, trust, accept. I feel to heal. I surrender, trust, and accept. I feel to heal.

As you repeat this mantra, silently to yourself, you can sit and practice this at another time, and practice for at least 10 minutes. And allow yourself to really sink into those words and just gently return to those words if your thoughts wander. But for now, let's go ahead and open our eyes and continue.

So, this soul inquiry follows the soul mantra. You do a meditation to sort of put yourself in that grounded, aware state and open, open to your own inquiry. Then you ask the questions. And then you journal the answers, uncensored. That's the important part. Just allow yourself to journal. Just say other day, my friend was sharing with me that she was doing this process, and she was just amazed at what was coming out. Things that she never even considered she was dealing with something, and she never even considered these things that were just coming out of her coming from her pen. And that's how healing journaling can be. Your soul inquiry could be "What's your message in the mess?" as we talked about earlier.

So, what I'd love for you to see right now is that you do have choices amidst adversity. Sometimes we stand at the fork in the road of our choices, and your pivot toward healing could be a very important choice that you make. I know that I saw my choices early on in my grief, about 48 hours after Richard died. I was sitting at our fireplace, and I remember seeing very clearly that I could go down two paths. One might be that I wouldn't pull the covers up over my head; even though I had girls in high school, I still could see that that was a choice that I would just stay in bed and I wouldn't survive this loss, I wouldn't go on with my life. And the other was that I could see myself honoring Richard, doing right by my children, and standing in what was given to me. That I knew that I didn't have a choice, I knew I couldn't change this, but I knew that I could step in and I could move forward. Here's the great teaching here: and that is that we don't live at the affect of our circumstances, when we choose not to be the victim. This is the pivot toward acceptance and rebirth. All of what happens is there for our growth. All of what happens is happening for us, and it's the stories we tell ourselves that matter most.

Now I'm going to talk about moving forward and leaning in, embracing the unknown with gentleness and self-compassion is key. This is the result that happens, and this is what you'll find after you practice surrender, trust, and accept as a mantra for living and healing. But first, we have to address your fears. Some people don't have much fear in change, but I would say most of us have plenty of fear in change. It's normal to feel fear during big life change. Few of us automatically embrace immediately something that presents us with this identity crisis. So, most of us, again, we need to address our fears. So, let's talk about how to embrace fear and lean in.

Moving through your fear, you can think of it like I do, and that is there is a hoop of fire. And this hoop of fire is in front of you, and on the other side of that hoop of fire is actually, there is a gift. There's something beyond that hoop of fire. But this hoop of fire is pretty big, and it's screaming warning, warning! Now I'm going to tell you that you hoop of fire is created by your ego. Why? Because you're going through a loss of identity, and your ego screams in loss of identity. Your ego wants to put that fear in front of you because it's saying it's not a safe place to be to go beyond and into your authentic self, into your true nature, into your highest expression of who you are.

So, in this way, we can actually start to look at fear when it's emotional fear, as being that guide. This is how I think about it. I think when I have an emotional fear, like let's say something simple. It's not exactly fear, but sometimes if I'm going to do a personal growth workshop where I'm going to participate, I have a little resistance to that. And I would think that when I have that resistance come up, I start to think I should follow that resistance. You feel like you don't want to do this, so you need to do this, Kris. That's what I tell myself.

Well, emotional fear is the same thing. A lot of people have the fear of public speaking, for example. That's an emotional fear. You know think of that as the hoop of fire. But if you can break through that hoop of fire, and on the other side the gift, the other side of fear as you lean into it is that as you move through that fear and you come into being a public speaker or whatever, then you're able to express from this very authentic place from outside of your fear. I mean really what is there to be scared of? I mean you could be teaching some sort of workshop or something on mindfulness! How is that scary?

So, if you start to think of our fears as just something to move through, lean into, and actually be your guide, you'll start to feel almost excited when you feel that sense of fear. Not scared anymore, because it's telling you that you're out of your comfort zone, and that's a really good thing, to be out of your comfort zone. It means you're stretching yourself.

So, your greatest fear may have been something like mine was, which initially was being alone. But you know that you don't have to be alone in loss. Nobody said you have to be alone. There's no rules in loss. You can do loss the way you do it. You can design your own plan. You can lean into loving again after heartbreak, or not. This is your choice. But I will say this, that a lot of people will immediately try and fill that hole, that gaping hole of loss of any kind, with something else. And I'm going to encourage you to think of filling that hole with nothing but the present moment. Don't go right out if you've gotten divorced or you're in loss from a loved one. Don't go right out and try and find somebody else to replace that person. Spend some time with yourself and spend some time in reflection.

So, I'm going to share a story about a woman named Karen, and she came to one of my heartbroken open circles. I used to have these circles in my home or I would invite people that were going through a loss. And a lot of women were divorced or they had lost their spouse, and they would come to my home and we'd sit in circle together. And when Karen first came, she was really, you know, understandably a mess. And she had just lost her husband to a train accident. Very, very tragic accident.

And I listened to her, we all listened to her. She left. And then one day I was at the supermarket and Karen ran up to me. But I didn't recognize it was Karen. She was glowing. She looked so different. A few short months later and she said, "Kris, Kris, I have something to tell you!" And I said "What's that?" She said "Your advice really worked." And I thought uh oh, what advice is that? "So what did I tell you?" And she said, "You told me that if I needed to I could find a companion, and I didn't have to go right out and fall in love. I didn't have to address my fear in that way, but I could find a healing companion. And that I should just think of it that way, as a healing companion. I shouldn't think of it and turn it into something else. So, I've done that and it's really, really helped me. I'm still going through grief, I'm still in loss, but I'm not alone."

So, this is your choice. You don't have to be alone going through loss. Nobody should be alone. But you don't have to run out and have anybody take the place of your loved one either. That's purely up to you.

But, if we don't address our fears and we allow our fears to create out that block, that can be a true barrier, can really put us in a place of waiting. It can make us feel like we're dangling in this place, it can stop our healing in this place of waiting, where we're not here, and we're not there. So, when you've leaned into your fears and healed, this one question can become your guide to a new dream. Something new is going to emerge from you as you open, as you heal, and your adventure begins and you get to choose to have a great love affair with your life. This one question will lead you on this love affair, and that is what is your deepest desire and passion? Follow that.

So, the other side of release and letting go is receive. Remember that mantra, that star mantra? It's rebirthing a new life and a new dream. There is this time when you feel better, and it's different for everyone. I remember wondering when is this grief thing going to be done? Sometimes you just wonder how much of it you're going to endure, or you can endure. There's no real timeline for anyone. But I remember about two years in, I came in late one night, I was out with some girlfriends. And I didn't think about it. And for the first night in a long time I slept all night long. And when I woke up the next morning, I felt different. I felt better. I felt like myself again. And you know what? I woke up on Richard's side of the bed. I had gone to sleep on Richard's side of the bed for the first time in 25 years, and I felt better.

And that's I'm saying to you, is you just don't know when you're going to suddenly be out or when you're going to feel better. And I'm not saying that you're going to be completely out, but boy, I'll take feeling better over being in deep grief any day. And it feels a little bit like when you've had the flu or something, you know, you're lying on the floor and you think I just want to die right now. And suddenly you feel better. And boy you want that steak or you want to go eat something really good, well this is the time that this happens. You know when you have accepted this change, when you have released a lot of emotion and feelings, you do receive this new life. And there's this just delightful sense of awareness that comes in this awakened heart state that you have well earned. You feel so much more alive and everything. You go outside and you feel the breeze on your face, you smell smells you've never smelled, things that in your other life were completely invisible to you are suddenly profoundly alive to you. It's an amazing thing because you are awake to life.

This profound awakening is a true engagement in the present moment. You are living way more presently than you ever have. And that's what loss, that's what heartbreak, can really teach us. It can bring us right into mindfulness, it can bring us right into the present moment. You are seeing the ordinary as extraordinary. That's a *Don't Sweat the Small Stuff* chapter. That's one I understand really well. All the ordinary things become extraordinary.

So, I am always reminded, when I talk about this, of Joseph Campbell and this wonderful interview that I watched on this documentary that he did with Bill Moyers. And I remember Joseph Campbell saying, and exploding actually, "You know, by God I'm suffering, but by God I'm alive!" I just love that because that's the truth, isn't it? Yeah you're suffering but you're feeling and you're feeling alive. And this is what the journey is. This is what embracing the journey means. It means that we're really bracing and embracing more life.

So now going to talk about recovery, rediscovery, and discovery. Because as you heal and you begin to see this new life is coming, this is a great opportunity to discover who you are now. So, when your identity is shattered, but you can take a look back to see what you left behind, those aspects, those passions, that self-expression. Remember when you were five years old and somebody asked you what did you want to be when you grew up? Well they asked you what did you want to be when you grow up, but you have grown up now. Think about those things, those things that were just natural passions to you. A lot of times what we find is that we've left those behind to live the life that we've lived. And identity crisis can be an opportunity to reclaim and rediscover those passions. All those innate qualities, those things that have been left dormant in your career, dormant in your relationship, or whatever you've identified with so strongly, that has overshadowed something else that has kept you from feeling whole.

So, what you have lost actually helps you discover what you value presently. And now that you see the world through a new agreement with reality and a new lens, who are you after this career, this breakup, this loss? What did you leave behind in the past to live the life that you've lived? Your dream's shattered; now is the time to dream again. Look to your passion. What excites you? What excites you ignites you, that is for sure. What gives your life meaning now?

Three months before Richard died, he said to me something that came back to me time and time again as I was going through grief. He said, "You know Kris what I love most about the human spirit?" And I said "What, honey?" And he said, "I love that there are people that take their greatest tragedy and allow it to move them forward in life so that their life has greater meaning than it might have otherwise had."

Now I'm not sure everything in life happens for a reason. I believe that it is our job to find the reason why things happen. Perhaps the greatest adventure of all is living in and open to the mystery of the unknown and allowing it to unfold. I've learned that the unknown is actually a really exciting place to live, because it's so creative. It's not restricted by plans. It's not restricted by anything. But being present is the key that puts you in the flow.

And in closing, I'd love to share a story with you that shows that there are miracle moments of grace and presence. When you are truly present and tuned into your deepest desire, and you ask for something that serves all, you don't miss the nuances of spirit. And the spirit delivers the answer to your prayer, and your feelings guide you.

So about two years after Richard's transition, my daughters and I were flying back home from Eugene to San Francisco. We had been visiting my parents, and they'd had this 50th wedding anniversary party. And it was about Christmastime, a little bit before Christmas. And we walk up to the ticket agent at the airport and the ticket agent says to us, "Did you know you're not seated together on this flight?" And we look at each other and I ask the girls does that matter and they say no it doesn't matter. I say it's okay, we're okay, it's a short flight. It was a little commuter jet from flying from Eugene to San Francisco. And he takes it upon himself to rearrange our seats on this plane. And so, he says as we know are walking away calls out, he said "I got you seated together!" And I was like "Oh, great, thanks!"

So, we go we get seated on the plane and the girls are in the window in the aisle and I'm seated in the aisle, and the window seat is open, and a man walks up to sit in the window seat. And I remember getting this really odd feeling come over me, super odd, almost a chill. I remember thinking, "Wow, that's a weird feeling I'm having." And my kids let out a giggle. Now they were 19 and 17 years old. I mean, they're not giggling age, you know, but they let out this giggle. And I thought that's odd too. This guy sits down and I think to myself I really want to talk to this guy; I really want to talk to him. But he pulls his laptop out and he starts to tap away and I'm like okay I'm not going to bug him, he's clearly working.

So, I quiet down and settle in my seat. On the descent of the flight, about 45 minutes later, I still have that super strong feeling that I want to talk to this guy. So, I ask him "Hey is this a workday for you?" And he said "I am really sorry, I would have loved to have chatted with you, but I have a meeting this afternoon." We talk about how he was visiting his sister and I was visiting my family. He says "What about you, is it a workday for you? I notice you have your laptop with you." And I said "No, it's not a workday, but I'm a writer, and so potentially every day is a workday. I always take my laptop with me." And he said "Oh, have you been published? Anything I might know of?" And I said "Well possibly, but you'll probably be more aware of my late husband Dr. Richard Carlson's work, he wrote *Don't Sweat the Small Stuff.*"

Well, the guy did something like this. He kind of sat back and looked up and got a little uncomfortable. He even turned color a little bit, like he got very uncomfortable. And I said "What? Did you know him?" He said "No, I didn't know him." And I said "What?" "So did your husband die on a flight to JFK a little over two years ago?" And I said "Yeah he did. How did you know he died going to JFK?" And he said, "Because I was seated directly behind him on that flight. I was the first to assist. I helped to lift your husband's body out of his seat." You can imagine how that felt for me. And I said "What are the odds of that?" And he said "There are no odds that this could happen."

But what he didn't know was that my deepest prayer, the thing that I wanted more than anything in the world, was to meet somebody who had been on that plane with Richard. Who had been holding space for him, who was with him when he died. So, that meant everything to me. And that was such a miracle. And it was such a miracle of grace. And it also verified to me that when you're present and you listen to your feelings, when you're in the present moment you don't miss the nuances of spirit. Nobody missed their cue that day. Not the guy that changed our seats, not my daughters, and not me. That story marked the hugest pivot turn in my growth, and I'm so grateful to know that we are loved and that we are divinely guided. And that when we're mindful, and are mindfully aware pays great dividends in our lives.

Thank you so much for being here and listening. It's been a great honor to share this time with you.

A MINDFUL APPROACH TO ANGER

LESSON 7

This lesson explores a mindful approach to anger and the importance of taking time to get to know your own darkness—your own shadowy stuff—which includes uncomfortable emotions, such as anger. When you can generate compassion for yourself and your own darkness, then you are better suited to be with other people in their shadow. This is a form of compassion; it's how you tend to those you love.

EXPLORING ANGER

Anger is one of the most stigmatized emotions. It gets a bad rap in society, in large part because of the things that are connected to it, such as violence and aggression. So, there's good reason that it gets a bad rap. But because of this, we have not taken the time to truly get to know anger—to create a relationship with it.

Anger inevitably arises because we're human and we have boundaries, and sometimes we don't hold them well or sometimes other people trespass them. When anger does arise, we go in one of two main directions: We express our anger in an unhealthy way, so we get overidentified with our anger and fuse with it; or we try to suppress, bypass, or morph our anger into more convenient or comfortable emotions, such as sadness and depression.

When we can come into a healthy relationship with our anger, we can really mine the wisdom it has to offer us and come more into our power and take appropriate action. And mindfulness is the most important tool to support us in creating this balanced, healthy relationship with anger.

When anger arises, we usually express it unhealthily by fusing with it and overidentifying with it. Essentially, we let anger drive the car. Or we want to get rid of it, so we stuff it in the trunk. This point can be illustrated by this metaphor: Anger is like a child. You don't want to let it drive the car, but you certainly don't want to stuff it in the trunk either.

When anger comes up, you can use this metaphor to slow things down and ask yourself a few questions: Who's driving the car right now? Is my anger driving the car, or am I driving the car? Am I stuffing my anger in the trunk? You want your anger to be in the passenger seat or back seat with you.

STEREOTYPES OF ANGER

There are some stereotypes about anger that can influence how we view this emotion. When we think of anger, some of the things that we tend to think of are that it's ugly, bad, wrong, unenlightened, primitive, and perhaps even unfeminine. We get some of these stereotypes from our families and in school as well as from religion, society, and the media.

Have you ever asked someone, "Are you angry right now?" only to have him or her respond, "No, I'm not angry; I'm just a little annoyed"? This can actually be considered "anger light." Words like "annoyed," "irritated," "frustrated," and "irked" are all anger; they are just lighter versions of anger. But sometimes it can feel a little easier or more comfortable to use those words. There's also "anger heavy," which encompasses words like "enraged," "aggressive," "hateful," and "hostile."

Heavy	Anger	**Light**
Enraged		Resentful
Aggressive		Irritated
Hostile		Annoyed
Wrathful		Frustrated
Hateful		Bothered
Livid		Irked

MEDITATION EXERCISE: DEEPENING YOUR RELATIONSHIP WITH ANGER

Get in a comfortable seated position. Start by taking some slow, deep breaths throughout your whole body, feeling your feet on the floor and your seat bones making contact with your chair or cushion. Come into the present moment.

When you're ready, close your eyes. Notice the sounds in the space around you.

Notice what arises in your body—what sensations bubble up—and where they are arising in your body when you consider the word "anger." Try to hold all that's happening with compassion and nonjudgment. Take some deep, slow breaths, just noticing what is here. Notice what's bubbling up inside of you, even if it's nothing.

Notice what arises when you consider the sentence "I feel angry." Take some deep breaths throughout your whole body, just noticing what is here.

Next, you're going to say these statements, either out loud or to yourself. And as you say them, notice what is here—what arises. Say "anger." Notice what happens inside your body. Take some deep, slow breaths, relaxing your shoulders.

Next, say "I feel angry." Notice what's here and see if you can say it with a little bit of force. Use mindfulness—compassionate nonjudgmental awareness—to notice what is happening.

For the final piece of this exercise, really come into your body, pressing your feet into the ground, feeling your seat bones in your chair or cushion, breathing through the whole length of your body, and letting your breath really massage your insides. Then, imagine that the essence of anger is standing in front of you. This isn't the stereotypical version of anger; this is the core of what anger truly is.

Take some deep breaths, noticing how anger shows up for you. Try to not judge how it's showing itself to you. Hold all of it with an open mind, breathing and staying curious.

Then, imagine that you can talk to your anger and ask some questions. And imagine that your anger can speak to you.

> "Anger, what are you?" Be open to anything it wants to share with you. It might be in the form of words, images, or feelings. Just open into what arises, continuing to breathe.

> "What is the one thing you most want me to know right now?"

Take some final deep breaths through your body, wiggling your toes and pressing your feet into the ground. When you're ready, open your eyes.

Take some time to journal about some of the things you discovered by doing this exercise and reflect on your experience, considering the following questions:

> When you considered the word "anger" and the sentence "I feel angry," what arose for you? What sensations did you notice in your body? Where were they? Were you able to stay with yourself?

> When you said "anger" and "I feel angry," what arose for you? Where did you feel your anger? Or was it difficult to stay with yourself in that? Was it difficult not to judge your experience?

> When you met your anger, what did it look like? What did it tell you that it was? What did it say to you that it most wanted you to know?

Part of creating a relationship with anger is taking the time to get to know it, and this is what you're doing in this journaling exercise.

THE ESSENCE OF ANGER

Anger is protection of self, other, or what we care for most. Anger is our boundaries. Anger is also our unclaimed power; it's our right to be here, have a voice, and take a stand for the things we care for most.

It's not about getting rid of our anger; instead, it's about creating more of a relationship with this emotion by understanding it, getting to know it, and learning to sit with it, even the discomfort of it. When we do that, we support the growth of our joy, our love, and our heart.

In Karla MacLaren's book *The Language of Emotions*, she says that anger is "a mix between a stalwart castle sentry and an ancient sage. Anger sets your boundaries by walking the perimeter of your soul and keeping an eye on you, the people around you, and your environment. If your boundaries are broken (by the insensitivity of others or in any other way), anger comes forward to restore your sense of strength and separateness. The questions for anger are: 'What must be protected?' and 'What must be restored'?"

These two questions are helpful ways to slow us down and allow us to come into contact with the anger that's in the present moment so that we can mine the gems of wisdom it might have to offer us.

THE GIFTS OF ANGER

We often think of anger as something that is bad and that needs to be gotten rid of, but there are many gifts that anger can offer us, even though sometimes it can be difficult to see these gifts.

Anger can illuminate our boundaries, our authentic no, and our unclaimed power.

Anger can inspire us into action and to take a stand for what we care for most.

Anger can be thought of as "destroy for love." We love our freedom and our joy so much that anger can inspire us to end, eliminate, or destroy something that's no longer good for us, such as a relationship or a job.

Tara Brach calls anger "discriminating wisdom." Anger helps us see clearly—to know that something is a little off and that we should listen to it. There is a wisdom in anger.

Karla McLaren says that anger is the "healing of trauma." The inner roar of anger has this ability to thaw us out of the freeze, or the dissociated state that we're in as a result of trauma. When our psyche feels us fiercely taking a stand for ourselves, anger helps us come home more fully into our bodies.

MEDITATION EXERCISE: REFLECTING ON YOUR RELATIONSHIP WITH ANGER

In your journal, answer the following questions about anger to reflect on your relationship with it. In this way, you can create a deeper understanding of your history with anger and even your current experience of anger.

> What experiences (from childhood and beyond) have shaped and informed your current view of anger?
>
> How would you describe your current relationship with anger? What do you do (or not do) when you feel angry? When others feel angry?
>
> What is the scariest thing about creating a deeper relationship with your anger?

Describe your ideal relationship with anger. What would it look like to have a healthy relationship with this emotion? How might this impact your relationships, health, and work?

A MINDFUL APPROACH TO ANGER

[Introduction by Shauna Shapiro]

Juna Mustad is a highly developed mindfulness coach, author, and expert in mindful anger. She brings an unparalleled depth and nuance to her teaching. She works with *Fortune* 100 companies, organizations, and individuals all over the world, coaching them in emotional intelligence, mindfulness, and skills for building healthy and effective relationships.

[End of introduction]

Hello! My name is Juna and I'm delighted to be here with you today as we explore a mindful approach to anger. And so, to get us started, I just want to share one of my favorite quotes that kind of illustrates a little bit about what we're going to be doing today. And this is by Pema Chodron, and she's a world-famous meditation mindfulness teacher. "Compassion is knowing our darkness well enough that we can sit in the dark with others." And so, to me, this quote really signifies the importance of taking that time to get to know our own darkness, our own shadowy stuff, which includes our uncomfortable emotions like anger. And when we can do this, when we can generate compassion for ourselves and our own darkness, then we are better apt, better suited, to offer this to other people. To be with them in their shadow. And this is how we love people. This is how we tend to those that we love. And this is a form of compassion. So, this is really what we're going to be doing a little bit of today. So, let's go ahead and get started.

What we're going to be exploring is anger. And anger is one of the most stigmatized emotions out there. Anger gets a pretty bad rap in our society, in our world, in our religions, at home with our families, in our schools. And in large part, anger gets a bad rap because of a lot of the things that are connected to it: violence, aggression. And so, there's a lot of good reason that it gets this bad rap. But because it gets the stigma, we have not taken the time to truly get to know anger, to create a relationship with it.

So, when anger arises, which invariably it will because we're human and we have boundaries and sometimes we don't hold them well or sometimes other people trespass our boundaries. So, when anger does arise, we either go into one of two main camps with our anger. We express our anger in an unhealthy way so we get over identified with our anger. We fuse with our anger. Or we try to suppress our anger. We try to bypass it or we try to morph it into more convenient or comfortable emotions like sadness, depression, give up.

So, those are two reactive things we tend to do with our anger. But when we can come into balance, into a healthy relationship with our anger, we can really mine the gems, the wisdom it has to offer us, and come more into our power and take appropriate action. So, this is what we're going to be exploring today. But how do we do this? Well this is where mindfulness comes in. Mindfulness is the most important tool to support us in creating this balanced healthy relationship with anger.

So, what we're going to be exploring today, to start, we are going to be unpacking anger, getting to know what it is, clarifying what it's also not. And we're going to be exploring the neuroscience of anger, what's happening in our brain, what's happening in our physiology when anger is here. We're also going to be generating some greater understanding for our anger, exploring your own personal relationship with it, your history with it, and what happens in your body when it arises. And we're also going to be using some mindfulness practices to help you come into greater balance and harmony with it.

So, I have a few goals for us today, and one of the goals is to support you, and just at the very basic level, having a deeper understanding of what anger is. A second goal is to support you and creating a healthier relationship with this emotion, and maybe even, possibly an appreciation for it, for the gems it has to offer you. So normally, when anger arises, in the fire and heat and passion of it, we can't see clearly. The waters are muddied. And so, using mindfulness—which is really a tool to help us see clearly—we can better get to those gems of wisdom that our anger is trying to share with us.

So, I have a few goals for this section for today. And so, one of the goals is really to start to help you to create a deeper understanding of what anger really is. A second goal that I have for today is to help you create a healthier relationship with your own anger, and maybe even an appreciation for the gems it has to offer you. And the last goal I have for this section is really to help you come into greater balance with this relationship, as I shared a little bit before. And there's a great quote that I really appreciate that illustrates this point: "Anger is like a child. You don't want to let it drive the car, but you certainly don't want to stuff it in the trunk either."

So, for me, when anger comes up, I like to use this metaphor to slow things down and really ask myself, "Hey, Juna, who's driving the car right now? Is my anger driving the car or am I driving the car?" Or "Hey Juna, am I stuffing my anger in the trunk right now? Because I want her to be actually in the passenger seat or the back seat with me." So, this might be a helpful quote for you as we're going along in this section today.

So, let's start by unpacking anger a little bit here. There are some stereotypes about anger, and those can really influence how we view this emotion. So, I want you to think right now, what are some of the stereotypes that you have about this emotion? When you hear the word anger, what comes to mind for you? And so, you might be thinking right now it's ugly. This is a bad emotion. This is a wrong emotion. Maybe you're thinking it's unenlightened, it's kind of primitive. Maybe you're thinking it's even unfeminine. So, these are some of the things that we tend to think of when we hear that word anger.

So, where do we get some of these stereotypes about anger? We get them from our families growing up. We get them in school. We get them from our religions, from the society we grew up in. We get them from the media. And again, I share all this just to help us really see some of these stereotypes really color and influence our perspective of this emotion.

So, another question I have for you: Have you ever asked someone "Are you angry right now?" only to have them respond with, "No, no, no. I'm not angry I'm just a little annoyed."

So, what I would offer is that that is actually anger light. So, words like annoyed, irritated, frustrated, I'm irked right now. All of those are anger, they are just a lighter version of anger. But sometimes it can feel a little easier or more comfortable to use those words. And then there's also anger heavy, which encompasses words like rage, aggression, hate, wrath, hostility. And all of these are actually words to describe the same thing: anger.

So, what is anger really? What is really the essence of this emotion? So, in a moment we're going to be diving into exploring what anger is. But before we do that, I want to give you a felt experience of meeting this emotion, contacting it in your body, so that we're not going to color any of what you're going to experience with any of the content I'm going to share.

So, what I'm going to invite you to do is go ahead and get in a comfortable seated position. Just start by taking some slow, deep breaths throughout your whole body right now. Feeling maybe your feet on the floor and your sits bones in, making contact with your chair or cushion. Just really coming into this present moment right now. As you're ready, closing your eyes. Noticing the sounds in the room around you, in the space. We are going to be generating some of the themes of mindfulness as we go into this practice. And so, some of those themes are going to be opening to some— having some curiosity. Generating some compassion for our experience. Practicing nonjudgment for whatever arises, even if it's uncomfortable and it might be.

And so, to start here, I'm going to count to three and I'm going to say a word, and I'm going to invite you to notice what's arising in your body. What sensations are bubbling up? Where are they arising? What's going on for you? And see if you can hold all that's happening with compassion, with nonjudgment. One, two, three: anger. Taking some deep slow breaths. Just noticing what is here. What's bubbling up inside of you? Even if it's nothing at all.

And again, on the count of three, I'm going to say a sentence, and you're going to do the very same thing. You're just going to notice what arises. One, two, three. I feel angry. Taking some deep breaths throughout your whole body. Just noticing what is here.

Now again, this time you're going to actually be saying some of these statements. And as you say them out loud or to yourself, I'm going to have you notice what is here, what arises. So, on the count of three mean what have you say "anger." And again, notice what happens inside your body. One, two, three: anger. Taking some deep, slow breaths, relaxing your shoulders. And on the count of three, I'm going to have you say "I feel angry" again, noticing what's here and see if you can say it with a little bit of force. One, two, three: I feel angry. Using mindfulness, using this compassionate nonjudgmental awareness to notice what is happening.

And we have one last part of this exercise. For a moment here, just really come into your body, pressing your feet into the ground, feeling your sits bones in your seat. Breathing through the whole length of your body, letting your breath really massage your insides. You are doing a beautiful job here. This is not easy work.

For this final piece, I want you to imagine that anger, the essence of anger, is standing out in front of you, maybe about 10 feet away. And this isn't the stereotypical version of anger. This is really the core of it. What anger truly is. So, go ahead and see it out in front of you, and take some deep breaths, just noticing how it shows up for you. And see if you can not judge how it's showing itself to you. You can really hold all of it with an open mind, breathing and staying curious.

Then, we're going to imagine for a moment that you could actually talk to your anger and ask it some questions. And we're going to imagine that your anger can actually speak to you. So, the first question for your anger is, "Anger, what are you? What are you?" Really open to anything it wants to share with you. It might be in the form of words, images, feelings. Just opening into what arises. Continuing to breathe.

Then one final question here for your anger. And again, just imagining it can speak to you, it can share with you. The last question is, "Anger, what is the one thing you most want me to know right now? What is the one thing you most want me to know right now?" Just taking some final deep breaths through your body. Again, wiggling your toes, pressing your feet into the ground. And as you're ready you can begin to open your eyes.

Thank you so much for doing that practice. I know it's not easy to dive right in like that, especially into such an uncomfortable emotion like anger. So, I really appreciate your willingness. And now that I'd love for you to do is take some time to actually journal about some of the things that you discovered here.

So, in a moment, you're going to pause this video and journal on the following questions. And the first one is: When I said anger, when I said I feel angry, what arose for you? What sensations did you notice in your body? Where were they? Were you able to stay with yourself?

The second one is when you said anger, when you said I feel angry, how was that for you? What arose for you? Again, where did you maybe feel your anger? Or was it hard to really stay with yourself in that? Was it hard to not judge your experience? And again, all of this is data. We're just documenting what you found, what you discovered.

And the final piece to journal about is when you met your anger, what did it look like? What did it tell you that it was? And what did it say to you that it most wanted you to know?

So, go ahead and pause the video and take some time to journal and reflect on your experience, and then we'll come back together.

So, part of creating a relationship with anger is really taking the time to get to know it. And you are doing that right now, even through doing some of these journaling exercises. So, I asked you some different questions and I just want to reflect a little bit about what participants in the past have shared or even clients of mine have shared when they've done some of these exercises.

So, in the past, when people said "I feel angry," they would notice tension in their shoulders, in the back of the neck, the jaw, sometimes even in their fists. So, anger tends to reside in these areas of the body, and in my experience, it can also cause issues in these areas. So, undigested anger, unmetabolized anger can actually cause issues in our body that hang around. And being someone who had chronic TMJ, acid reflux, and neck issues, yes, I can say that that I can certainly attest that this certainly happens.

When people asked anger, what are you? They heard the words protection. They heard the words boundary. Some people got really afraid when they met their anger, and they felt themselves dissociating and leaving their body a little bit during the meditation. Other people enjoyed meeting their anger. So, these are just some of the things that might have arisen for you as you did this exercise.

So now we're going to take some time to actually explore what anger is. So, as we shared already, anger is protection of self, other, or that which we care for most. Anger is our boundaries. And I know what I would also say that anger is our unclaimed power, our right to be here, to have a voice, to take a stand for the things we care for most. And as we dive into exploring anger a little bit more, I want to share a little story with you.

Thich Nhat Hanh is a Vietnamese Buddhist monk and a world-renowned mindfulness teacher. And he was sitting up on stage, asking the audience some different questions, and then they were asking him questions of him. And this little cute little girl raised her hand and he called on her and she looked really troubled. And she said "How do I get rid of my anger?" And he looked down at her and he said, "Anger is like the mud. And you cannot grow the lotus flower without the mud. And the lotus flower represents our joy, our love, our happiness."

And so, what he basically said to her is it's not about getting rid of our anger. Instead, it's really about creating more of a relationship with this emotion, understanding this emotion, getting to know it, and learning to sit with it, even in the discomfort of it. Because when we do that we support the growth of the lotus flower, which is our joy, our love our heart. And so, I appreciate this story because, as I'll share a little bit, that was not my perspective of anger as at all growing up. I was much more similar to that little girl.

Karla McLaren wrote the book *The Language of Emotions*, and she has a beautiful quote about anger she says:

> Anger is a mix between a stalwart castle sentry and an ancient sage. Anger sets your boundaries by walking the perimeter of your soul and keeping an eye on you, the people around you, and your environment. If your boundaries are broken by the insensitivity of others or in any other way, anger comes forward to restore your sense of strength and separateness. The questions for anger are: What must be protected? What must be restored?

So, I really appreciate this quote by Karla McLaren, and those questions have stayed with me. So just like that that quote about the car and not wanting anger to drive the car, or putting it in the trunk, these two questions are also questions I use, I use with clients and in my lectures. What must be protected? What must be restored? These are really helpful ways to slow us down and actually come into contact with the anger that's here in this moment. Again, mining the gems it might have to offer us.

There are many gifts that anger can offer us. And again, it can be sometimes hard to see this, but it's also really important to illustrate. So, anger can illuminate, as I said before, our boundaries, our authentic no and our unclaimed power. Another gift of anger is that it can inspire us into action, to take a stand for the things we care for most. If we feel that there is some kind of injustice happening, anger is that motivating energy to take action, to start a movement, to make a change.

One of my colleagues also calls anger "destroy for love," and I really appreciate this idea of anger. I kind of imagine the Hindu goddess Kali with her big, huge sword. And she's cutting through illusion, she's cutting through things that no longer are serving, because we love ourselves so much. We love our freedom, our joy, so much. So, anger can also inspire us to end a relationship, to end a job, to end something, to eliminate something, to destroy something that's no longer good for us.

Tara Brach also calls anger "discriminating wisdom." So, one of the ways that we can look at anger is that it helps us actually see clearly. It helps us actually know something's fishy here, something's a little off here, and I'm going to listen to this. There is a wisdom in anger. And Karla McLaren says that anger is the healing of trauma. And this was an interesting one for me, because this is something that I've certainly experienced. So, the inner roar of anger has this ability, this capacity, to actually thaw us out of the freeze, the dissociated state that we're in as a result of trauma. When our psyche, our soul, feels us here with ourselves, advocating for ourselves, fiercely taking a stand for ourselves, maybe for the first time in our lives, this anger actually helps us come home to ourselves more fully into our bodies. So, these are some of the gifts here of anger that I wanted to share with all of you.

I didn't always see these gifts. In fact, I might have been a little bit more like you and certainly like that little girl with Thich Nhat Hanh, where I thought anger was something that is bad to be gotten rid of. And what I'd like to share with you is a story from my past. Something I've experienced and it's a little vulnerable to share, but it also feels important, because it helps you see why I have such a passion for sharing the wisdom of this emotion.

So, I grew up as a good girl. I grew up with a loving, amazing family. And my mom was also the quintessential gold star-earning good girl. And I really enjoyed the benefits of being a good girl. People like good girls. But growing up, I think one of the things that I can see now that shaped my inner good girl was growing up with a father who's an amazing man, an inspiring man, a loving man. But he also had a really unhealthy relationship with his anger.

So, in our household growing up, sometimes he would just erupt in a fit of anger. He was never physically violent, but he would yell and he would scream, and I never quite knew when he was going to get set off. Sometimes it would be from maybe going into the kitchen and leaving a cupboard open. Maybe it would be because I left something on the hallway floor. But suddenly he'd be yelling. And his yells terrified me. Being an empathic child, a sensitive child, I think that they were extra scary for me.

I remember being maybe about 10 years old and sitting in a restaurant with my family. And my dad started to yell at the waiter for serving him warm red wine, and the waiters started to cry. And I actually remember sitting back in my chair and quietly vowing to myself that I would never, ever do anger. I thought anger was ugly and bad and a primitive emotion, and it only just did bad things that only hurt people.

So, that was a significant moment where I chose to adopt a personality much more similar to my mom's and chose not to do any of that ugly, bad anger stuff like my dad. So, growing up as a good girl, there was many benefits to it. I was liked. I smiled. People enjoyed me. And this coping strategy worked for a while. People tend to like us good girls. But it hit a point where it wasn't starting to work anymore.

I remember in college starting to get some feedback from people where they said "Juna I really like you, but I feel like you're a little fake or I don't really know if I trust you when you tell me what you're feeling or what you're really thinking." And I was horrified. What? But I thought I'm doing everything right. I didn't know how to show up differently.

So, this is the way life works sometimes—and maybe you've experienced this yourself—but at a certain point, we'll create something big enough, hard enough to help us actually see that the strategies we're using are really, truly not working for us anymore. And that's what I created with my own inner good girl. I didn't have a sense of my boundaries. I didn't have enough of a sense of self because my largest commitment in this life was to being good, to doing it right, and maintaining connection above all else.

So, at a certain point in my late 20s, I got into a relationship. I started dating this amazing, charismatic really smart man, and I fell head over heels in love with him. And then I started to lose myself. And then I started to second guess myself. But the love was so good and the relationship was so amazing, and I didn't really pay attention to those other things. It got to a point in that relationship where I had fully lost myself, and any time I tried to hold my boundaries I was punished. And it wasn't physical abuse, which is somebody hitting you, it was psychological abuse, where he would overtly withdraw his attention, his love, his adoration of me, sometimes for hours, sometimes for days. Now who doesn't do this in relationships? Where we love someone, they do something that triggers us, we pull away because we're hurt.

Well there is a big difference between that and strategic, systematic, regular, kind of in a way pulling away our attention as a way of training someone to a certain way of being. I started to recognize I was on hyper alert to always want to do whatever he wanted me to do in order to maintain the love and connection above all else.

So, year three of that relationship, something began to happen. And for those of you who live in California or earthquake country, you might know this. But when an earthquake is coming, sometimes you can actually hear it before the earth has been actually, before the earth has started to shake. And this is what started to happen in my being. I started to almost feel an earthquake was coming. And I didn't know what it was, but it terrified me.

And that last year of our relationship, I remember saying to him, "I feel like a volcano is about to explode, I feel like something's happening inside of me. And I don't know what it is and it's really scaring me."

And when my inner earthquake finally came, my volcano blew up. I broke up with him, which was terrifying. And I was seething, I was fuming with anger. My anger was so, so mad at him, at myself for all the ways I had trespassed myself in that relationship. And there was some pretty acute and significant ways.

And then my anger rose again to show me it was so angry at all the ways I had trespassed myself my entire life, and this anger was uncomfortable. It was really the first time in my life I was actually feeling anger, and I wanted to make this emotion go away. I wanted to do whatever I could just to get rid of this emotion, but it wouldn't go away. In fact, it got larger even after the breakup. And so, I'd go on walks, I journal how do I get rid of this anger, someone tell me what to do. Nothing was happening. Nothing was changing the situation.

So, months later, maybe even a year later, it wasn't until I actually started to turn towards my anger to really face it just like you've done here today, and to actually create a relationship with it, that it began to show me things, it began to tell me things. I began to come back home into myself. I began to see all the ways I had left myself trespassing my own boundaries, not listening to my authentic yes, my authentic no, allowing other people to trespass my boundaries. All of this just started to become super clear.

And finally, my anger began to move. And this was a really powerful time— not comfortable; very, very uncomfortable in fact—and one of the most significant experiences of my life. Because for the first time I was coming home to me. For the first time, I felt like I had a voice. For the first time, I learned how to be in my body. I didn't have to be dissociated, kind of hovering above my body, sweetly smiling all the time.

So, this was a really powerful experience, and has really informed how I show up in the world, how I communicate in the world. And it was also a challenging experience. And there was some messy parts of it as well.

So, anger is not a clean emotion. It can be very messy, but it's really important to recognize that that's a phase, and as we apply mindfulness to this emotion, as we apply really taking the time to get to know this emotion, we begin to come in to right relationship with it.

So, some of these tools, some of these techniques that we're using today are the very same ones I use with my clients who also have had a challenging relationship with anger; where either they stuffed it consistently or they were only able to feel sadness instead of anger. Or as I said before, they overly fuse with it, overly identify with that.

Thank you so much for hearing my story, it's definitely vulnerable to share, and it also feels important. So now I'm going to invite you to journal and reflect on your own relationship with anger. And in a moment, you can pause this and take some time to journal and create a little bit of a deeper understanding of your history and even your current experience of anger.

So, the first question is: What experiences from childhood and beyond have shaped and informed to your current view of anger?

Number two: How would you describe your current relationship with anger? What do you do or don't do when you feel angry? When others feel angry?

Number three: What is the scariest thing about creating a deeper relationship with your anger?

And the last question, number four: Describe your ideal relationship with anger. What would it look like to have a healthy relationship with this emotion, and how might this impact your relationships, your health, your work?

So, go ahead and take some time to journal on these four different questions, and then we'll come back together and do a little bit of reflection.

GETTING TO KNOW YOUR ANGER

LESSON 8

This lesson further explores anger, with a focus on the neuroscience of anger and how mindfulness can help.

CHANNELING YOUR ANGER

There is the pure emotion of anger, and then there are all the things we do with our anger. These are not the same thing. Anger and aggression are not the same thing. Hate and violence are also not the same as anger. When anger arises, we choose to channel it into avenues that are not anger. But anger itself is often conflated with all the things we do with it because it has the strongest impetus to act out of all the emotions, so anger is seen as violence or rage or hate.

When anger arises, we can choose unhealthy ways of relating to it: expressing it in an unhealthy way or suppressing it. We can express anger in an unhealthy way by channeling it into aggression, bullying, hate, or violence. We can suppress this emotion by just sitting on it, stuffing it under the rug, or morphing it to more convenient emotions, such as sadness and depression. When we go in the direction of these unhealthy aspects, we tend to recycle the emotion of anger. We don't support ourselves in moving all the way through the emotion, so it tends to linger.

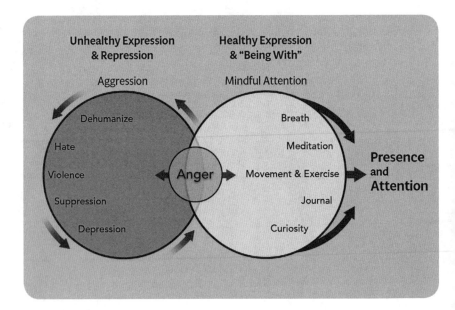

When anger arises, we can choose to deal with it in a healthier way by expressing it in a healthy way or by just being with it. We can mindfully attend to it. We can pause, take a deep breath, and meditate with it; go on a walk with it; journal about it; get in our car (or other safe space) and let ourselves speak or yell or move some of the energy; or get curious with it and ask some questions. When you are with your anger in these healthy ways, you support the emotion in moving all the way through you. Then, you can come back into a greater presence with yourself. This supports you in taking appropriate action for the situation you're facing.

Research has shown that emotions tend to not last longer than about 90 seconds if we don't feed them with our thoughts.

THE NEUROSCIENCE OF ANGER

The human brain is often called the triune brain because it's broken up into three main parts:

> The **cortex** is the thinking, aware part of the brain. It's flexible in its ability to respond. It's also the reflective part of the brain; it can self-reflect. The prefrontal cortex is the wise part of the brain that can rationally assess what's going on in a particular moment.

> The **subcortical** region is the older part of the brain. It's more reactive. It's the source of emotions. It acts quickly and can also act on autopilot to ensure our survival. The limbic part of the brain is where the amygdala, hypothalamus, and hippocampus are housed.

> The **brain stem** controls our basic bodily functions.

The limbic part and subcortical region of our brain is constantly scanning our environment, looking for threats. When it detects a threat, the amygdala, which sits in the command center of the brain, sets off the alarm bells.

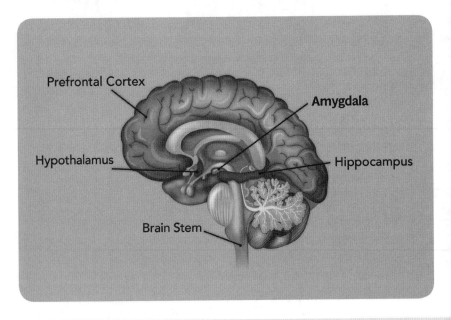

The amygdala judges whether the threat is something that we can fight and win or not. If it judges that we can fight this threat and have a chance of winning, it will engage the fight response. If, on the other hand, it judges that we will probably not win this fight, it will engage either the flight response so that we can get away or the freeze response.

If the amygdala determines that the threat is a worthy opponent to fight, it then signals its neighbor the hypothalamus, which triggers a release of chemicals throughout the body. Cortisol, adrenaline, and norepinephrine flood the body, engaging us and readying us for the fight response. The heart rate increases, and blood from other areas of the body is diverted to the muscles to prepare for a fight.

There are some challenges associated with this threat response system. When it is activated, we flip our lid, losing contact with our prefrontal cortex—the wise, aware part of the brain that can rationally assess what is going on. The prefrontal cortex determines whether a situation is appropriate to fight or to flee, or whether there is a different way we can respond to it. This is why it's difficult to think rationally and see clearly when you're activated in anger.

Another challenge with this system is that it doesn't adequately differentiate between different kinds of threats. If a tiger is chasing us, that will certainly engage the fight-or-flight response, but what could also engage this response is receiving a snarky email from a coworker.

THE BENEFITS OF MINDFULNESS

Mindfulness can support us in having a deeper connection with the prefrontal cortex in those moments when the threat response system is engaged. Mindfulness practices have been shown to grow the regulatory fibers from the prefrontal cortex to the lower structures of the brain, such as the limbic region and the amygdala.

In essence, practicing mindfulness—slowing down, generating compassion and curiosity, and taking deep breaths—strengthens our ability to get our prefrontal cortex back online once the limbic region of our brain and the amygdala have hijacked us.

There are specific mindfulness tools that help us reconnect with the prefrontal cortex, even in the heat and fire of our own anger. We can apply the tools of mindfulness to our anger or experience when anger arises in a six-step process:

Be self-aware. Daniel Goleman, author of *Emotional Intelligence*, says that one of the first aspects of emotional intelligence is self-awareness—knowing ourselves better, watching what's going on, and noticing what's arising.

Slow things down using the breath. Research has shown that taking deep breaths during an anger episode, when the threat response system is activated, not only helps us come more into the body, but also helps us activate the prefrontal cortex.

Label your experience. Research has shown that affect labeling works to engage the prefrontal cortex. This simply involves saying, "I feel angry right now"; "I'm noticing sensations of tension in my stomach, shoulders, and neck"; or "I'm noticing heat rise through my body." This supports you in coming back more fully to yourself and less in the story of what's happening.

Generate compassion. It's difficult to channel anger into aggression or violence when you are connected to your heart, so place your hand on your heart and try to feel some compassion for yourself, for the experience that you're imagining, or even for the other person involved.

Be curious and inquire. Ask your anger some questions to get to know it a little deeper and to mine its gems of wisdom. What is your anger trying to communicate with you?

Take action. Anger doesn't just want us to see clearly; it wants us to take action and make changes. Sometimes this can be the most challenging part of the process, but it's very important.

The mindfulness exercise that follows applies these mindfulness tools.

MINDFULNESS EXERCISE: MINDFUL ANGER

Get in a comfortable seated position. When you're ready, close your eyes. Take some slow, deep breaths down the length of your spine, relaxing your jaw and shoulders and feeling yourself melting into your chair a little more.

Call to mind an experience from your past where you felt angry—for example, a challenging situation with a partner or when someone cut you in line at the grocery store. If feeling anger is a challenge for you, you can call to mind a situation where you should have felt angry.

Imagine that this experience is on a movie screen in front of you. Rewind this experience all the way to the beginning, before the anger started to come up for you. Then, play this experience in slow motion as you continue to breathe. Notice what sensations are arising within your body. How can you hold or tend to these sensations with nonjudgment and compassion? Notice what feels familiar here. Anger is rising up. What does it feel like? How can you maintain curiosity as you're noticing your anger rise?

Take some slow, deep breaths. As you're watching the situation play out, use your breath to soothe your whole body and to help you be in your body in the present moment.

Practice labeling your experience with kindness. How can you say what you're experiencing? "I'm feeling angry right now." "I'm noticing some sensations of tension in my shoulders and my jaw." Play with naming what these sensations feel like. "They feel prickly." "They feel tight and knotted."

When you're ready, place a hand on your heart to generate some compassion for yourself. Maybe you reacted in this situation from the past by saying or doing hurtful things. Or maybe the other person or other party did. Take a deep breath into your chest and feel your own heart. Making contact with your heart is one of the most powerful ways of not letting your anger morph into hate or aggression, or other hurtful things. Breathe through your whole body, feeling your feet on the ground and rolling your shoulders while still seeing the situation play out in front of you.

Ask your anger some questions, being open to anything that arises—even if it's nothing—and holding all of it without judgment.

> What does my anger most want me to know about this situation?
>
> From my past, what does this situation remind me of?
>
> What most needs to be protected or restored here? What action do I need to take?

Take some deep breaths, pressing your feet into the ground and wiggling your toes and fingers.

Before you open your eyes, take a moment to appreciate yourself for being willing to do this exercise—for having the courage to get to know anger and generate some compassion and gain some clarity for this situation from your past. Take a moment to say thank you to yourself for doing this work. It's not easy.

When you're ready, open your eyes, letting the light in. Stretch if you need to.

After completing this exercise, journal on some of the things that you noticed. What arose for you during this practice? Which of the mindfulness tools were the hardest? Which were the easiest? Then, play with answering the questions you asked your anger during the exercise, taking time to journal what arose for you.

Even if this is a situation from your past and it's too late to take action, open to seeing whatever that was. Maybe you can still take action. Open to that awareness.

GETTING TO KNOW YOUR ANGER

Thank you for taking the time to journal on these questions. And one thing I'm going I really welcome you to do is to continue to ask yourself some of these questions, you know what really, what experiences from my past really have impacted me here? And what is the scariest thing for me about deepening with anger? So, as you continue on this journey of creating more of a relationship with this emotion, you might notice some of these fears that you've written down today start to bubble up. And now, that you've really isolated them you can more fully see them and choose whether they influence your experience or not.

So, now we're going to be going into exploring a little bit more about anger, the neuroscience of anger, and then leading you through another mindfulness practice to support you in deepening your relationship with anger.

So, to start here what I would offer you is that there is the pure emotion of anger and then there are all the things that we do with our anger and these are not the same thing. So, anger arises and then there are actual things we choose to do with our anger, they're actual avenues we choose to channel our anger into that are not anger. But anger itself is so often conflated with all the things we do with it because out of all the emotions it has the strongest impetus to act. And we'll be exploring that a little bit further as we go into the neuroscience. But first I want to tease apart this point here.

So, anger and aggression are not the same thing. Anger and hate, anger and violence are not the same thing. Anger arises and we can choose to express it in an unhealthy way, or we can also choose to suppress it. And both of these are unhealthy versions of relating to anger. So, anger arises and I can channel my anger into aggression where I dehumanize others. I can channel my anger into bullying. I can channel my anger into hate or violence. And anger also arises and I can suppress this emotion. So, I can actually just sit on my anger. I can stuff it under the rug, or I can morph it even to more convenient emotions like sadness, depression, give up, as I said before.

So, those are all unhealthy things that I can do with my anger. And what you'll notice is when you go in that direction of doing some of these more unhealthy things with anger, unhealthy expression or suppressing it, you tend to actually recycle the emotion anger. It's almost like putting your anger in the washing machine and spinning it again and again and again. You don't actually support yourself in moving all the way through this emotion. It just tends to linger.

So, another version of doing anger is anger can arise and we pause. We take a deep breath. We meditate with it. We go on a walk with it. Maybe we journal. Maybe we get in our car and we just let ourselves speak or yell or move some of the energy. But we're doing it maybe in a safer space. Anger might arise and we mindfully attend to it. Maybe we get curious with it and we ask it some questions like you've done today.

So, all of these are healthier ways of expressing our anger and also being with our anger. And what you may notice when you are with your anger in these kinds of ways, you support the emotion in moving all the way through you. I like to imagine emotions are like a wave: they rise, they hit a peak, and they fall. And some research has shown that emotions tend to not actually last longer than about 90 seconds, if we don't feed them with our thoughts.

So again, when you attend to your anger in these healthy ways, being with the emotion, expressing the emotion in a healthy way, you support the rise and fall of this emotion and then you can come back into a greater presence with yourself. And what this supports you in doing is then taking action that's congruent with the situation at hand—appropriate action. So, this is a little bit here about what it's like to be with anger and channel it either in unhealthy ways or healthy ways.

So why is anger so often conflated with all the things we do with it? Well, as I said anger has the strongest impetus to act of all the emotions. So of course, it's seen as violent or rage or hate, but now what want to do is deepen our understanding of that a little bit more. And we're going to start by looking at the brain and the neuroscience of anger.

The human brain is often called the triune brain because it's broken up into three main parts. And Dan Siegel in this course talks about the human brain and he actually has us do a fist. So, go ahead and right now put your hand into a fist. And the top part of your fist here where the knuckles are and the fingers curl over, this is called the cortex, and this is the thinking part of our brain the aware part of our brain. And it's flexible in its ability to respond. It's also the reflective part of our brain, it can self-reflect. And this area where the knuckles are is the prefrontal cortex. And so, this is really the wise part of our brain that can rationally assess what's going on in a particular moment.

And if you lift up your fingers with your thumb still on the inside of your palm, you'll notice the palm where your thumb is and even your wrist. This is all called the subcortical region of your brain, and this is the older part of your brain. It's more reactive. It's the source of emotions. It acts really quickly, and it can also act on autopilot. And it does this all to ensure our survival. So, for hundreds and thousands of years this part of our brain has ensured our survival. It's a smart part of our brain in that regard. And where our thumb is resting in our palm, this has often been called the limbic brain. This is where the amygdala, the hypothalamus, the hippocampus are. And the brain stem is where our wrist is, and this area controls our basic bodily functions.

So now I want to talk a little bit about what's happening in our brain when the threat response system is engaged. So, the limbic part of our brain and the subcortical region of our brain is constantly scanning our environment, looking for threat. And when it detects threat the amygdala sends off the alarm bells—it really sits the command center of the brain. It says uh-oh, threat is here. And it will look at the threat and basically judge, is this threat something that I can fight and actually win? And if it judges that this is a threat I can fight and have a chance of winning, it will engage the fight response. If it takes a look at this threat and it says no I will not probably win this fight, but I can get away, it will engage the flight response. And if it looks at this threat and says nope can't win, can't get away, then the amygdala will engage the flight or even the freeze response. So, this is how the threat response system works in our brain.

And there are some challenges to this system. Number one is—and this is something that Dan Segal has talked about often—but when this threat response system is activated, we literally flip our lid. And so, you can just imagine this right now with your fist. Go ahead and lift-up your fingers and actually flip your lid. You lose contact with your prefrontal cortex. This wise part of your brain that can rationally assess what is going on. Is this an appropriate situation to fight or to flee? Or is there a different way I can respond in this situation? So, that's what the prefrontal cortex does for us.

So now I want to talk a little bit about the fight response. So basically, what's happening here is that the subcortical region of our brain and the amygdala are scanning our environment looking for threat, and they find that threat is here, and the amygdala assesses this is a worthy opponent, we can actually maybe win here. And it sends some chemical signals, some electrical signals to the hypothalamus, which is its neighbor. The hypothalamus then triggers a release of chemicals throughout the body. Cortisol, adrenaline, norepinephrine, flood the body engaging us, readying us for the fight response. So, the heart rate increases pumping four liters of blood per minute—up to 20 liters of blood for a minute—and the blood on the surface of the skin and other areas of the body is then diverted and moves into the muscles. All of this is done to engage us, to ready us for fight.

And as I spoke to before, when the fight response happens, we flip our lead. We lose contact with this wise, aware part of our brain, and that's why when you're activated in anger and the fight response, it's so hard to think rationally, to see clearly. The other challenge with this part or this threat response system is that it doesn't adequately differentiate between different kinds of threats. So, whether a tiger is chasing us, that will certainly engage the fight response or the flight response, but we might also get a snarky email from a coworker and that could also engage the fight response, flight, faint, any of those other responses as well.

So, losing our prefrontal cortex, losing contact to this area of the brain, is one of the great challenges here. And this is really where mindfulness comes in, because mindfulness can really support us in growing those pathways, support us in having a deeper connection with the prefrontal cortex in those moments when the threat response system is engaged.

And mindfulness practices have been shown to grow the regulatory fibers from the prefrontal cortex to the lower structures of the brain, such as the limbic regions and the amygdala. So in essence here, practicing mindfulness—the slowing down, generating compassion and curiosity, taking deep breaths—all of this strengthens our ability to get our prefrontal cortex back online once this region, the limbic region of our brain and the amygdala, have really hijacked us.

So, this is what we're going to be now doing together is taking some time to explore specific mindfulness tools that are going to help us really, actually connect, again, with this prefrontal cortex. Even in the heat and fire of our own anger.

So, I have a six-step process that I want to lead us through. And first what I'll do is explain it, and then I will invite us all into a mindfulness exercise that we're going to do together to support us and actually deepening our relationship with anger and applying mindfulness to it.

The first step here is self-awareness. So, Daniel Goleman, the author of *Emotional Intelligence*, says that one of the first aspects of emotional intelligence is actually self-awareness, knowing ourselves better, watching what's going on, noticing what's arising. And so, this is the first step of our practice today.

The second step is then slow things down. And one of the most profound ways to slow things down is using our breath. I remember growing up and hearing the saying if you're angry just take 10 deep breaths. Well that actually does work. And research has shown that taking deep breaths during an anger episode, when that threat response system is activated, helps us come not only more into the body, but again helps us activate our prefrontal cortex. So, slowing things down, taking deep breaths.

The third step of this process is labeling your experience. And what we call this is an affect labeling. And again, research has shown that affect labeling really works to again engage this prefrontal cortex. So, what that is, is just saying "I feel angry right now. I'm noticing sensations of tension in my belly and my shoulders, in the back of my neck. I'm noticing heat rise through my body." All of that helps you come more into the body. All of that supports you and coming back more fully to yourself and less in the story of what's happening.

The fourth part of this process is generating compassion. And so, what I literally do when anger is here is I put my hand on my heart. I take some deep breaths and I make contact with my own heart. It's hard to actually channel our anger into aggression or violence when we are connected to our heart. I think it's actually probably impossible to do so. So, one of the things that I would really invite during this exercise, though it might feel challenging, is place your hand on your heart and see if you can feel some compassion for yourself, for this experience that you're imagining, or even for the other person involved.

The fifth step here is opening, having more curiosity, and being able to inquire. So, we can ask our anger, what do I most need to see right now? What needs protection? What needs to be restored? Those are Karla McLaren's questions that I really appreciate. But slowing things down enough to actually ask our anger some questions, to get to know it a little deeper, and to again open to some of those gems. What is my anger trying to communicate with me?

And the last step here is taking action. So, anger doesn't just want us to see clearly. Anger wants us to make changes, to actually take action. And sometimes that can be some of the hardest most challenging parts, but it's really important. So again, these are some questions we're going to be asking to support you in cultivating a more mindful relationship with your anger.

So, in a moment here we're going to be doing a final mindfulness exercise. And what I want you to do to start is to just start to think about an experience from your past. An experience where some anger came up for you. Could be a challenging situation with a partner, a coworker. It could be sitting in traffic on a Friday evening when you just want to get home. It could be a situation where someone cut you in line at the grocery store. Just go ahead and think about an experience you want to use for this mindfulness practice.

So, we're now going to lead you into a final mindfulness practice of getting to know your anger and applying some of these mindfulness tools and themes that I just went over to this exercise. And I just want to note that this is not comfortable stuff. This takes a lot of courage to do this work. And so, I really appreciate that you're taking the time to do this. And if that discomfort arises, how can you attend to that discomfort with this very same compassion, with this kindness, that we're using here today?

So, let's just start by again getting in a comfortable seated position. And as you're ready, closing your eyes. Taking some slow, deep breaths, down the length of your spine. Relaxing your jaw, your shoulders, and feeling yourself maybe even melting into your chair two percent more. Just relaxing that body of yours.

I want you to now call to mind the experience from your past, the situation where you felt angry. And for those of you who maybe have a challenging relationship even feeling anger, you can also call to mind a situation where you should have perhaps felt angry. Go ahead and see this experience in your mind's eye, and continue to breathe.

And what I'd like you to do is imagine this experience is out on a movie screen, out in front of you. And maybe you can even hit the rewind button and rewind this experience all the way to the beginning. Maybe even before the anger started to come up for you. And we're going to play this movie. We're going to play out this experience in slow motion. So, go ahead and start to watch what's happening, and as you're doing it continuing to breathe.

As you're seeing this experience, this challenging situation begin to play out in slow motion, start to notice what sensations are arising within your body. And how can you hold, how can you tend to these sensations with that nonjudgment, that compassion? Noticing what feels familiar here. Anger is rising up. What does it feel like? How can you actually maintain a little bit of curiosity as you're noticing your anger rise?

Now taking some slow, deep breaths. As you're watching the situation play out, take some deep breaths right now, using your breath to start to soothe your whole body, helping you really be here in your body in this moment. Now practicing labeling your experience with kindness. How can you say what you're experiencing? I'm feeling angry right now. I'm noticing some sensations of tension in my shoulders and my jaw. Play with naming what those sensations feel like. They feel prickly, they feel tight and knotted. And again, affect labeling really works to help us reengage our prefrontal cortex when anger is here. Continuing to breathe, watching this scenario play out in front of you.

And when you're ready, go ahead and place a hand on your heart. Now we're generating some compassion for ourselves. Maybe we really reacted in this situation from the past. Maybe we said hurtful things or did hurtful things, or maybe the other person did or the other party did. But what I'm going to invite you right now to do is take a deep breath into your chest and feel your own heart. Make contact with your heart right now. This is one of the most powerful ways of not letting our anger morph into hate or aggression or other really hurtful things. Breathing into your heart, breathing through your whole body. Again, feeling your feet on the ground, even just pressing them into the ground, rolling your shoulders and still seeing the situation playing out in front of you.

I want you to play with asking your anger some questions. What is my anger most want me to know about this situation? What does my anger most want to know about this situation? And open to anything that arises. Holding all of it without judgment.

The next question you can ask is you're watching the scenario play out: From my past, what does this situation remind me of? From my past, what does this situation remind me of? Again, opening to anything that arises, even if it doesn't make sense. Even if it's nothing at all.

The last question to ask here is, what most needs to be protected or restored here? What action do I need to take? Again, really opening yourself to anything that bubbles up. Really trusting the first thing that arises. Taking some deep breaths here, pressing your feet into the ground, maybe wiggling your toes and your fingers a little bit.

Before you open your eyes here, I'm just going to welcome you to take a moment of appreciating yourself for being willing to do this exercise. Appreciating yourself for having the courage to actually get to know anger, and generate some compassion, gain some clarity for this situation from your past. Just taking a moment to say thank you—thank you to yourself for being willing to do this. This is not easy work. And as you're ready began to open your eyes. letting the light in. Feel free to stretch if you need to.

I appreciate you doing that mindfulness practice with me. And what I'd like you to do now is again, take this into a journaling exercise. So, in a moment you can hit pause, and I want you to journal on some of the things that you noticed. What arose for you doing this practice? Which of the mindfulness tools were the hardest? Which were the easiest?

And then also play with answering some of these questions—when you asked your anger some of these questions take some time to journal what actually arose for you. And so, the first question was, what does my anger most want me to know about this situation? The second question was from my past, what does the situation remind me of? And the final question was, what most needs to be protected or restored here? And what action do I most need to take? And even if this is a situation from your past and it's too late to take action, go ahead and open to seeing whatever that was. And maybe it's action that you can even still take, now. So just opening to that awareness here.

Thank you for taking the time to journal and reflect on that mindfulness practice. And what I would just share is that when I've led clients through this, or participants through this exercise, for some of them it's been really challenging. It was not an easy thing to look at that experience from their past. Some of them experienced quite a bit of shame from how they reacted in unhealthy ways with their anger. Some of them it was really challenging to see how they let other people bully them or treat them poorly, and they wish that they had had a voice in those moments, to express their anger in a healthier way instead of stuffing it. So, there's a whole variety of responses you may have had here. But I really appreciate you taking this time. And again, what we're doing is helping you build a relationship with this emotion which most people don't do. And mindfulness, these tools that we're using today, are really a potent way to support us in doing this.

So, we're going to be bringing in this section to a close here, but I really appreciate being on this journey with you. I don't know if you can feel my passion, but I have such a love for sharing the wisdom of emotional intelligence, specifically with some of the emotions that tend to be more unsavory—namely anger, also fear and sadness. And a lot of the exercises we did today can be applied to all our emotions, to help us come back into balance with ourselves, when anger or fear or sadness are driving the car.

And so, what I'd really welcome for you is to remember that metaphor. If anger—if you don't want anger to drive the car, you also don't want to put it in the trunk either. You want to cultivate some kind of balance with this emotion and it's not an easy thing to do. Have patience with yourself. This requires a lot of practice. And as we shared, when we went into the neuroscience of what's going on in our brain when anger is here, taking that time to slow things down, to breathe, to generate compassion, to ask questions. All of that supports this wise, aware part of our brain, the prefrontal cortex, in coming back online so we can respond to the situation at hand appropriately instead of from a reactive place.

I hope you really enjoy the rest of this course, because mindfulness is such a powerful tool to weave into all areas of your life. And specifically, with emotional awareness, developing a better relationship with our emotions. This can have a huge impact on our lives, on our relationships, on our health, on our well-being, and on the work that we do in the world. And so, it's been truly an honor to be here with you. And I hope you take some of these practices and deepen with them.

So, the next time anger arises, just really pause take some deep breaths, ask yourself, "I wonder what is the gem here that my anger is trying to communicate with me? I wonder what needs to be protected or restored here?" So, practicing mindfulness, generating curiosity, compassion, all of these are going to be a huge support for you as you move forward on this journey.

Thank you so much.

MINDFULNESS AT WORK: THE POWER OF AUTHENTICITY

LESSON 9

This lesson is about the importance of authenticity: honesty without self-righteousness and with vulnerability. Being authentic takes courage, but when we are authentic, not only does it liberate us, but it gives other people permission to be authentic, too. It's also one of the most important aspects of being mindful and effective at work.

AUTHENTICITY

There is a misconception of what authenticity means. When people think about authenticity, they often think of honesty, or transparency, or directness, or originality instead. Instead, think of authenticity as a continuum ranging from phony to authentic, with honest in the middle.

The Authenticity Continuum

Phony	Honest	Authentic

While it is easy for us to notice when other people, especially coworkers, are being phony or inauthentic, a better observation—particularly from a mindfulness perspective—is to consider where, when, why, or with whom we find ourselves being inauthentic. It's important to pay attention to this side of the continuum so that we can become self-aware, even self-compassionate, and start moving along the continuum in a more authentic direction.

Being honest is halfway down the continuum because while it is good to be honest, it can be tricky. We can be honest about something and it causes a problem, such as upsetting or offending someone. As a result, most of us have learned different ways to massage the truth so that we're being honest, but only mostly honest or honest in a politically correct way. This is often how we operate in the world, particularly in our professional lives. But it takes an enormous amount of energy and effort to remember how honest we can be with each individual.

Authenticity is where real freedom and power lies. To get there, we not only have to have the courage to be honest, but we also have to remove self-righteousness from our honesty and add vulnerability to it.

The Authenticity Equation:

Honesty - Self-Righteousness + Vulnerability= Authenticity

SELF-RIGHTEOUSNESS

Generally, when we're self-righteous about something, we think that we're right and someone else is wrong. This causes separation and disconnection.

From a mindfulness perspective, there's an important distinction between self-righteousness and conviction. With self-righteousness, you think that you're right and another person is wrong.

But with conviction, you believe something to be true and are willing to speak up about it, perhaps even debate about it, but you have enough humility and self-awareness to realize a few things: that you might be wrong or that there might be other ways to look at the issue.

Being mindful at work is about being willing and courageous enough to show up and be who we are—authentic and real.

VULNERABILITY

Dr. Brené Brown, who has been studying vulnerability for more than a decade, defines it as emotional exposure, risk, and uncertainty.

There is almost nothing that is meaningful or important that we accomplish or experience in life, personally or professionally, that does not involve emotional exposure, risk, or uncertainty. But at the same time, when we are emotionally exposed, taking a risk, or uncertain in a situation or relationship, we're usually not very comfortable. But it's necessary. And the more we can lean into the discomfort of vulnerability, the better.

Two important things about vulnerability are that it's the key driver in human trust and connection and that it's the birthplace of innovation, change, and creativity—anything new and different. We have to be willing to be vulnerable. And that takes real courage, especially in a professional setting.

MINDFULNESS EXERCISE: IF YOU REALLY KNEW ME

This exercise is based on the simple but powerful metaphor of the iceberg. All we can see of an iceberg is the tip above the surface of the water, but the vast majority of the iceberg is below the waterline. That's like how we are in life, but particularly at work. We let our professional side pop up above the surface, but how we really think and feel is below the waterline.

For us to show up more authentically in our work and in our lives, we have to consciously choose to lower the waterline on the iceberg, expressing or exposing more of who we really are. And that takes courage, but it's one of the best ways that we can build our muscle for vulnerability and authenticity with the people we work with.

In this exercise, two people—for example, coworkers—are paired up.

Each person has a few minutes to complete the phrase "if you really knew me" with something the other person does not know about you. It's an opportunity for that person to authentically, vulnerably share whatever is true and real for them in the moment. The person who is listening does not comment, interject, give advice, or disagree. He or she just listens.

Once the first person has gone, then the second person goes. Once both people have gone, then they talk about what they thought about the exercise and what they noticed.

This exercise reveals that on the surface, we're all different—we look different and have different backgrounds, ages, and genders—but the farther below the waterline we go, the more similar we become.

By doing this exercise, many people find that they can relate to their partner. The natural human response to vulnerability is empathy, so when people get real, not only is it liberating for the person who's getting real, but the other people around them can see themselves in that person.

CREATING AN ENVIRONMENT OF AUTHENTICITY

Being authentic takes courage for us individually and for the people we're around. The following are some specific steps we can take to create an environment of authenticity:

Look for opportunities to lower the waterline. This might involve sharing or revealing something deep and personal, or it might involve sharing something more mundane. At the beginning of a meeting, for example, take a few moments to quickly check in, asking participants how they feel and if they have anything they want to say. This grounds us and makes us more present and connected. We remember that there are a bunch of other human beings in the room. It's important for us to find ways to make human connections.

Ask for help. Most people like to help others, but few people are comfortable asking others for help. When we ask for help a few things become available. First, we might actually get some help. Second, we give other people the opportunity to do something that most love to do, which is help. Most people don't ask for help because they're afraid that they will be judged for asking, perhaps appearing weak, unable, or incompetent. People are also afraid that they'll get rejected. Some people are so controlling that they don't ask for help because they're afraid another person will do it "wrong" or not the way they'd do it. But all of this creates a ton of stress for us, and the act of asking for help and then receiving help can be both liberating for us and build much stronger connections with the people around us.

Be willing to engage in difficult conversations with people sooner rather than later. This is not easy, but it's important with respect to our relationships as well as our personal journey. Most people are not huge fans of difficult or uncomfortable conversations, such as giving feedback or talking about emotional issues. There are two aspects of emotional intelligence: the self and the other. Consider self-awareness and self-management: How do I feel about having difficult conversations? Is there a way I can manage myself more effectively in those situations? Also consider social awareness and relationship management: Who am I talking to and what are we talking about? What's needed to have effective, even difficult, conversations?

MINDFULNESS AT WORK: THE POWER OF AUTHENTICITY

LESSON 9 TRANSCRIPT

[Introduction by Shauna Shapiro]

Mike Robbins is a speaker, an author, an expert in bringing mindfulness to the workplace. He helps leaders and organizations be more compassionate more authentic and more effective. We are privileged to have him as part of this *Masters of Mindfulness* course.

[End of introduction]

Hi, I'm Mike Robbins. Thanks for joining me here. We're going to be talking about mindfulness at work. You know, I've been passionate about this topic for many years, and my introduction into mindfulness and specifically mindfulness at work actually came from my background as a professional baseball player. So, I grew up playing baseball as a kid, and was pretty good at it. I actually got drafted right out of high school by the New York Yankees. I didn't end up signing a contract with the Yankees because I got an opportunity to play baseball in college at Stanford University, so I went to Stanford, played there. Then I got drafted out of Stanford by the Kansas City Royals.

And the way that it works in professional baseball—I mean you get drafted by a Major League team like the Royals or the Yankees or any other team, you have to go into what's called the minor leagues. So, I go into the minor leagues. I signed my contract at the age of 21. And unfortunately for me, when I was 23, still in my minor league career, I tore ligaments in my elbow and my career ended. Two years later, after three surgeries I had to walk away from baseball. So, it was disappointing for me personally, but as much as I love baseball and the game I was fascinated by two specific aspects of it.

On the personal side, I was really fascinated by the time I got further along in my career when I was playing in college and then professionally, I noticed that so much of my success or my failure, as well as my fulfillment or lack thereof, had a lot more to do with the mental, emotional process I took towards the game than the game itself. And from a team perspective, I also found it fascinating that sometimes I was on teams where we had really good talent but the team wasn't very good. And some other times I was on some teams where the talent was pretty good, you know but not great, and the team was fantastic. And that didn't make any sense to me. And in baseball we sort of called this "chemistry." No one could quite define what that was, but you knew and you had it and you definitely knew when you didn't have it. And it made a big difference in terms of how we performed as a team and also individually.

And when my baseball career ended and I moved back home to the San Francisco Bay area where I still live and got a job working in the tech world, I immediately noticed a couple of things. On the personal level, I noticed that it wasn't always the most talented people that were the most successful, and it wasn't always the most successful people that were the most fulfilled. And on a team level, I also noted that same phenomenon, that it wasn't always the most talented teams that were the most effective teams. It had more to do with that team chemistry, which in business we call culture.

So, after a couple of years working in the tech world I got so fascinated by this, I actually started my consulting business about 18 years ago, because I really wanted to understand this at a deeper level. On a personal level but also collectively. What are some things that we could do— mentally, emotionally— to be more successful and fulfilled? And what can we do as teams collectively to be more successful? And what I stumbled upon in those early days of my own study was meditation and mindfulness for myself, which really helped me calm myself down and be more effective at what I was doing. But I also stumbled upon a lot of research around emotional intelligence and some group and team dynamic work that really fascinated me. And I started to study more the psychology of teams.

And over all my years of study and over the last 18 years with all the great clients I've had a chance to work with and the books that I've written, what I have found are the two key drivers in our own individual success and fulfillment at work, as well as the teams and groups that we're a part of, are authenticity and appreciation. Really simple concepts, but very important aspects of emotional intelligence and ultimately of mindfulness. So, we're going to talk about those two things here.

The first thing we're going to focus on is authenticity. So, when you hear the word authentic or authenticity what comes to mind? What do you think of? When I talk to people about this, people say things to me like honesty or transparency or directness or originality. Different words and terms. But one of the things that I've noticed over many years of studying this and looking at it, particularly at work, is that the idea of authenticity, I think we sometimes have a bit of a misperception of what it actually means.

I was speaking at an event a number of years ago and I was giving a speech on authenticity. And I got done speaking and I walked off stage, and this guy comes over to me and makes a beeline right over to me he gets right in my face and he says, "I'm authentic. I'm authentic all the time." And he was like upset, so I said, "All right man. What's the problem?" He said "Well I've lost some jobs because of that." I said "Really?" He said "Yeah, not everybody can handle it."

Right now, at this point I didn't know this guy, but I was getting a pretty strong sense of his personality. And I'm not sure what prompted me to ask him this somewhat provocative question, but I did. I looked him right in the eye and I said "Now tell me the truth. Is it authentic or obnoxious?" And he was a little shocked. I was actually a little shocked, like I can't believe I said that. But after his moment of shock, he kind of laughed and he said, "Well maybe a little bit of both." And I said, "All right man, I appreciate the honesty. I appreciate the self-awareness." I said, "Look, I don't know for sure, but if I had to guess, I bet it was the obnoxious that got you fired, not the authentic."

So, authenticity isn't just simply speaking our mind. Yes, it's about being honest. But the way that I like to think of authenticity is think of it more on a continuum or sort of on a scale. On this side of the continuum, say over here on the left-hand side is what we'll call phony, inauthentic. We all know what that looks like, we know what that sounds like, we know what that feels like, what's it like to interact with someone who's being phony or inauthentic with you. It's kind of off putting, right? It's annoying, it's obnoxious, it can actually be downright disrespectful when we're interacting with someone in life, and particularly at work and we feel like they're not actually being real with us. And as easy as it is for us to point the finger at other people and notice when other people are being phony or inauthentic, a better place, particularly from a mindfulness or self-awareness perspective, for us to take a look at is where or when or why or with whom do I find myself being inauthentic?

It's not usually malicious. It's not like we wake up in the morning and say to ourselves, "Ha ha ha, you know what I'm going to do today? I'm going to lie to everybody. Going to manipulate people." No not at all. But in the course of our life, in the course of our work, we have agendas we're trying to accomplish, we have goals, we have different things, and what we'll end up doing is we do certain things or say certain things that are phony or inauthentic. And it's important to pay attention to that.

Sometimes we're unconscious about it or more oblivious. Other times we're aware of it but we justify it. I hear people say things to me all the time in my consulting work, "You know Mike, you can't really be authentic around here with that person or in this situation or in that meeting or when you're talking to this client or this leader," or whatever the case may be. And my response is like, Look I know it can be hard, it can be challenging, but the issue isn't that we can't. It's that we won't. So, we're choosing to be inauthentic or phony. And it's important to pay attention to this side of the continuum, because if we pay attention to this we have some real self-awareness, even some compassion with ourselves when we find ourselves there. Then we can start to move along the continuum in a more authentic direction.

Halfway down the continuum, this is where we'll put honest. Now honest is good, right? I mean how many of you were taught—my mother used to say to me all the time "Honesty's the best policy." She would say that all the time and she was right. Honesty is definitely the best policy. Although if you ever had a situation in your life, particularly your professional life, where you were honest about something and it caused a problem? You were honest about something and it upset someone. We're honest about something and it offends someone. We're honest about something and we put our foot in our mouth. We're honest about something and we speak out of turn. One way, shape, or form, we've all learned sometimes the hard way that being honest can be tricky.

So, most of us have learned different ways to massage the truth. We say to ourselves, okay I'm not going to be phony or inauthentic, I'm going to be honest, but like mostly honest, right? Like politically correct honest. Like makes me look good honest. I was at an event a few years ago and someone yelled out from the audience "I mean like HR honest?" And everybody laughed and I was like, yeah, like that kind of honest, right? Honest so that we cover our you know what. Don't get ourselves into trouble.

And while this all totally makes sense, this is often how we operate in the world, particularly in our professional lives. The issue is that it takes an enormous amount of energy and effort because I have to constantly remember how honest can I be with you, and how honest can I be with you, and okay, I don't know you that well. We're constantly having to navigate that line, so to speak, and it takes a lot of mental, emotional, and just energy from us that can be put in better directions. So, where there's real freedom and there's real power for us is on the other side of honesty.

This is where authenticity lies on the continuum. And in order to get there, yes it's about being honest, so we have to have the courage to be honest, but we have to remove something from our honesty and we have to add something to it. The thing we have to remove from our honesty is our self-righteousness.

Self-righteousness? Now what do I mean by that? Do you like me have a lot of opinions? And do you like me think your opinions are right? Yeah, that's what we call self-righteous. There's nothing wrong with your opinions. I've got tons of opinions; you have tons of opinions. We have passionate opinions about all kinds of stuff, not just work and business related, but about life and about the world and about politics and about spirituality and all kinds of stuff. And we're entitled to every opinion that we have. And in today's world, for better or worse, we have more ways to express our opinion than ever before. The issue isn't with our opinion. It's not even with the passion with which we hold the opinion. It's the self-righteousness that we hold the opinion that becomes the problem. Because when I'm right about something like self-righteous, if you don't agree with me what does that make you? Wrong. Now we have a problem. I'm right, you're wrong. Separation. Disconnection.

Now usually I don't know, again, the environment in which you work or where you operate. But for the most part, when we're self-righteous about something, we think we're right and someone else is wrong, we don't usually get right in their face and say I'm right, I think I'm right, and I think you're wrong, and maybe we do. That's not usually the way we go about those kinds of discussions. The way I see it play out, particularly in the business world with teams, is that there's a discussion, maybe even a disagreement. We go okay, great. Okay, I'll take that into consideration. And we walk out of the room and then what do we say in our head? I'm right, they're wrong, or in fact, not only are they wrong, but they're an idiot. And then we go find other people who think they might be an idiot or whatever. And then we get together with people who agree with us and disagree with them and there's more separation, more disconnection.

And the thing about self-righteousness—and this is where it becomes a really important mindfulness practice—is that when you and I are being self-righteous, we don't think we're being self-righteous. We think we're right. And one of my favorite quotes of the many great quotes from Dr. Martin Luther King, he said, "We have no morally persuasive power with those who can feel our underlying contempt for them."

Think about that: "We have no morally persuasive power with those who can feel our underlying contempt for them." So, we're trying to influence people. We're trying to get them to see our way our idea. They can't do it or see it or be influenced by us if where we're coming from is a place of contempt. And it could be contempt for them personally, I don't like them, I don't trust them, I don't—or could just be I disagree with their idea or their approach.

I see this happen all the time with my clients. Two individuals. It could be one team and another team. It could be one office and another office. It could be people who live in this place versus people who live in that place, or someone who works in marketing and someone who works in sales or someone who works in engineering, or even for people who have their own businesses. Oh, I'm more of a creative person, that person is like this. So, we not only prejudge them, but then we decide I'm right, or I'm this way and they're that way. Separation. Disconnection.

So, I'm not saying water down your opinions. I'm not saying don't believe what you believe. However, from a mindfulness perspective, there's a really important distinction that we all need to understand: the difference between self-righteousness, which is I'm right, you're wrong, and conviction, which is I believe this to be true, I'm willing to speak up about it, I'm willing to even engage and challenge you and debate about it. However, I have enough humility and self-awareness to realize a couple of things.

First of all, I might be wrong. Have you ever been convinced you were right about something only to realize you were actually wrong? Yeah. Happens all the time. Right? It's humbling. It's not the most pleasurable experience, but it happens. Sometimes we're convinced were right and realized, "Oops! I was wrong." Or if we can't even acknowledge that we might be wrong, maybe we can at least acknowledge there might be some other ways to look at this same issue, different than the way I'm looking at it. So, can we remove our self-righteousness—not water down our opinion, not sell out on ourselves, and not speak up—but be honest without self-righteousness? And then the thing we have to add to our honesty is vulnerability.

Vulnerability. This is what I call the authenticity equation: honesty minus self-righteousness plus vulnerability, that's authenticity. However, vulnerability is difficult. It's challenging. I love the definition that Dr. Brené Brown at the University of Houston gives for vulnerability. She's been studying vulnerability and other human emotions for 15 or so years, and she defines vulnerability as emotional exposure, risk, and uncertainty. Emotional exposure, risk, and uncertainty.

Can you think of anything meaningful or important that you've ever accomplished or experienced in your life, personally or professionally, that did not involve emotional exposure, risk, or uncertainty? I can't think of anything. Not if it really matters to us. And at the same time, I don't know about you, but for me, when I'm being emotionally exposed, when I'm doing something that's risky or when there's a ton of uncertainty in a situation or a relationship or a project or anything, I'm usually not super comfortable. It's not my favorite place to hang out. However, it's necessary. And the more we can lean into the discomfort of that vulnerability the better.

You know I was speaking at an event a few years back in Japan. I got invited to speak at this leadership conference and it was for one of my clients that's based here in the US, but they have people all over the world, and I'd spoken at this same leadership conference. They'd had it for their employees and some of their leaders in different parts of the United States, and they said Mike would you come and deliver the same keynote at the same event to kick things off? The only difference is that all of these leaders are from Japan and we're actually going to do a simultaneous translation into Japanese. And I said sure. And I've spoken at some events internationally before and it's always a bit of a challenge for me from a communications standpoint. I've got to be really mindful about, okay, I need to slow down and how I speak. And also, as much as I try to be as aware culturally and socially aware of things, my world view is very American. And as soon as I step outside of the United States, I'm always aware of that.

So anyway, I show up to the event and one of the things about the way that I present at most conferences, I don't use slides, I tell stories and try to engage the audience. And so, for a translator, that can be a little nerve-wracking. They don't have a script to go on, they don't have slides, so the translator comes up to me and she's pretty stressed out, she's like,

"Can you tell me a little bit about what you're going to talk about?" And I said, "Well I'm going to talk about a few things. We're going to talk about the importance of authenticity." And I said to her here's how I define authenticity. It's honesty without self-righteousness and with vulnerability. And she says, "Vulnerability?" And I said, "Yeah. Vulnerability." And she says, "Vulnerability?" And I said, "Yeah. Vulnerability." She said, "There's no word for that in Japanese." I said, "Really?" She goes well there is a word, but it's a bad word. And now I was fascinated, right? I was like oh what is it? She goes it means weakness. I said, hmm, that's interesting. I said most people think that's what it means in English too. Then she looks at me and now she's like mad. She says, "Why would you tell anyone to be vulnerable?"

And I said, well, my research and my experience has taught me two really important things about vulnerability. I said first of all, it's the key driver in human trust and connection. So, for everybody here at the conference, their leaders they want to have trust with their teams and with people and their customer—everybody they've got to be willing to be vulnerable. And I said secondly, it's really the birthplace of innovation, of change, of creativity, of anything new and different. We've got to be willing to be vulnerable. She wasn't buying it.

So now I'm having a standoff with the translator before this event. I was already feeling nervous about giving this speech to 300 people who don't speak English and all of that, and I looked at it and I said, "Listen, do me a favor. I said translate what I say as best you can. I said if it doesn't make sense, if it doesn't translate appropriately or if it's not culturally consistent or just... I'll figure it out."

Now the truth was I didn't know how was going to figure it out. I just wanted to stop talking to her because she was scaring me. So, she walks away and then I'm thinking to myself maybe I shouldn't talk about vulnerability. Maybe it's insensitive. Maybe it won't translate effectively. Maybe it won't make sense. But I'm up on stage. I'm in the middle my presentation and I get to the point where I'm defining what authenticity is and I'm thinking I've got to talk about vulnerability, so I do.

But at that moment, I start looking in a little translation booth at the back of the room and I'm thinking, what is she saying to them right? I have no idea. I don't speak Japanese. She could be saying anything like, "Don't listen to this crazy American" or "I have no idea." But it seemed like it was translating or resonating. I couldn't quite tell. Then I decided to actually pair up the group. There was 300 people in there and pair them up and actually have them do an exercise which I'll explain in just a moment. And as they started to do the exercise, even though I didn't understand the language, intuitively at a mindful level, if you will, I could feel in the room. Okay. I could feel that there was more vulnerability, there was more authenticity just in the way that people were interacting with one another. But it was still a little odd, the environment, right?

I get done with my speech. I walk offstage. I go to the back of the room. The next presenter came up after me. He was speaking Japanese. He did not need her translation services, so she gets out of the translation booth. I'm at the back taking my microphone off at the audio-visual table. She walks across the back of the ballroom to me. She walks over to me she says thank you for your presentation. I said, "You're welcome." She said, "I don't think I understood exactly what you meant about vulnerability when we were talking before, but after hearing your presentation and seeing the exercise, I think I understand now." She said vulnerability's not bad, it's just hard. I said you're right, it's hard. It takes real courage for us to be vulnerable, particularly at work, particularly when our livelihood is at stake. We're very invested in our professional credibility.

And look, it's not that professional credibility is not important. It is. But there's two types of credibility. There's professional credibility, which is about our resume and our track record and our title, or the nature of our business or where we went to school or whatever the case may be, and professional credibility matters. Right? I wouldn't be sitting here having this conversation with you if I had no professional credibility to have this. You wouldn't have the job you have or do the work you do or have the business you have if you had no professional credibility to have it. Absolutely.

But when we think about mindfulness we think about influence; we think about really wanting to have impact on the people around us. And we want to have meaning in our own work. It doesn't come from our professional credibility, it comes from our personal credibility, and what's personal credibility? Can I trust you? Can I relate to you? Are you a real living breathing human being where I can find some common ground and we can work things out? That's where it's really important for us to be mindful in how we build relationships with other people, but also how we go about our work.

The exercise that I did with that group in Japan is an exercise I've been doing for many years. And it's based on a metaphor, a really simple metaphor, but I think a powerful one and it's the metaphor of the iceberg. Do you think that the iceberg metaphor, which gets used for lots of different things, right? Just the tip of the iceberg pops up above the surface of the water. That's all we can see. But the vast majority of the iceberg is down below the waterline, right? That's like how you and I are in life, but particularly at work. We let our professional side pop up above the surface. That's what we show people. But how we really think and feel, what's really going on is down below the waterline. And so, for us to show up more authentically, in our work and in our lives, what we've got to do is consciously choose to lower the waterline on the iceberg. Express or expose more of who we really are. And that takes some courage for sure, but that's one of the best ways that I've seen that we can actually build our muscle, if you will, for vulnerability and authenticity with the people that we work with.

So, when I was at that event in Japan—and I do this often when I'm speaking to a large group of people. I also do it with smaller groups in a workshop setting or even with smaller teams, intact teams that I work with—and the way the exercise works is this: The exercise is what we call if you really knew me. So, if it's just two people paired up, like that group in Japan, one person would start. And I usually would set some context. Talk about the iceberg and about the importance of being vulnerable and lowering our waterline.

And I'll often go first and I'll just say, look one person is going to go first, and then the next person is going to follow him when it's your turn, you'll have about two minutes you just repeat the phrase, "If you really knew me you'd know this about me." And it's really an opportunity for that person to just share whatever is true and real for them in the moment. Think about it from a mindfulness perspective. It's just like really checking in what are my physical sensations? What thoughts are going on in my mind? How am I feeling? What's happening in my life right now?

And again, I always set it up but then I start and go first. So, I'll just, you know say stand up in front of a group and again it could be a big group, a couple of hundred people in a room, it could be 50 people and they're broken up into small groups or into pairs or it could be 10 people sitting around a table who all work together. But I go first and just lower the waterline on my iceberg and share with them authentically, vulnerably how I'm actually feeling in that moment.

Sometimes it's in relation to being there. Like in Japan that day I was able to say to them, if you really knew me you would know I'm excited to be here. I feel really excited and nervous. I'm out of my comfort zone here. I'm in a completely different country, in a different culture, hoping that this will resonate. Right? Sometimes it's about whatever's going on in my life at the time, whatever might be real or true or at home or you know, there's no right or wrong way to do the exercise and I try to just model it in a way that being real and being vulnerable is actually something that's liberating. And then I invite them to go. And again, if it's a whole big group of people the first person goes and everybody goes and I let them know the person listening is not going to comment, they're not going to interject, they're not going to give you advice, they're not going to disagree, they're just going to listen.

And then once the first person has gone then we switch and the second person goes. Again, or if it's a small group of people or even a larger group everyone goes one at a time until everybody's had a chance to go. And once we're done with the exercise then the conversation is, how is that? Or what did you notice? Or some you know de-brief and maybe they debrief in pairs or in small groups or if it's a group of 10 or 12 people sitting around a table will debrief altogether. What's interesting about that and what I've seen and learned over the years of doing this exercise with people is there's a paradox, if you will.

On the surface, we're all really different, we look different, we have different backgrounds or different ages and genders and all kinds of aspects that make us different and unique and diverse, which is beautiful. And simultaneously the further down below the waterline we go, the more similar we become.

You know the natural human response to vulnerability is empathy. So, when people get real, what ends up happening is not only is it liberating for the person who's getting real and being vulnerable, the other people around can see themselves in that person. I'll often ask the group, whatever the size of group, how many of you could relate to what your partner or what the people in your group are talking about? And everybody's hand goes up every time, because they can relate. You can't always relate to the specific circumstance. I mean I could be partnered up with a woman who's pregnant and she could say if you really knew me you'd know I'm dealing with being pregnant, and I can't relate to that specific situation circumstance. I mean I have two girls at home, but my wife was the one that was pregnant and not me. I mean there's a lot of circumstances we may not be able to relate to but when people start to share about their real experience and they start to share the emotional experience they're having, we can almost always relate to that emotional experience. Even if the specific circumstances aren't things we can relate to.

And what's amazing, again back to that group in Japan, I don't know exactly what they were saying to each other because there was a whole big group of people talking all at once—and, oh by the way they were speaking a language, Japanese, that I don't speak. But I do know what they were talking about. They were talking about the same things that every other human being that I work with, in group that I work with, is talking about they're talking about being human. They were talking about joys and fears and excitement and anger and curiosity and frustration and all of what it is to be a human being. So, being mindful at work is really about as being willing and courageous enough to show up and be authentic. Be real. Be who we are. Right?

The most recent book that I wrote is called *Bring Your Whole Self to Work*. Like all of who we are: the good, the bad, everything. And that takes a lot of courage for us individually, and it also takes a lot of courage for the people that were around to create that kind of environment. So, what are some things that you can do, specifically? Let's talk about that.

One thing that we can do is start to look for opportunities for where we can lower the waterline, so to speak. And sometimes it might be sharing something or revealing something really deep and personal, and sometimes it might be something more mundane if you will or just on a day to day basis. One of my favorite activities to do with groups of people who work together is, even if we're not going to do the whole "If you really knew me" exercise to just take a few moments as we started a meeting or a gathering or a phone call or a videoconference to just do a quick little check-in. Right?

There are some situations in some environments where it would be completely appropriate to do a mindfulness practice where we all close our eyes or we're just silent for a minute or two minutes or five minutes. In some environments that wouldn't be appropriate or that would seem strange. But in almost every environment you can do, Hey, can we just take a few minutes for everybody, just briefly check-in. How you feeling? What's going on? Anything you want to say? One or two words or, you know, 30 seconds or a minute or something simple. Most meetings, even as busy as we are, we have time to do that. And what that does is just grounds us, makes us more present more connected. We remember, oh yeah there's a bunch of other human beings in this room or on this call or having this conversation with me at the same time, particularly given how connected we are with all of our technology. It's important for us to find ways to just make little human connections.

Another thing that we can do is ask for help. If you're anything like me and most people that I know, you probably like helping other people. But if you're also anything like me and most people that I know and work with, you might have a bit of a challenge asking other people for help. Most of us love to help, but very few of us are comfortable asking for help. And one reframe on that, if we can remember that when we ask for help a couple of things become available. Number one we might actually get some help. Number two we give other people the opportunity to do something that most people love to do, which is what? Help.

Most of us don't ask for help. Why? Because we're afraid, either they'll judge us for asking. They'll think we're weak. They'll think something's wrong. They think we can't do it, or we're afraid that we'll get rejected. Right? They'll say no. I make myself vulnerable. I put myself out there and then they say no. And then some of us, this isn't for everybody, but I know this can relate to me sometimes too, some of us are so controlling we don't ask for help because we're afraid if we ask someone to do it they'll do it wrong or they won't do it our way, so then we do it ourselves. But all of those things create a ton of stress for us and just simply the act of asking for help and then receiving the help can be both liberating for us and build much stronger connections with the people around us.

And a final thing that we can do, and this one is not easy, but it's super important with respect to our relationships and also our own personal journey, is be willing to engage in difficult conversations with people sooner rather than later. Now look, most people that I know, and this is true for me as well, are not huge fans of difficult or uncomfortable conversations. Giving feedback or talking about things that might get emotional or might be uncomfortable, right?

But thinking about emotional intelligence, so we think about emotional intelligence, right? There's two aspects of emotional intelligence the self aspect and the other aspect if you will, it's about self-awareness and self-management. So how do I feel about having difficult conversations? Right? And is there a way I can manage myself more effectively in those situations. And then also social awareness and relationship management. Who am I talking to? What are we talking about? What's needed to have effective, even difficult conversations?

Think of something that a mentor of mine said to me a number of years ago that I never forgot. He said, "Mike, you know what stands between you and the kind of relationships you really want to have with people?" I said, "What's that?" He said it's probably a 10-minute sweaty palm conversation you're too afraid to have. He said if you get really good at those 10-minute sweaty palm conversations you'll have fantastic relationships he said. But if you do like most of us and you avoid them because they're uncomfortable, because sometimes they can go sideways or get a little messy, he said then you'll just be a victim of who you work with and who you live with.

He said, but if you're willing to lean into the discomfort and have those conversations sooner rather than later you'll build trust with people. You'll resolve conflicts. You'll be able to work with just about anybody and deal with just about anything. And he was right.

So, you think about what we've been talking about the importance of authenticity, right? Honesty without self-righteousness, with vulnerability. A willingness to lower the waterline on our iceberg, to show up as authentically as we possibly can. It takes courage, yes, but when we do that not only does it liberate us, but it gives other people permission to do the same. And it's one of the most important aspects of us being mindful and effective in the work that we do.

In the next segment, we're going to talk about the power of appreciation which is another really important aspect of us being mindful and successful in our work.

MINDFULNESS AT WORK: THE POWER OF APPRECIATION

LESSON 10

In addition to authenticity, the subject of the previous lesson, appreciation is another important aspect of being mindful and successful at work. Although these are both relatively simple concepts, at least to understand, they can be challenging in practice. But when we do appreciate the people we work with and are grateful for the work we do, it allows us to be more effective and ultimately more fulfilled.

APPRECIATION VERSUS RECOGNITION

When appreciation exists in relationships and within teams, such as work groups, people thrive. When it doesn't, people get stressed out, burned out, and upset.

Appreciation is a simple concept, but we often confuse it with recognition, particularly in professional settings. While both are important, they are different.

> Recognition is positive feedback based on results or performance. It's a reaction to something you did or produced. Sometimes it's formal, such as receiving an award or bonus, while other times it's just someone telling you that you did a great job.

> Appreciation is about people's value—who you are.

In other words, recognition is about what we do, while appreciation is about who we are.

Mindfulness and emotional intelligence are about having social awareness. What does this particular person need? Appreciation is about letting people know what we appreciate and value about them. Recognition is reacting to people's performance. We recognize people when they deserve recognition, but we appreciate people all the time.

It doesn't matter how successful or accomplished a person is. We all want to be seen and heard, and we want to know that not just what we say matters, but who we are also matters. This is something we can all do for everybody around us. It takes a certain amount of awareness and mindfulness, because we have to make a human connection with that other person. That sounds simple—and it is—but in today's world, with the pace at which we work, showing appreciation is sometimes a profound act.

When people are asked to think of a time when they felt specifically appreciated, they don't usually recount some big deal. Instead, they recount some small, simple interaction, such as a note or message someone sent them. Just a little bit of appreciation goes a long way.

MINDFULNESS EXERCISE: THE APPRECIATION SEAT

This is a simple but powerful exercise that can be done with teams or groups of people. If the group is large, it can be split into smaller groups of four or five people. A group of 10 or 12 people who all work together is ideal. Regardless of group size, the idea of the difference between recognition and appreciation is introduced to the group.

Each person in the group gets to sit in the appreciation seat for a few minutes (a timer can be set to regulate this), and everyone in the group takes turns expressing appreciation for the individual in the seat. And as difficult or uncomfortable as it may be for the person in the appreciation seat, his or her job is to just sit there and receive the appreciation from the people in the group.

When one person expresses appreciation for another, it raises the serotonin level in both people's brains, making them happier and less stressed. If this is done in a group setting, such as when this exercise is done with a team, it increases oxytocin levels in the body, which physiologically connects people with each other.

As people express their appreciation for each other, there are laughs, pats on the back, hugs, and even tears. And inevitably, the exercise always goes longer than expected because people have so much appreciation to share for their team members.

After the exercise is completed, the group discusses what they thought about the exercise as a whole. Most people will acknowledge the most difficult or uncomfortable part of it is receiving the appreciation. But people also say that it feels really good to express appreciation.

What people really want in today's professional environment is authentic appreciation.

A study conducted by Glassdoor found that 52 percent of people said they would have stayed at their company longer if they felt more valued and appreciated, and 81 percent of people said they're more motivated to work harder when their boss or manager actually appreciates them. But only 37 percent of people said they were more motivated to work harder when their boss was hard on them or when they feared losing their job.

There are opportunities for us to express appreciation all the time. We just don't do it. We're waiting for some event, or activity, or result. But what if we just did it proactively, for no particular reason, just because we wanted to let people know that we appreciate them? Expressing our appreciation is important because it lets people know the value they bring based on who they are, not just what they do.

GRATITUDE

If we're going to be able to express and experience appreciation around us at work, the mindset we have to take is one of gratitude. The thing about gratitude is that it's so simple, but it's easy for us to forget. How often do we stop on a daily basis and ask ourselves, What am I grateful for right now?

Gratitude is a mindfulness practice, and we can bring it into the workplace in many different ways. For example, the next time you are in a meeting, try starting the meeting by asking everyone to share what they are grateful for in that moment. Some people will inevitably not be that into this at first, but over time, this practice can help build the connection among the people in the group, resulting in more trust and understanding of each other.

Making gratitude sharing a regular practice can make the members of a group feel safe to share things they have struggled with or times when they have failed. It can create more psychological safety, which is basically trust at a group level.

CREATING AN ENVIRONMENT OF APPRECIATION

Where can you infuse appreciation and gratitude in your work environment? There are a few simple practices that are helpful in creating such an environment:

Simply ask this question: What are you grateful for?

Look for opportunities to express appreciation for the people around you. When can you make it safe and conducive to express appreciation for the people that you work with? Perhaps you can write someone a thank-you card and drop it on his or her desk.

Start receiving appreciation from other people more graciously. Just say thank you, especially if you don't agree with what they're saying. It's perhaps not possible to be overappreciated, and most people probably feel underappreciated. This is partly because people get weird when others express appreciation for them. So, if you become more comfortable receiving appreciation, you'll get more, and you will make it more conducive to the environment in which you work for appreciation to be expressed.

From a mindfulness perspective, we can become more mindful of what we're grateful for and what we appreciate about the people around us. We can not only express it more effectively, but we can change the culture of the team or the people with whom we work.

MINDFULNESS AT WORK:
THE POWER OF APPRECIATION

LESSON 10 TRANSCRIPT

Welcome back. I'm Mike Robbins and we're talking about mindfulness at work. And in the first segment we talked to all about the power of authenticity. In this segment, we're going to talk about the power of appreciation. So, you ever had something taken away from you in your life only to realize how much you appreciated it after it was gone? Probably so. This happened to me a number of times in my life. Probably the most significant experience I had of that was when my professional baseball career ended.

So, as I mentioned in the first segment, I played baseball growing up, had a chance to play in college, and then got drafted by the Kansas City Royals out of Stanford. I was in the minor leagues when I injured my arm—I tore ligaments in my elbow. I had three surgeries on my pitching arm, tried to come back, I wasn't able to make it back. And you know as disappointed as I was when I finally realized that my baseball career was over, when I realized I wasn't going get to play anymore, I started to reflect on the whole experience and look back on it. And as I was reflecting on it I started to ask myself some questions over and over again and one of the questions that I had was did I have any regrets?

You know if I could do anything different what would I do? If I could go back. And the truth was I didn't regret a lot of the stuff that I thought I would have, like the bad games that I had or the bad pitches that I threw or the times I really blew it. None of that stuff mattered to me anymore. The only regret that I had was that I didn't fully appreciate it while it was happening. I was too busy trying to make it.

You know I was this kid who was raised by a single mom. We didn't have a lot of money. I was going to make it to the major leagues. I was going to be successful. I was going to be famous. And you know, I figured I'd appreciate it once that all happened. But up to that point in my life, when I got injured at the age of 23, even though I was pretty good, I spent most of my time thinking that I wasn't good enough, comparing myself to everyone around me, and literally like holding my breath hoping that I didn't mess it up. And when it was all said and done and I hadn't made it, I thought to myself, oops, I think I missed the point.

Maybe you can relate to this in your own life in some way. It was very significant for me at that point in my life. I didn't know the full significance of that lesson if you will at that time. But as I mentioned in the first segment, when I left baseball and got into the business world, I got a job in the tech world. I started to notice some similarities, some things that were similar to my own experience as an athlete, both individually and within the team, as I got into the business world. And I realized, oh some of these things, some of these intangible qualities that go into success or failure for me as an individual as well as for the team are relevant at work.

And one of the most important things that I noticed right away as I started to reflect on my experience as an athlete and look around at some of the people I was working with was appreciation. Most of the best teams I'd ever been on, there was a lot of appreciation for what we were doing, for each other, from the coaches, to me as an athlete, and then as I started to look at work teams I started to see the same thing: that when appreciation exists in relationships and within teams, people can thrive. When it doesn't, people get stressed out, burned out, and upset.

So, what is this appreciation really mean at work? It's a really simple concept, but one of the things I've learned over studying this and talking to lots and lots of people about this around the world is that we confuse two things that are both important, but they're different, particularly in our professional lives. We confuse recognition and appreciation. They're both important, but they're different.

Here's what recognition is: Recognition is positive feedback based on results, based on performance. You produce a result, hopefully you get recognized for it. Sometimes it's formal, sometimes you might get an award or some kind of bonus, or some kind of award or something. Sometimes it might just be someone saying, "Hey, great job. Way to go." A pat on the back. But it's a reaction to something, a job well done, something that we've produced. Appreciation, on the other hand, is about people's value. Recognition is about what we do. Appreciation is about who we are.

The best way I know to describe the difference between these two things and why they're important, I'll give you an example from my baseball career. Now whether you know anything about baseball or not you may know what happens to the pitcher—which is the position that I played—in the baseball game and the pitcher doesn't do well. Do you know what happens? Yeah, they stop the game and in front of everybody, the manager, the guy in charge, literally walks out to the middle of the field, takes the ball from you and makes you leave and you have to walk out off the mound out of the game. It's pretty embarrassing.

I mean imagine you're at work doing whatever kind of work you do and you make a mistake, like kind of a big one, and someone bursts into the room and says, "Stop right there!" and you have to stop in the middle of whatever you're doing and get up and leave and some other person comes and sits down in your chair and starts doing your job for you. And imagine thousands of people are watching this happen. You would probably feel a little embarrassed, don't you think? That's what it's like to get taken out of the baseball game as the pitcher.

But the worst part of the whole experience was when I would go to sit down on the bench where all my teammates were, nobody would talk to me. Even if you don't like baseball, if you have a chance to watch an American baseball game just watch it—it's best on television because the camera will literally follow that guy in and you'll see what happens is, it's like an unwritten rule in baseball. Leave him alone, he's upset.

And yes, I was upset. I had just pitched bad enough they took me out of the game. But you know what I could've used after just having a bad game and sitting over there on the bench? What do you think? Some appreciation. Not recognition. I mean if I had done a bad job what are they going to do? Come over, "Hey Robbins, way to go, great job!" No, that would be phony. That would be inauthentic. Appreciation isn't phony recognition. I didn't deserve any recognition if I'd failed. I hadn't done my job.

So, like, look, we all have to do our jobs. We have expectations. In that situation, if I didn't pitch well we're probably going to lose the game. So, me not doing a good job was both my responsibility and my personal failure but also the team's failure. However, what I could have used and almost never got in all those years of playing baseball was for someone to come over and actually appreciate me, personally, not for what I had done, but for who I am.

What could they have said? I don't know, they could have said hey man that was rough, but you know you're an important part of the team. Or hey, you know we got your back. We believe in you, right? Mindfulness and emotional intelligence is about having some social awareness. What does this person need? Appreciation is about letting people know what we appreciate and value about them. Recognition is reacting to people's performance. They're both important, but if we separate them out we recognize people when they deserve recognition. We appreciate people all the time.

You know, I heard Oprah Winfrey speak a few years ago, and she said this really simple but powerful thing she said, "I've interviewed thousands and thousands and thousands of people in my career. I've interviewed everybody. I've interviewed presidents, I've interviewed prime ministers, I've interviewed celebrities, I've interviewed children, I've interviewed criminals I've interviewed—you name the type of person," she said, "I've interviewed them." She said, "For all these years and all these interviews," she said, "you know that just about every single person asks me some version of the same question. When the interview is over interview's over, camera shuts off, they lean over and they say 'How did I do?' or 'Was that okay?'" Some version of that question.

She said "Early in my career I used to be really confused by this question because I would be sitting across from someone who's very successful, very accomplished. I'd be wondering to myself, 'Are they really that insecure? Do they really need the validation? Like why are they asking me how they did?'" She goes, "Then I realized something. They're not actually asking me how they did. You know what they're really asking me? Did you see me? Did you hear me? Did what I say matter to you?"

She said—and I agree with her—everybody's asking those questions, all the time. It doesn't matter how successful or accomplished they might be. We all want to be seen, we want to be heard, and we want to know not just what we say, but who we are matters. And that's something that we can all do for everybody around us. It takes a certain amount of awareness. It takes some mindfulness. We have to put our phones down or sometimes close the laptop and actually connect with someone eye to eye and heart to heart. If we're on the telephone with them or on a video-conference, it's actually making a human connection with that other person. And that sounds simple, and it is. But in today's world, with the pace at which we work, it's actually sometimes a profound act.

Glassdoor.com recently did a study, and they always are looking at how people like where they work, if you will. You can leave reviews on Glassdoor for places where you work or when you leave someone, somewhere, to let people know how is it actually working there. And they did a study recently and they found that 52 percent of people said I would have stayed at my company longer if I felt more valued and appreciated. They also found that 81 percent of people said I'm more motivated to work harder when my boss or my manager actually appreciates me. Where only 37 percent of people said they were more motivated to work harder when their boss was hard on them or they feared losing their job. So, the way that we work in today's world and what people really want is authentic appreciation.

Now again the difference between recognition and appreciation is an important one. I was speaking at an event a few years ago for one of my clients, I often get invited to speak at recognition events where people are getting awards, where they're being honored and recognized for a job well done, or for producing a result. Which are pretty cool events to be at because everyone's in a good mood. It's for a very positive thing.

I was at this event, a couple hundred people at this event, and as I got up to speak about the difference between recognition and appreciation I said "Hey, everybody here just pair up with someone in the audience and talk a little bit about what was it about winning this award that had you feel most appreciated?"

And they paired up and I gave them a few minutes to talk to each other, and then when everybody came back I said "Does anybody want to share what they were talking about with their partner?" and a few people raised their hands and they were sharing. This one man raised his hand and he stood up and he said "You know Mike, I never really thought about it." He said, "Winning this award is a big deal. I was surprised. You know getting to come here. It was a trip, (they got to take a trip) I get to bring my wife. You know being here, we don't usually travel without our kids so just it's really an amazing experience just to be here." He said, "But when you asked us that question and I paired up with my partner, I shared with him the moment for me that was the most meaningful of this whole experience." He said "When I went home and told my family that I won this award, my son told me he was proud of me." He said, "That was the moment for me." He said, "Look the trip's great, the award, the whole thing, it's all great, but that's the moment that I really felt appreciated."

And when I asked this question of people all the time, to think of a time where they felt specifically appreciated, it's usually not some big deal, it's some simple little interaction. It's a note that someone sent them, a message someone left for them, it's just something simple. And there's an exercise that I love to do with teams, and if you work with a group of people this is a really simple but powerful exercise that you can do. I call this exercise the appreciation seat exercise. And this exercise I will use often. I can do it with a larger group and split people up into smaller groups of four or five which is great. The best way is when I'm with a group of 10 or 12 people. They all work together, and I'll introduce the idea of the difference between recognition and appreciation.

I'll say, here's what we're going to do: We're going to go around the table and each person is going to have a few minutes to be on the appreciation seat. Now what that means is when it's their turn—so let's say Suzy's sitting over here to my right—when it's Suzy's turn everyone in the group is going to have a few minutes to just express some appreciation for Suzy.

Now I usually set it up because I've done this before like, look we may not get to everyone. I'll put three minutes on the clock here and then the timer will go off and everyone will have time in that three minutes to say some things they appreciate about Susie. And Susie's job, as difficult or uncomfortable as it may be for her, is to just sit there and receive the appreciation from the people on her team.

And what's amazing is we have a lot of resistance, by the way, to receiving appreciation, which is kind of funny. We have all these weird social norms that we do. You know what you're supposed to say by the way when someone expresses appreciation for you? You know you're supposed to say? Thank you. Then shut your mouth. All you have to do is say thanks, but if you listen to yourself and most other people what comes after the thanks is almost always weird and insincere. We either give them a compliment right back—You too, you too, you're great too— and sometimes we mean it, but sometimes it's just like a knee jerk reaction.

I often think of it like a birthday gift. It would be strange if I came over to your house on your birthday with a gift and I said happy birthday and you went "Oh thanks," and then you ran into the other room and came out with a gift for me. That would be weird, right? But even worse, we argue with people when they give us a compliment or express an apology: "Oh no, it's nothing Oh no, stop." Which is always odd. What are you expecting them to say in response, by the way? "Oh, you're right. You're an idiot. I was just kidding." Like it's the weirdest thing. Where I'm giving you a gift, a birthday gift, happy birthday, that would be like you taking the present and smashing it on the floor and going, "I don't deserve that." I wouldn't give you any more gifts, by the way. You would offend me and you'd ruin the gift.

But so, the exercise itself, the hardest part, is often sitting there and just receiving the appreciation. You know what's amazing about this when one human being expresses appreciation for another human being? It raises the serotonin level in both people's brains. It physiologically makes us happier, less stressed. If we do it in a group like when I do the appreciation seed exercise with a team, it actually increases our level of oxytocin which connects us, physiologically connects us with each other.

So again, three minutes for Suzy on the appreciation seat. We all take turns in and as many people as can go express some appreciation for her. Then we'll go to the next person, let's say it's Antoine. Now it's his turn. Again, three minutes for Antoine. And at first, usually when we do the exercise people are a little funny at first or they are a little goofy or making jokes, and I usually know just to kind of ride through that a little bit and keep reminding people you know be real about this. But usually by the second person or the third person, the waterline on the iceberg—which I talked about in the previous segment—people start getting more real.

And what's amazing is what gets shared. And sometimes there's some laughs and there's some pats on the back and there's some hugs and even some tears as people express their appreciation for each other. And we go around the room and everybody has a few minutes on the appreciation seat, and inevitably, no matter how many times I've done this exercise, it always goes longer than I think. People start yelling at me. Turn off the watch, turn off the timer, I have more to say and I want to go! And it's amazing that I've sat with the group of 10 people and we've spent an hour and 45 minutes having that conversation. And it always blows me away that just a little bit of appreciation goes such a long way.

I was at an event a few years ago in Las Vegas for a company, it was their all company event. They had people all over the country in the United States, and they get together once a year for an annual conference. And I had talked to a few of the people who were at the event on the phone before the event started. And one of the women that I talked to told me a story about when she got promoted to be a manager a few years earlier, one of the executives from the company had called her and left her this voicemail where he just celebrated her and was so excited for her and she said you know that voicemail made me feel so good when I got it, I save it on my phone, and when I'm feeling bad or I'm feeling down, sometimes I'll just listen to it.

And so, I'm at the event before I go to speak and everyone's wearing name tags and I recognize the woman's name as I'm standing in line to get some food because I talked to her on the phone. And I was like, hey we talked on the phone and I said, "Do you really have that voicemail on your phone?"

And she pulls out her phone and she plays it for me. And it was a really passionate, very excited message from one of the executives. And I saw the executive who had left the message because I had actually talked to him on the phone as well. And I said, "Does he know that you have that voicemail?" And she said no and her face got a little red. And I said do you want to share it with him and she was a little embarrassed but she was like okay.

So, we walk over to him tell the whole story, play the voicemail. He listens to it. We all have a nice chat about it. She walks away. And he looks back at me and says "Mike, I don't even remember leaving that message." He said it's something that I do when people get promoted, particularly when we promote people from within. It's a big deal, I like to make sure I thank them and acknowledge them and make a big deal about it, but he's like, but I don't remember leaving that message. But she had it on her phone and she listens to it every few months when she needs a little pick me up. And it was a great reminder for him in that moment, but also for me, as he and I were having that conversation. A little bit of appreciation goes a long way.

When we do the appreciation seed exercise with teams what I'm always amazed by when we get done, when we debrief I usually ask people, how was that? Most people will acknowledge the most difficult or uncomfortable part of it is receiving the appreciation. Although I often say to them I promise you, you won't forget anytime soon what people said to you today. And on the flipside, though what people say is it feels so good to give appreciation, to express it. And what we often realize is there are opportunities for us to do that all the time. We just don't do it. We're waiting for some event or some activity or some result or some something. But what if we just did it proactively, for no particular reason, just because we wanted to let people know?

Look from a mindfulness perspective why this is so important, we talk about mindfulness at work, is because appreciation, while it's expressing our appreciation, letting people know the value that they bring for who they are not just what they do, the mindset we have to take, if we're going to be able to express and experience appreciation around us at work, is a mindfulness or a mindset so to speak of gratitude.

Now the thing about gratitude is it's so simple, but it's easy for us to forget. Right? It's how often do we stop on a daily basis and just ask ourselves, what am I grateful for right now? It's one of my favorite questions to ask. By the way if you call my office, on the voicemail, you know what it says? And it's been on there for about 15 years. I've changed the message many times, but it's "Hey, sorry we missed you. Leave a message and in your message let us know something that you're grateful for." We get the coolest messages in the office. People call to like sell us stuff and they'll be like, "Uh. I wasn't prepared for that question. Let me see. I'm grateful for my kids or I'm grateful for my health. I'm grateful for something simple."

And what I learned many years ago about asking this question—it's a personal practice that I have—I want to inspire gratitude in other people. But there's a self-serving part of it because when I ask other people what they're grateful for, you know what it forces me to do? Stop and think about what I'm grateful for. At least once a week, sometimes two or three times a week, I did it earlier today, I just go on social media and I'll post the question "What are you grateful for in this moment?" Because gratitude is a practice. It's a mindfulness practice and we can bring it into work in lots of different ways.

I think of a woman named Erica Fox who I did some work with Google a number of years ago. And at the time Erica was running a learning team that was spread out all across the United States, so a virtual team, which can be challenging. She doesn't get to see her team on a regular basis and she was struggling with how do I bring this team together given that the way we meet is by video-conference once a week and we don't always get a chance to be in person with one another? And she said after she came to one of the sessions that I delivered, she decided to come up with some creative ideas for how to engage and connect her team. And she said, "What I did on the very next video conference meeting that we had, I said to everybody, 'Hey listen we're going to go around and I want everyone to share something that they're grateful for. Could be something about work, it could be something about life, whatever it is it doesn't matter. Just share what you're grateful for and then take out a Post-it Note and write the thing on the Post-it Note that you're grateful for. And then what I'd like for you to do is post it somewhere in your desk or workspace. Like hide it from yourself, because then you'll find it later.'"

And she said at first she got some eye rolls and people kind of thought it was a little corny. But she said, "What happened was everybody shared something they were grateful for," and she goes, "I noticed that it actually allowed us to connect with each other a little more personally and it set the meeting tone if you will in a positive way to begin with. The next week I did it again. And there were still a few eye rolls, but people got into it a little more. So, the third week I did it again and after three weeks in a row I thought, you know maybe I'll stop. Maybe we'll try something different and I get on our meeting for that fourth week and just jumped into the meeting and all of a sudden people were upset. 'Wait, wait hold on, hold on, I got my Post-it Note. I'm ready to share the thing I'm grateful for!'"

And she said, she realized that even some of the people on her team who weren't that into it at first had really gotten into it. And she said over time, what she found was that it started to really build up the connection amongst the people on her team. There was more trust, there was more understanding of each other. And she said when they would get together every couple of months in person, which they did, they started as a team to have a practice where they not only would share things that they were grateful for and they wanted to celebrate. But it made them feel safer, if you will, to share things that they were struggling with or where they'd failed. It actually created more what we call psychological safety for her team. Psychological safety is basically trust at a group level.

So, think about how this relates to you, to your own work, to the people that you work with, to the work that you do. Where can you infuse appreciation and gratitude? There's a couple of simple practices that I've found to be really helpful. One is ask that question, what are you grateful for? Years ago, a mentor of mine said to me this great thing he said "Mike you know gratitude and victimhood can't coexist." So, when we're at a place of gratitude we can't simultaneously be in a place of victimhood. And one of the things that derails us individually and collectively at work is feeling like we're victimized by whatever's going on around us: the other people we work with, the technology, what's going on in the market, you name it, the customers. There's all kinds of stuff that we can justifiably feel like it's not fair but if we come from a place of gratitude it's very difficult to get stuck in that place.

Another thing that we can do is look for opportunities to express our appreciation for the people around us. As simple as that sounds, we've got to find opportunities to do that, right? Like that appreciation seat exercise. Where can you make it safe and conducive to express appreciation for the people that you work with. Maybe you actually write a physical card. You will blow people's minds, by the way, if you actually write them a thank you card. Put it in an envelope put their name on it maybe drop it in the mail, unless you work with them, drop it on their desk. We don't give cards to each other like we used to.

And another thing that we can do, and I mentioned it earlier, but start receiving appreciation from other people more graciously. Just say thank you, even and especially if you don't agree with what they're saying. Right? Your opinion about my expression of appreciation for you is actually not that interesting to me.

And you know what's interesting? Here's something that I've learned over many years. You know I've interviewed tons of people about this particular topic in my work. And you know what I've never heard anyone say to me? "You know what, Mike? I'm just too appreciated. It's just too much, just bugs me. My coworkers, my spouse, my kids, my friends, my family. They just appreciate me too much. Just gets on my nerves." I've never heard anyone say that.

You know why? Because I don't think it's possible to be over appreciated. And if we're honest most of us feel underappreciated. And one of the reasons why we feel underappreciated is because we get all weird when people express appreciation for us. So, if we actually become more comfortable receiving appreciation, a couple things will happen. First of all, we'll get more, and second of all, we'll actually make it more conducive to the environment in which we work for appreciation to be expressed. Right?

We talked about in the first segment authenticity and vulnerability, expressing appreciation for other people and receiving it is actually a bold and courageous act and creates a certain amount of vulnerability for us as human beings. And so, from a mindfulness perspective, we become more mindful of what we're grateful for, what we appreciate about the people around us.

We can not only express it more effectively, but we literally can change the culture of the team or the people with which we work. I've seen this happen many times over the course of all these years of doing this work.

And as a way to start to wrap up this particular segment, I want to tell one poignant story about this. Because in all my years of doing this work with different types of teams and groups and people in a variety of different work environments, one of my favorite places to get to do work—and I don't do it all that often—but given my sports background, from time to time in addition all the companies that bring me in to work with their teams and their leaders, I do get invited to work with athletes, particularly baseball players.

And a few years back, this was actually in the spring of 2010, I got a telephone call from the San Francisco Giants, one of the two local professional baseball teams in the San Francisco Bay area where I live. And I was honored to get that phone call and they asked me, "Hey Mike would you come in and give a talk to the organization about the power of appreciation?" And I said of course. And I went in and I gave that talk, and the message really resonated. And I got a chance to work with the team a bit and the organization over the course of that season. And I've actually had a chance to work with the San Francisco Giants since then. And what's interesting is the San Francisco Giants actually won the World Series or the championship in baseball that 2010 season. And it was a really big deal, not just because they'd never won the championship since the team moved from New York in the late 1950s—so it was a big deal both in sports but also culturally—but it was also a big deal because they won that championship and they didn't have the best talent.

All the experts on paper, when they got into the playoffs the very last day of the season, people said, oh they're not going to win. They don't have a good enough team and they won each round to the playoffs and then they won their championship and people were like, "Wow!" But baseball is kind of a funny sport like that. Sometimes you can get hot at the right time and win a championship even if you don't have the best players. But then two years later in 2012, the San Francisco Giants won the World Series again.

They won another championship. Two in three years which is very difficult to do. And similarly, that 2012 team, on paper, didn't look like it should have been the best team. They shouldn't have won another championship. And then two years after that, in 2014, they won another championship. So, three championships in five years, each time with teams that weren't supposed to win. But somehow figured out that whole team chemistry, team culture thing, in a way that allowed them to be incredibly successful. And because I've had a chance to watch them both from the outside as a fan, but also worked with them inside the organization, I got some insight on this. And there's two things that happened in back to back seasons at the end of the 2013 and 2014 season, to me that really epitomize the power of appreciation.

The end of the 2013 season, the Giants weren't going to the playoffs, they weren't going to win another championship. They were disappointed with how the season had turned out. I was at the ballpark. One of the last games of the season, they give out a big award that gets voted on by the other players and coaches to basically their most inspirational player. And the player that won that award that year is a guy named Hunter Pence. And Hunter was an all-star player, really good player on the field, but kind of their spiritual or sort of passionate motivational leader in the clubhouse in the locker room so to speak. And he got voted that most inspirational player that year.

And when he was receiving his award on the field right before a game, there's about 40,000 people in the stands that night, I was one of them, he walks out onto the field and they had a whole ceremony for him and he received the award and he thanked everybody. And at one point in his speech towards the end, he's looking at all of his teammates and he gets kind of serious and he says "Listen, I want each and every one of you to know that I love you." And he said, "I know some of you get uncomfortable when I say that because you think it's soft." He said, "I don't think it's soft. In fact, I think it's the most important thing that we have."

And I'm sitting in the ballpark listening to him say this to his teammates in front of all those people and I was really touched by it. I was like, "Wow!" He very passionately, vulnerably, expressed his love for his teammates.

And it wasn't because they were winning a championship or celebrating something specific, although he was winning an award. It was authentic, it was real, it was full of appreciation and love. And it really touched me.

Fast forward to the end of the next season, it's 2014. They're back in the World Series, they're back in the championship, it's game seven. They're on the road in Kansas City. The tying runs on third base, there's two outs in the bottom of the ninth inning. Madison Bumgarner, a big burly pitcher for the San Francisco Giants from North Carolina—he's about 6'5, about 220 pounds—he gets the final out of the World Series. The guy from Kansas City pops up, the Giants win their third championship in five years. And as they're about to celebrate, Bumgarner runs off the pitcher's mound towards home plate towards the catcher, a guy named Buster Posey. Another big strong guy from Georgia, these two burly manly men go to embrace each other in the middle of the diamond. As they embrace, Bumgarner leans over and whispers into Posey's ear, "I love you." And the whole team comes and jumps on them and they are celebrating their championship and I'm sitting in a hotel room in Arizona watching the game on television. Super excited that they won, but at that moment, when I see Bumgarner say that to Posey I think to myself, "That's it. That's it right there. That's what really makes a championship team."

It's that love. It's that appreciation for one another. It's so simple, but it's powerful, in the work that you do, in the work that I do, in the work that all of us do. Can we be mindful enough to pay attention to the people around us, to the work that we're doing, to appreciate the people that we work with? Not just recognize them when they do something worthy of recognition, and to be grateful for the work that we do for the opportunity to do it. For the ability to support ourselves and the people that we love. There's so much for us to be grateful for if we choose to pay attention to it.

So, you think about the two things that we've talked about here, in the first segment we talked about the power of authenticity. And in this segment, we talked about the power of appreciation. Relatively simple concepts, at least to understand. The more challenging aspect is to be able to practice it.

And when we do practice being authentic and we do practice appreciating not only the people that we work with but being grateful for the work that we do, it allows us to be more effective and more successful and ultimately more fulfilled. And it allows us to have the kind of impact we want to have on the people around us.

And that's what it really takes for us to be mindful at work.

Thanks.

THE BENEFITS OF BRAIN TRAINING

LESSON 11

This lesson is about cognitive training: the notion that our cognitive functions, the core systems of our brain, can or cannot be trained. The lesson addresses cross-sectional studies as well as randomized controlled studies that have been conducted to study neuroplasticity of the brain: the ability of the brain to change in structure and function as a result of experience and training.

TRAINING THE BRAIN

How do we train the brain? Unfortunately, there's a lot of lore around the idea that playing brain games like puzzles or sudoku might help the brain, but research shows that doesn't seem to be the case.

There are three main categories of reasons that motivate people to train the brain: People want to feel better, perform better, or age better.

Feeling better has to do with improving psychological well-being.

Performing better involves improving cognitive functioning.

Aging better has to do with doing something on a regular basis—in the same way we might engage in physical activity for physical health—to protect against age-related diseases, such as Alzheimer's disease.

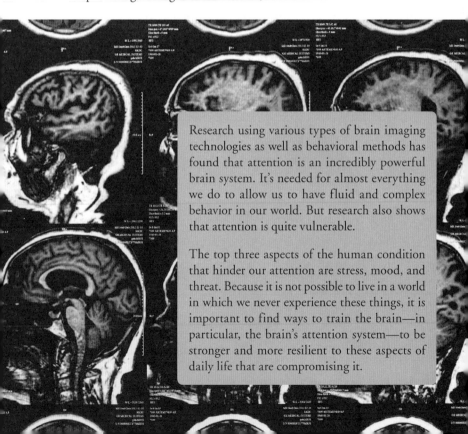

Research using various types of brain imaging technologies as well as behavioral methods has found that attention is an incredibly powerful brain system. It's needed for almost everything we do to allow us to have fluid and complex behavior in our world. But research also shows that attention is quite vulnerable.

The top three aspects of the human condition that hinder our attention are stress, mood, and threat. Because it is not possible to live in a world in which we never experience these things, it is important to find ways to train the brain—in particular, the brain's attention system—to be stronger and more resilient to these aspects of daily life that are compromising it.

Beyond this, many people have the self-interest of wanting their brains in peak shape so they can be of better service to our world.

There are many reasons we'd like to train the brain, including to be more effective in our job; more resilient to life's challenges; more giving, kind, or connected; or more joyful in life.

CROSS-SECTIONAL STUDIES

In the broad topic of neuroplasticity, researchers are interested in seeing how the experience and activities that the human brain engages in may alter brain structure and function, ultimately to improve its performance. One of the questions that researchers in this realm aim to answer is this: Are there individuals who have a type of daily life experience, maybe through their profession, that causes their brain structure to be different from most people's?

One very intriguing group is cabdrivers—in particular, those who navigate the circuitous landscape of the city streets of London. It is very difficult for people to know how to get from point A to point B unless they are highly familiar with this jungle of streets, so London cabdrivers have to have three years of formal training to get very familiar with the maps of the city.

Researchers designed a study using this unique group to analyze the notion that engaging in certain activities may change the brain's structures. They scanned the brains of London cabdrivers, who constantly had to navigate unknown routes, and compared the scans with those of bus drivers, who also drove all day but had well-defined paths on which they traveled back and forth.

Using structural MRI, researchers found that there were brain differences between London cabdrivers and bus drivers—specifically in the region involved in spatial navigation, the hippocampus. Cabdrivers had larger hippocampi—which were more densely packed and looked structurally healthier and more robust—than the bus drivers. Even more striking was that the size of the hippocampus was tied to how many years the cabdrivers had been cabdrivers: The longer time they'd spent navigating the streets of London, the larger the size of their hippocampus.

This finding suggests that there is some correspondence between how the brain is organized and how people spend their time. In addition, driving itself appears not to cause the brain change; the spatial navigation demands appear to change it.

This notion of experience altering or shaping the brain is not unique to cabdrivers. The hippocampi of people who play video games (such as Tetris) or who juggle tend to look healthier and more robust than matched control groups, in terms of age and education, of people who don't engage in that activity.

Within the field of cognitive neuroscience, brain training (along with its benefits) is one of the most hotly studied topics.

Although this study does a great job of connecting a particular brain structure to function, it is an opportunistic, naturalistic type of experiment. They didn't recruit drivers in London to be part of the study; they sought out people that happened to drive as their profession.

This is called a cross-sectional study because researchers are studying individuals who just happen to be different because of their life circumstance; they are not asking individuals to engage in any particular training. Cross-sectional studies allow us to compare distinct groups of people and ask specific questions, and benefit from what's already happening.

But who decides to become a cabdriver? What if it's the case that people that choose to be the cabdrivers just happen to have hippocampi that are larger? It becomes a question of cause and effect. It may not be that the circuitous route navigation leads to the structural change; instead, it may be that people choose to do this type of job because they already have larger hippocampi that allow them to do it well.

RANDOMIZED CONTROLLED TRIALS

Cross-sectional studies may not give us the strongest test of neuroplasticity because of this design limitation. A better way to ask the question of whether experience and training changes the brain is by using the gold standard of how research is conducted: the randomized controlled trial.

In this type of research design, people are invited into a study who have an interest in a broad topic—for example, brain training—and then are randomly assigned to be in either a condition of interest—for example, one that includes a particular brain-training protocol—or another condition, called the control group.

The control group is either a no-training control group, which involves doing nothing, or an active-comparison control group, in which participants in a computer-based brain-training study, for example, can watch movies or read books instead of doing the training. The control condition serves as a comparison for the treatment condition.

A longitudinal study is one in which researchers track participants over time.

The industry of computer-based programs and apps for brain training is a very popular one. In fact, it's valued at about a billion dollars. Therefore, a lot of effort and financial investment goes into this strategy for brain training.

In a particular randomized controlled trial on the effectiveness of brain training, the goal was to determine if brain function could be improved as a result of people engaging in the study itself. The study involved a very popular way that people choose to engage in brain training: computer-based programs or apps.

In this study, researchers randomly assigned participants either to use Lumosity, a brain-training app, for 70 days or to engage in fun, intensive video game playing for 70 days. The first condition was intended to be training for the brain while the other was just intended to match the amount of screen time and engagement the people in the brain-training condition experienced.

Researchers tracked the performance of participants by using an index from the Lumosity program. Overall, everyone showed improvement over 70 days. Their scores continually increased, until at some point they plateaued, but the data showed a strong learning and improvement effect, which is very encouraging.

By analyzing this data, researchers also learned that how much time and effort people spent engaging in this brain-training protocol impacted how much they benefited. People who had low adherence and didn't always do the assigned homework didn't improve as much as those who had high adherence.

Lumosity Performance Index

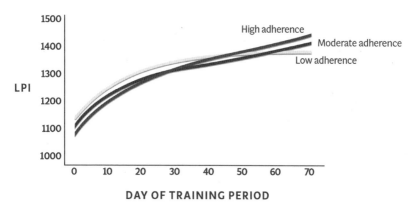

The intention of Lumosity's brain-training protocol is to improve attention, and attention-related processes, that might eventually help a person be better at decision making in the real world. So, the true test of this brain-training method came when the researchers in this experiment studied whether the benefits participants gained from training certain operations—such as attention, inhibition control, and deliberation—through the Lumosity program carried over into a real-world decision-making task.

A review paper on brain training found little evidence that training enhances performance on distantly related tasks or that training improves everyday cognitive performance. This suggests that although people may download an app and choose to use it and even get better at the brain-training games, it has virtually no impact on the rest of their lives. And this probably means that it's not worth their time, because nobody's really playing these games for the sole purpose of getting better at playing them.

THE BENEFITS OF BRAIN TRAINING

LESSON 11 TRANSCRIPT

[Introduction by Shauna Shapiro]

Dr. Amishi Jha is a neuroscientist and associate professor at the Department of Psychology at the University of Miami. She studies the neural basis of attention, working memory, and the effects of mindfulness based training programs on cognition, emotion, and resilience. Amishi is one of the most extraordinary thinkers and researchers of our time and I'm delighted that she's joining us on this journey.

[End of introduction]

It's my great pleasure to talk to you today about the neuroscience of mindfulness. Obviously, this is a very big topic, and to give you a sense of the kind of slice through it that will take, I'd like to give you a little bit of background on who I am and the kind of research I do in my own laboratory, so that you know where I'm coming from with regard to the perspectives I'll take and some of the research that we've conducted.

So, I am a cognitive neuroscientist, which means that I study how it is that the brain is it is able to instantiate the mind in different cognitive functions. In particular, the functions of attention. So, in my laboratory, we use various types of brain imaging technologies, functional MRI, event related potential's or ERP's, as well as behavioral methods. And through these methods what we've been able to learn is that, and maybe this is obvious to most, attention is an incredibly powerful brain system. It's needed for almost everything we do, to allow us to have fluid and complex behavior in our, in our world. But it ends up that we've learned through this research that attention is also quite vulnerable. And the top three aspects of our human condition that actually cripple, or in some sense can be thought of as kryptonite, for attention are stress, poor mood, and threat. If it were possible to live in a world in which we never experienced these things that would be tremendous. But that's not that's not the human condition.

So, what we've been very interested in doing is trying to see if there are ways in which we might be able to train the brain—in particular train the brain's attention system—to be stronger and more resilient to these aspects of functioning in daily life that are compromising it. That's how our work comes to mindfulness training. So, you'll understand that the perspective I take is really with regard to brain training as it relates to mindfulness training.

In my lab, we look at a whole host of populations and what one thing they happen to have in common is that they experience what we call a high stress interval. These are demanding periods of time over which they have not only to perform well, but they may have to learn new tasks, get training in new types of content. And this could be a few weeks to several weeks. So, some of the examples are students going through the academic semester, or elite athletes or college athletes that are enduring pre-season training, or accountants and other business professionals in which they have to dedicate and use their attention in a very precise fashion over multiple months, for example, tax season. And a very large group that we work with are military personnel as well as military spouses. We track them and work with them over pre-deployment training intervals in which the demands are intensive. But the whole intention is to ready them so that they're best prepared for the deployment itself.

So, as I mentioned these are all high stress groups, and we want to work with them and see if there's ways in which we might protect their attention. Not only so that their training is optimal and their learning is optimal, but so that at the end of this intensive demanding period of preparation, they're able to perform well. Whether it's taking final exams or actually being deployed to a war zone. We want to make sure attention is in peak shape. So, let's broaden our conversation a little bit and we'll return back to some of the studies we've done with these populations.

I'd like to just review with you some of the key questions we're going to be covering. First, I'd like to tell you a little bit and talk to you about what cognitive training is: this notion that our cognitive functions of attention and working memory, these work core systems of our brain, we want to find out if they can be trained and what that even means.

And then narrow in a little bit on the topic of attention. How does it work in the brain? How are we able to perform well under pressure? And how does our attention system allow us to do so? And then we'll finally talk about sort of the heart of the matter which is mindfulness training. Is this an effective cognitive training tool? If so, how does it actually work in the brain, and what impact does it have on our cognitive performance? So, we will go through each of these key questions in turn.

And now I'd like to take a little bit of an historical journey with you. How is it that we come to even ask such questions? So, let's take our mind back in time a little bit, let's say a little bit over 100 years ago. At this point in our history, if anybody said that in 100 years people would willingly get on a bicycle that's had its back wheel removed to pedal as hard and fast as they can, for 30 minutes at a time, to get nowhere, we would have thought this is absolutely preposterous. Nobody would do this. But of course, every day people take spinning classes, right? This is something we do and we might do it quite frequently, maybe three times a week, four times a week. So, the question is this: Why do people do this? Why do we engage in this type of activity, this type of daily physical activity?

And part of the answer is this: In today's day and age we all have the very clear cultural understanding that physical activity is necessary for physical health. Our leaders, our public policy experts, whether it's the Center for Disease Control, or Disease Prevention, the surgeon general of the United States, for example. These are all resources that we go to as our public health officials to provide us with exquisite and precise evidence-based guidance and what we can do to keep our bodies physically fit, right?

So, whether it's 30 minutes a day a couple of days a week, or an hour and 15 minutes of vigorous exercise, there are prescriptions that we get from our medical professionals and what we need to do to keep the body physically fit. It's so common and so prevalent at this point that anyone if asked this question— "Does physical activity improve physical health?"—would say, of course, it's obvious. And I think that there's a lot to say about this. It says a lot about sort of the cultural norms we hold, of how to preserve and work with our own wellness.

So, let's shift gears here a little bit. Let's try to understand why it is that we're able to hold such a cultural norm. And this is where people like me, scientists, researchers, I think have had a very big role to play. I would argue that one of the reasons this is our common cultural understanding is because the evidence base is quite robust. In fact, since 1980, there have been over 300,000 articles that have been published on the topic of physical exercise and physical health.

And how is this large and vast research literature actually parsed? We could think of it as kind of folded into four different silos of research that of course talk to each other. The first is to see what the physiologic effects are on the body when somebody is engaged in exercise. Right? How is it that the heart rate changes, that the blood pressure changes? And we can observe that the kind of systematic changes that happen while engaging in exercise. Or we can take somebody who's quite physically fit—an athlete—bring them into the laboratory and just see what they look like in terms of their resting functioning, what's their baseline heart rate? Right? And this allows us to get a sense of what a very well-trained person who has physical exercise as part of their daily routine, what health benefits they may enjoy. We can also look at structural changes in the body. So how is it that the physical structures, the muscles for example, change as a function of engaging in daily exercise?

And of course, the last sort of area, which is probably the one that most of us care about the most, is our ability to perform and behave in the world. Whether it's the… whether it's the goal to be in a 5k or a half marathon or a marathon or just your ability to walk up and down the stairs with ease without any pain or a sense of your health not being in optimal conditions. All of these different research aspects lead us to being able to say exactly why it is that physical exercise is necessary for physical health. And I'm really using this to set up where we are today with regard to another very important topic, which is our mind.

So, let's take a step back and think about what it might be that the body needs or enacts as a function of getting physically fit. Basically, it's this concept of plasticity—that engaging in certain behaviors will change the nature of the body's tissues, its muscles, its skeletal structure, and all of that gives it more pliability and more excellence and wellness as it functions.

So, we've been talking about the body. Let's now switch gears to talking about the brain and ask a broad question: Does mental exercise improve brain health? And if so, we might want to understand how? How do we train the brain? There are many ways in which people may choose to do this on their own, and unfortunately, there's a lot of lore around this idea that playing brain games like puzzles or Sudoku might actually help the brain. But it doesn't seem to be the case, I'm very sorry to tell you.

And really, even before we dig into successful and evidence based approaches that there may be to training the brain it's important to consider why people choose to do this anyway. Why do we want to train the brain? We've asked many people this question in our research studies and it breaks down into three main categories of reasons that motivate people to train the brain. These essentially boil down to people want to feel better, they want to perform better, or they want to age better. What does that really mean?

Well in terms of feeling better, it has to do with our psychological health. We'd like to engage in some form of brain training to improve our psychological well-being. When it comes to performing better, maybe cognitive functioning that we want to see is improved through brain training. And finally, with regard to aging, we want to see if there's something we could do on a regular basis in the same way we might engage in physical activity for our physical health. We may want engage in brain training to protect against age related diseases such as Alzheimer's disease. So, those are the three main reasons people say they'd like to train their brain: feel better, perform better, age better.

And of course, we can go beyond this to just the self-interest many of us want to have our brains in peak shape so we can be a better service and better use to our world, right? Whether it's being more effective in our job, or as a parent or a spouse, being more resilient to the challenges that life brings us, being more giving, or kind, or connected. Experiencing more awe and joy in our lives, there are many reasons we'd like to train the brain. This is just giving us a sampling of what that is.

So, with these lofty goals—but I would hope achievable goals—of how to improve our brain function, let's start moving into what we can do to train our brains and what is actually available to us, right now, sort of in the open marketplace to do this.

As we think about this know that all of these different forms of training, that we'll talk about in a few minutes, hinge on this notion that the brain is able to be changed through experience and training. And this is captured by the term neuroplasticity. So, in the same way we talked we talked about plasticity in the body, right, of ways of changing and improving the functioning of tissues, cells, our skeletal structure; neuroplasticity has to do with changing the structure and function of the brain to improve its functioning as well. And in particular, what we're going to do is look to see benchmarks of neuroplasticity. Are there brain structural changes and are there brain functional changes that correspond to for any form of brain training we might introduce to our participants in a research study, for example?

In the broad topic of neuroplasticity, we're very interested in seeing how the experience and activities that the human brain engages in may alter brain structure and function. And researchers became very interested in this topic. Broadly, we wanted to see if there were individuals who might have a type of daily life experience, maybe through their profession, that might lead their brain structure to actually be different than most of us.

One very intriguing group was cabdrivers. In particular, cabdrivers who had to negotiate the circuitous landscape of the city streets of London. Think about what it would mean—if you've ever visited the city of London you know it's quite dense. The streets are circuitous, it's not laid out in a nice Cartesian map, so it will be very difficult for people to know how to get from point A to point B unless they are highly familiar with this jungle of streets. So, it ends up that London cabdrivers have to have three years of formal training to get very well familiar with the maps of the city. And after they do this, of course, they might spend many years being a cabdriver.

So, in one study that was done to look at this notion that exercising the brain, engaging in certain activities in the brain, may change it structures, involved London cabdrivers. The reason they were chosen is because it ends up that there's a very specific brain structure called the hippocampus that is involved in spatial navigation and spatial maps. So, the researchers decided that they were going to scan the brains using structural MRI of London cabdrivers. They were going to hone in on the structure of the hippocampus and see if there were any structural differences between cabdrivers and other types of drivers in the city of London. In particular, they were going to compare cabdrivers who had to negotiate and navigate unknown routes with bus drivers who also drove all day, but had very well defined paths on which they went back and forth.

So, what was found was that indeed there are brain differences between cabdrivers and London bus drivers. And it's in the direction you might expect: cabdrivers had larger hippocampi, which means that they're the hippocampus—left and right hippocampi, two—was more densely packed, looked like it had more cells, it was structurally looked healthier or more robust than the same structure within bus drivers. What was even more striking was that this size of the hippocampus was tied to how many years they'd actually been a cabdriver. The longer time they'd spent on the streets of London negotiating and navigating, the larger the hippocampus.

This was a very exciting finding because it suggested to us that there was some correspondence between how the brain is organized and the way and manner in which people spend their moments of their life. Cabdrivers have more robust hippocampi.

Now this notion of experience altering or shaping the brain is actually not unique to cabdrivers. It ends up that if you look at the brains of people that play video games—*Tetris* for example, which also involves navigation and spatial maneuvering of just pieces on a screen as you play the video game— or people that engage in juggling as a regular hobby or even a profession, tend to have hippocampi that look healthier and more robust than matched control groups; age and education match control groups that don't engage in that activity.

So, what we learn from the London cabdrivers is that indeed it looks to be the case that those that engage in taxi driving as their profession, many hours a day for many years, actually have a brain structure that's different from bus drivers. It's a very elegant and simple way to see how driving itself may not cause the brain change but the spatial navigation demands may change it.

Now there's something really important to realize about this study: Though it does a very nice job connecting a particular brain structure to function, it is really relying on an opportunistic naturalistic type of an experiment. We didn't recruit drivers in London to be part of the study. We actually sought out people that happened to have this as their profession. So, for example, individuals who may choose to drive taxis versus those that may choose to drive buses.

We call this a cross-sectional study. So, we're taking individuals who just happened to be different because their life circumstances. We're not asking them to engage in any particular training. Cross-sectional studies allow us to compare distinct groups of people, so we could ask specific research questions. So, cross-sectional study designs are great because they're opportunistic, they allow us to benefit on what's happening. But here's a really important thing to keep in mind: Who decides to become a cabdriver? Right?

I know for myself I don't have great spatial navigation skills—if it weren't for my GPS, in some sense I might be lost often. It's not something I would choose to do, where I would say I'm relying on my own strengths to choose my profession. What if it's the case that people that choose to be the cabdrivers, especially those who are successful at it and maintain a career in this profession for many years, happened to just have hippocampi that are larger?

It becomes a cause and effect question. It may not be that the driving and the circuitous route navigation leads to the structural change; it may be that people choose to do this type of a job because they already have larger hippocampi that allows them to do this well. And that brings up a lot of questions with regard to what brain plasticity, neuroplasticity actually is. Cross-sectional studies may not allow us the strongest test of brain plasticity because of this type of design limitation.

So, what's a better way we might ask the question of whether experience and training changes the brain? One very common way in which this is conducted— I would say it's the gold standard of how research conduct is conducted— is something called the randomized control trial. What happens in this type of a research design is that people are invited into the study who have an interest in a broad topic, let's say brain training. And then from those individuals, they are randomly assigned to be in a condition of interest—let's say a particular brain-training protocol—and some other condition, whether it's doing nothing at all, which we'd call it no training control group, or an active comparison control group. Let's say it's a group that decides that they are they won't do brain training in terms of computer-based brain training, but they may choose to do brain training by watching movies or reading books. So, we have the treatment of interest and then the control condition as a comparison.

Now what's really a neat thing about this design is that we can match very well the type of individuals and each of these groups. And then we have them go through the training program itself. Let's say it's an eight-week program, and they get daily engagement in the training itself. One group gets brain training, one group watches movies. And then at the end of that eight weeks we would evaluate them again and look to see if the groups differ. The idea would be that if our hypothesis is correct and brain training, for example, improves functioning more so than watching movies or reading books, we might expect to see a group difference at the end of our training period of time. So, that's what we call a randomized controlled trial. Another description of this is a longitudinal study because we're following them over time.

Why do I mention this? Well we talked about London cabdrivers and cross-sectional studies. I'd like to move to a randomized controlled trial that was done in the context of brain training. This is a study that was very much interested in seeing if we could change brain function, improve brain function, as a product of people engaging in the research study itself. This study involved a very popular way that people choose to engage in brain training: using computer-based programs, and more recently computer based apps on their phone. This is a very popular industry.

In fact, it's valued at about a $1 billion industry. Billion with a B. So, a lot of effort and financial investment is going into this strategy for brain training. And within my field of cognitive neuroscience, this is probably one of the most hotly studied topics: brain training and the benefits of brain training.

So, I'd like to share with you one particular study that was done to see the effectiveness of brain training. Now remember as an attention researcher, my strong interest is in seeing if the brain's attention system can be trained with a program that's intended to make it stronger and more robust. Of all of these different brain training apps that are available, one that is commonly used and that was studied in the research study I'd like to tell you about is called Lumosity. And what they did in this study is that they invited people participants in, randomly assigned them to receive Lumosity for 70 days, or engage in a fun intensive video game playing time for 70 days. One was intended to be brain training, the other was just intended to match the amount of screen time and engagement the person might experience.

The intention for the Lumosity program's brain-training protocol was to improve attention, and we could say attention related processes, that might eventually help a person be better at decision making in the real world. So, the intention was always to see if brain training in this way helps our real-world performance. In fact, that's why most would say they do it: They want to be better outside the scope of just getting better at the game.

So, what happened in this study? They tracked folks over 70 days as I said, and every day they'd get an index from the Lumosity program itself that described their performance. Overall, everyone showed an improvement over 70 days. Their scores went up and up and up and up, and at some point, they plateaued, but it showed a strong learning and improvement effect which is very encouraging.

The other aspect of what they learned is that how much time and effort people spent engaging in this brain-training protocol really impacted how much they benefited. People that had low adherents and didn't always do the assigned homework didn't improve quite as much as those that had high adherence, which makes a lot of sense if you think of the analogy of deciding to do marathon training and only preparing a few days or weeks in advance versus four or five months, you might expect to perform better at the marathon or have a better time the more you've invested in preparing. So, this seems to be very similar: longer time spent, fuller engagement, better performance. Very exciting stuff.

Now of course the true test of whether brain training in this matter is beneficial was not just to see if the Lumosity scores improved. It was to see if the benefits carried over into some other kind of more real world decision making task. And so, the researchers in this experiment—it was Kable and colleagues—what they did is they had people perform decision-making tasks, in particular a decision-making task called delayed discounting. So, it would be something like saying you can have $20 now, or you can have $40 tomorrow if you wait. And they wanted to see if improving and training these operations through the Lumosity program of attention, of inhibition control, of deliberation, for example, might improve the delayed discounting performance.

And the bottom line is it did not. There was no evidence that even though their Lumosity scores improved that there was any carryover into another type of real world decision making task. Quite discouraging, but really important to know.

And I wanted to say a little bit about why this might be, it's something we call the problem of generalizability. Which is that when there's a good deal of overlap between the training task and the evaluation, we get very strong benefits, in the same way that the Lumosity performance itself on the Lumosity training task improved over 70 days, because the task itself that was used to evaluate whether the training was beneficial was the training task itself.

But as we make the overlap between the training context and the evaluation context more and more distant, it seems to be the case that the effects and benefits are weaker. So, that by the end, the training and Lumosity had no benefit on a decision-making task.

And this problem of generalizability unfortunately is not constrained to this study alone. It's a larger problem within the field of brain training. In fact, a recent review paper had this to say about the bottom line of what we know about brain training to date. They say that there is little evidence that training enhances performance on distantly related tasks or that training improves everyday cognitive performance. This was quite a blow to this billion-dollar industry, because what it suggests is that though people may download an app and choose to do it and even get better at doing the brain training games on the app, it has virtually no impact on the rest of their lives. And this probably means it's not worth their time, because nobody's playing these games really for the express purpose of getting better at playing them alone.

So, what we've discussed so far is that cognitive training is a tricky topic. It can actually be elusive in some ways. We talked about cross-sectional studies in which different groups may be involved into a research design to see if there's a correspondence between frequently performed activities and brain changes. We also talked about computer based training and the lack of evidence that there is actually successful generalizability for this.

So, I'd like to move now to the topic of mindfulness training and really ask the broad question: Can we think of mindfulness training as brain training?

MINDFULNESS AS BRAIN TRAINING
LESSON 12

Can we think of mindfulness training as a form of brain training? What type of training may be required to cultivate a more mindful way of being? And if somebody engages in this type of training, can we think of it as brain training? Put more plainly, if mindfulness training is training the brain, what is it training? What specific functions might it be strengthening? To understand this from the perspective of neuroscience, we need to understand how mindfulness training is cultivated through mindfulness exercises.

MINDFULNESS EXERCISE: MINDFULNESS OF BREATHING

This is a foundational exercise that is common to most programs in mindfulness training. You start by sitting in a comfortable upright posture and focusing all of your attention on the sensations of breathing.

> Select a particular sensation that is tied to your breathing, such as the coolness of air moving in and out of your nostrils or your abdomen moving up and down.

> Maintain your attention on that sensation for the period of time you're going to engage in the practice—for example, 10 to 15 minutes.

> Notice when your mind wanders away from the sensations of breathing. When you notice that it has wandered, gently return your attention to the sensations of breathing.

These three main components—select, maintain, and notice—are the central driving hypotheses of how we think mindfulness training may be altering the brain. Does mindfulness training allowing for process-specific training of attention?

SYSTEMS OF ATTENTION

One way to think about attention is that it's like a flashlight. And just like a flashlight in a darkened room, wherever our attention is directed, more information becomes available. We can have a laserlike focus, a very narrow focus, or a broad focus, but wherever that flashlight is directed, information is clearer and richer, more comes in, and you can direct it at will. This is the brain's orienting system of attention.

In contrast to the orienting system is the alerting system. This is like a caution sign. When you see a caution sign, you might not know exactly what the danger or potential threat might be, but the intention is to keep your attention in a readied state so that no matter what might come your way, you're prepared to deploy your attention in the service of benefiting your performance.

The brain's alerting system is the opposite of the orienting system. Whereas orienting the flashlight means narrowing and selecting, the alerting system is about broadening and preparing. And both of these systems are important tools for our attention and attention training.

Related to attention is working memory. This is like the mind's internal whiteboard. In fact, it's a whiteboard that has disappearing ink. Working memory is the ability to maintain and manipulate information over very short periods of time, from a few seconds to a few minutes. So, it works well with the brain's system of attention. Once information is selected into this system, working memory allows us to maintain it.

Our mind is exquisite at being able to engage in mental time travel. We can travel to the past and future with ease, but many times this ability can get our attention system into trouble.

Orienting, alerting, and working memory are core cognitive systems that are extremely important for our psychological health. They are functions that we all need in order to engage in fluid human behavior. And when they work well, we perform well. But these same three systems can also make us vulnerable to psychological diseases.

We can think of rewinding to the past not simply as a way to reflect on what's happened, but under conditions of stress and distress in particular, we may end up ruminating, reliving, or regretting experiences that have already happened. Or we fast-forward in a way that's not productive, possibly catastrophizing or worrying about events that not only haven't happened yet, but frankly may never happen.

This shows that attention can be hijacked in time. And when this happens, there are fewer moments for the mind to experience what's happening in the present—a mindfulness mode of being.

Another way to think about the hijacking of attention from the present moment is mind wandering, or having off-task thoughts during an ongoing task or activity. Mind wandering is not about just letting the mind flow wherever it will; it has to do with wanting to accomplish a goal and having your attention hijacked so that you are not able to accomplish that goal.

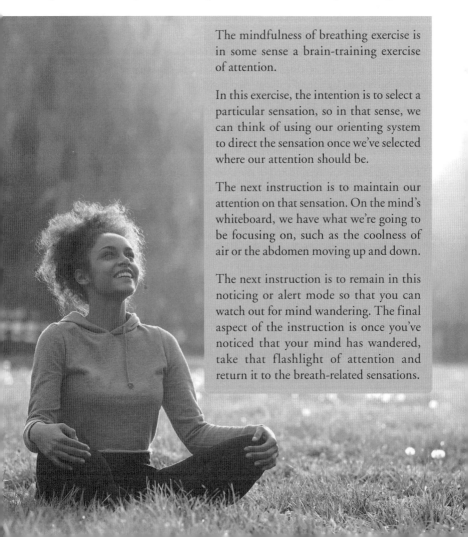

The mindfulness of breathing exercise is in some sense a brain-training exercise of attention.

In this exercise, the intention is to select a particular sensation, so in that sense, we can think of using our orienting system to direct the sensation once we've selected where our attention should be.

The next instruction is to maintain our attention on that sensation. On the mind's whiteboard, we have what we're going to be focusing on, such as the coolness of air or the abdomen moving up and down.

The next instruction is to remain in this noticing or alert mode so that you can watch out for mind wandering. The final aspect of the instruction is once you've noticed that your mind has wandered, take that flashlight of attention and return it to the breath-related sensations.

THE BRAIN SCIENCE OF ATTENTION

The broader cognitive neuroscience of attention literature has found that there are distinct networks that are tied to these three aspects of our functioning: our ability to select and maintain, our capacity to notice, and mind wandering.

> The central executive network, which involves the frontal lobes and parts of the parietal lobe, is involved in the capacity to select and maintain—the flashlight and the whiteboard.

> There are also networks that are distinct from the central executive network that are responsible for different aspects of functioning. For example, the alerting system, the noticing capacity of our brain, is subserved by the salience network, which is anchored in a region of the brain called the insula.

> The default mode network is the network that people typically associate with mind wandering.

These networks are established in the broader brain-imaging literature, and there are two important things to understand about brain networks—in particular these three attention-related networks.

> They're anatomically distinct from each other. In other words, the central executive network, the salience network, and the default mode network rely on different brain regions.

> They are mutually inhibitory, meaning that when one network's activity is prominent, the other two networks have lower levels of activity.

The reason these three networks are important is that they give us a clue into the brain regions that may be involved in brain training involving mindfulness.

RESEARCH ON BRAIN TRAINING AND BRAIN NETWORKS

There are many different ways we can look at brain changes. When we want to look at structural changes in the brain, we might analyze brain gyrification, which refers to how tightly packed and condensed the brain is. As we age, experience stress, or encounter brain-related disorders, the brain becomes smoother, or less gyrified. A less gyrified brain is a less healthy brain; a more densely packed brain is a healthier brain.

Research has shown that individuals who engage in long-term mindfulness practice have better gyrification—more efficient-looking brains. And it appears they have cortical gyrification in networks that are tied to the brain's attention systems. This is very interesting, because it suggests not only that certain parts of mindfulness practitioners' brains look healthier, but also that those same regions are the ones that are tied to the hypothesis that mindfulness exercises are training attention, noticing, and control over mind wandering.

There are also functional brain changes that are present in long-term mindfulness practitioners. One study found that the default mode—a brain network tied to mind wandering—has less activity in individuals who are long-term mindfulness practitioners. They are better able to control the activity of this network.

It was found that two important nodes of the default mode, the medial prefrontal cortex and the posterior simulate cortex, had less activity in mindfulness practitioners relative to age- and education-matched control participants. This suggests that not only are there structural changes, but functional brain activity profiles also seem to be aligned with better performance and better brain health.

These cross-sectional designs, though, have their limitations. For example, we don't know if long-term practitioners might have had brains that just happened to be more gyrified before they decided to start practicing mindfulness. In fact, it may be that there's a causal relationship the other way: People who have gyrified brains may end up choosing to meditate or practice mindfulness, and it has nothing to do with the mindfulness instantiating those changes.

A stronger test of this notion that brains can become healthier looking and function more efficiently as a function of mindfulness training requires us to test this with a randomized controlled trial.

Meta-analyses—sets of studies that are compiled to deduce a pattern of research—show that the brains or brain networks of long-term practitioners look healthier, are more gyrified, are more densely packed with gray matter, and function more efficiently. Meta-analyses also reveal that the kinds of structural and functional changes that are seen in randomized controlled trials of mindfulness training look very much like what's seen in long-term practitioners.

The fact that there are beneficial changes to the brain's structure as well as to the brain's functioning with mindfulness training is very exciting, but much more research is needed.

PERFORMANCE CHANGES

Some of the research studies conducted on the cognitive effects of mindfulness training look at many different groups of people who experienced some type of demanding interval. And for these individuals, in many cases, their attention can be the difference between success and failure—for example, for a student—or life and death, for a firefighter or military service member. Attention really matters.

Is it the case, as the brain data suggests, that the networks of the brain supporting attention are stronger and healthier? Is it the case that performance on tasks of attention looks like it's better in those engaging in mindfulness training?

For the groups of people that have been studied, unfortunately attention does not stay stable over high-stress intervals. If we index attention using simple computer-based behavioral tasks, we find that over multiple weeks of high demand and high stress, attentional performance declines.

The interest in these types of groups is to promote cognitive resilience, the ability to maintain or regain cognitive capacities—in particular, capacities like attention and working memory that are at risk for declining. We want to keep them protected against decline and keep them functioning well, even in the course of experiencing high demand.

In one study, undergraduates participated in a seven-week mindfulness training course in which they learned the foundational mindfulness practices. Individuals were randomly assigned to either get mindfulness training or not, in the case of the control group.

Students were recruited into this study during two time intervals: during the academic semester, when the stresses of a semester are high, and during summer break.

Over summer break, attention was stable over the seven-week period. But over the semester, for students who were not offered mindfulness training, attention significantly declined. These students were tested right before finals season, and that's when their attention was the lowest.

Unlike their counterparts who didn't get the mindfulness training and declined in their attention, those who received mindfulness training were able to stay stable in their attention and actually slightly improve in their attention over the seven-week period.

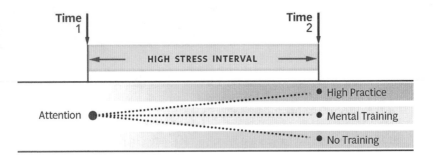

This is just one example in the education context, but the same pattern is seen in other studies: Reliable improvements are found with mindfulness training in different aspects of cognitive functioning, including selective attention, working memory, and mind wandering. This is quite promising from the perspective of thinking about mindfulness training as brain training.

In broad terms, mindfulness training may be a successful strategy by which to train the brain.

BRAIN TRAINING AND AGING

Our brains change over the course of our lifetime, and one feature of normal, healthy aging is that brain density in specific regions is reduced.

Recent studies have found that mindfulness practitioners seem better protected against this normal age-related decline.

PSYCHOLOGICAL HEALTH AND MINDFULNESS TRAINING

In a meta-analysis involving 47 studies on mindfulness training and psychological health, allowing people to engage in daily mindfulness training had effects comparable to a pharmacologic solution they may take to improve their psychological health. In addition, the more they practiced, the more their psychological health benefited. This is a promising route by which we may think of mindfulness training as brain training, even for psychological health improvement.

MINDFULNESS AS BRAIN TRAINING

I want to ask the broad question: Can we think of mindfulness training as a form of brain training? Well I think before we delve into the details of whether this can be answered in a in a way that's a yes or no, we need to understand more fully what I mean when I use the term "mindfulness training." And maybe even more broadly what mindfulness is.

So, from my point of view a great way to think about mindfulness requires the use of a simple metaphor. You could think of maybe a simple MP3 player or a video player with a fast forward or reverse and a play button. When I think of the term "mindfulness," I'm actually talking about "a mental mode, a way of making the mind, that's characterized by attention to our present moment experience without elaboration or emotional reactivity."

Now why the MP3 player metaphor? Well, I think that mindfulness can be thought of as a mode quite contrary to what the mind typically does. Typically, we can see our mind as being fantastic at mental time travel. We can rewind the mind to reflect on events that have already happened, or we can fast forward the mind to plan and think about the future. And we very easily and unfortunately quite often will see ourselves not in the present moment, but engaging in this rewind or fast forward.

So, when we think about mindfulness it is about keeping that button right on play, so we're fully living and experiencing the moment to moment unfolding of our lives. And what we want to understand is what type of training may be required in order to cultivate a more mindful way of being. And in particular, if somebody engages in this type of training, we want to understand if we can think of it as brain training. Or to put more plainly, if mindfulness training is training the brain, what is the training? What specific functions may it be strengthening?

To understand this as neuroscientists, we need to look under the hood, in the same way that understanding cabdrivers and spatial navigation or Lumosity and other brain training programs require us to know what it is that the person is engaging in as the mental training tool. We need to understand how it is that mindfulness training is cultivated through mindfulness exercises.

So, an example I'd like to give you, to give us a deeper dive and deeper understanding of this, is a foundational practice common to most exercise programs in mindfulness training. Something called mindfulness of breathing. And I'm just going to describe this to you in broad brush strokes so you get a sense of the sequence of events that needs to happen in this type of an exercise. You can think in many ways of mindfulness of breathing a sort of a central pushup of a mindfulness training program—the foundational exercise.

In mindfulness of breathing exercise, the instructions are quite simple, but if you've ever tried to engage in this exercise you'll understand it's not easy. So, what's required? For a dedicated period of time the instruction is to pay attention to sensations tied to one's breathing. And the first part of this instruction is to be very specific, to select a particular sensation, whether it's the coolness of air moving in and out of your nostrils or abdomen moving up and down. It's something tied to breathing itself. To select that sensation and then to maintain your attention on that sensation for the period of time you're going to engage in the practice. So, let's say 10 to 15 minutes.

The next important aspect of the instruction, after you've selected and are now maintaining this breath-related sensation, is to notice if the mind has drifted away. If the mind has wandered away. And when you notice that it has, the instruction is to simply return your attention back.

So, these three main components of select, maintain and notice, are going to be what we might consider the central driving hypotheses of how we think mindfulness training may be altering the brain. We can say that the larger question is, is it the case that mindfulness training is allowing for process specific training of attention? And in order to understand what I mean by this I think it's important that you get a sense of what we know about the broad field of attention research, because much is known about the common brain circuitry responsible for these different aspects of attention, aspects such as selecting, noticing, maintaining.

So, let's talk about that, different varieties of attention. And I think to delve into this topic it's also useful to have a few metaphors that we can use. So, one way we can think about attention is that it's like a flashlight. And just like a flashlight in a darkened room, wherever our attention is directed, more information becomes available. So, it is the case that we can have a laser-like focus just like a flashlight that may be of have a very narrow focus or a broad focus. But what happens is that wherever that flashlight is directed, information is clearer, richer, more comes in, and you can direct it at will. We call this the brain's orienting system of attention.

And in contrast to the orienting system is something we call the alerting system. The metaphor I use there is sort of a caution sign or even you might think of a flashing yellow light while you're driving on the road. When you see a flashing yellow light or a caution sign, you might not know exactly what the danger or potential threat might be. But the intention is to keep your attention in a readied state so that no matter what might come your way you're prepared to deploy your attention in the service of benefiting your performance.

So, we can think of the brain's alerting system as quite the opposite of the orienting system, whereas orienting the flashlight means narrowing and selecting, the alerting system is about broadening and preparing. And both of these are going to be very important tools for our attention and for attention training as well.

Related to attention, sort of a close cousin of attention, is something called working memory. And I use the metaphor of a white board—the mind's internal white board. And I want to push it a little further. It's a white board that has disappearing ink. The ink on the white board will disappear within a few to several seconds.

So, what is working memory? Working memory is the ability to maintain and manipulate information over very short periods of time from a few seconds to a few minutes. So, think about the last time you were at a restaurant and had to calculate a tip. Essentially you wrote on the whiteboard to do the simple math and then were able to produce the tip amount, but you don't need to keep that information in long term memory. You in fact don't want to keep it a long-term memory. Or think about the last time you might have been in a conversation with somebody and you were holding the idea that you wanted to express while you kindly let the person finish speaking. In that case, you also used your working memory, wrote on the mental whiteboard what it is that you want to say, and then of course once it was said it was gone. The ink was gone. So, working memory works very well with the brain's system of attention. Once information is selected into this system, working memory allows us to maintain it.

Of course, orienting, alerting, working memory, these are all functions that we all need in order to engage in fluid human behavior. And when these worked well, we perform well. Unfortunately, these same three systems can make us quite vulnerable to psychological diseases as well. That might be surprising for some of you who may understand that our cognitive function and our emotional health may be completely separate. And what I have to tell you is that that's not the case. These core cognitive systems are extremely important for our psychological health.

So, let me tell you what I mean by that. Think of these three disorders: depression, hypervigilance, and attention deficit disorder. We can characterize each of these, in some sense, as a problem with the brain's attention or working memory system. For depression, you might think of that flashlight of the orienting system being stuck on depressive genic content, so, that negative thoughts and memories may be the only place that flashlight chooses to shine. And it's very hard to remove our attention away from that type of content, which leads to this cascade of clinical disorder.

Or in the context of something like hypervigilance, that might happen in a disease like post-traumatic stress disorder. We can see that people might start observing in their world everything is a caution sign or a flashing yellow light. There's this propensity to see the need to be on high alert always.

And unfortunately, it might not serve us as we're just having a normal walk down a city street and there is no threat. But if our attention system is oriented this way, it can become quite problematic.

And finally, the example of attention deficit disorder. In some ways, we can think of this as an overly cluttered working memory or a white board that's got so much stuff on it, you can't make sense of what you need to do. In some types of attention deficit disorder, we can also think of it as a whiteboard whose ink disappears too quickly. The information is not able to be maintained long enough for us to actually execute our goals.

So, outside the context of attention systems going awry that lead to clinical disorders, many of us, even if we don't suffer from clinical disorders, may feel that our attention system can become compromised. And I'd like to return back to this metaphor of the MP3 player. Our brain, our mind, our attention system is exquisite at being able to engage in mental time travel as I mentioned. We can go to the past and the future with ease, but many times this function of being able to rewind and fast forward can get our attention system into trouble. In some sense, we can think of rewinding to the past, not as simply as a way to reflect on what's happened, but under conditions of stress and distress in particular, we may end up ruminating, reliving, or regretting experiences that have already happened.

So, we're rewinding the mind, and in some sense, intentionally rubbernecking to the past. It's like we can't help ourselves but go back in time.

Or we fast forward in a way that's also not productive. We may end up catastrophizing or worrying over and over again about events that not only haven't happened yet, but frankly may never happen. And I bring these up because what it tells us is that attention can be hijacked in time. And there's something that we can really think about with regard to this hijacking, which is that there are fewer moments for the mind to keep the button right on play, to experience what's happening in the here and the now, as what we describe as a mindfulness mode of being.

Another way to think about this hijacking of attention from the present moment is something called mind wandering. Mind wandering has to do with having off task thoughts during an ongoing task or activity. So, think about the last time you were trying to read a book. We might glaze over, our eyes may be moving down the page, we get to the bottom of the page to realize we have no idea what we have just read. This would be a very salient, and unfortunately for many of us, a common experience of mind wondering. What happened there? What happened is that attention was not actually aligned with perception; attention may have been gone up that may have gone off in many other directions.

So, this mind wandering is very important for us to understand because it's not about just letting the mind flow wherever it will. It's not mine wondering in some sense or daydreaming or in psychology speak what we might call conscious internal reflection, right? Having a spontaneous thought that'll go anywhere. Mind wandering has to do with actually wanting to accomplish a goal and having your mind hijacked away, your attention hijacked away, from being able to accomplish that goal.

So, let's now with these concepts in mind—the basic systems of attention, working memory, the vulnerabilities of attention with regard to mind wandering—let's return back to our question with regard to mindfulness training. If mindfulness training is training the brain, what is it training? As I mentioned we need to think about the under the hood kind of components of the training exercises themselves. And as we already reviewed, the mindfulness of breathing exercise is a foundational training exercise. So, let's return to that exercise. And now we're going to think about these components of mindfulness of breathing exercise as it relates to these aspects of attention and working memory we just reviewed.

So, recall back that in the mindfulness of breathing exercise the intention is to select a particular sensation. So, in that sense we can think of using our orienting system to direct the sensation, once we've selected it to where our attention should be. Next, the instruction is to maintain our attention on that sensation. We're having it up on the mind's white board what it is that we're going to be focusing on: the coolness of air or the abdomen moving down, whatever it is, that's what's going to be maintained on the white board. The next part of the instructions to remain in this noticing or alert mode so that you can watch out for mind wandering. And then the final aspect of the instruction is to once you've noticed that your mind has wandered simply return it back. Or you could say take that flashlight of attention and return it back to those breath related sensations.

So now that we can see this mindfulness of breathing exercise as in some sense a brain training exercise of attention, we want to start being able to build our hypotheses about what regions of the brain, what brain networks, may be strengthened or impacted by engaging in such an exercise. And to get into this topic, we need to learn a little bit more—or I need to provide to you a little bit more—about what is already known with regard of the brain science of attention. And there's three things I'd like to share with you that have to do with these aspects of attention we've already reviewed: this ability to select and maintain, our capacity to notice, as well as mind wandering.

The broader cognitive neuroscience of attention literature has found that there are distinct networks that are tied to these three aspects of our functioning. Something called the central executive network, which involves the frontal lobes and parts the parietal lobe, are involved in these capacities to select and maintain. Or in our shorthand, the flashlight and the whiteboard.

There are also networks distinct from the central executive network that are responsible for different aspects of functioning. So, for example the alerting system, this noticing capacity of our brain, is subserved by a network called the salience network, where prominent structures of region call the insula. And the third network that I'd like to describe to you is something called the default mode network. This is the network that people typically associate with mind wandering.

Now why am I bringing up all three of these networks to you? Mainly it's to say that these networks are established in the broader brain imaging literature and of course there are many other networks. As I speak, I'm sure that these networks are being updated and modified in the literature.

But the broad categories will probably still hold. And there's two important things I'd like you to understand about brain networks, in particular these three attention related networks.

One of them is that they're anatomically distinct from each other. So, the central executive network, the salient network, the default mode network, really rely on different brain regions within each of the networks. The second thing I'd like you to understand about these networks is they are mutually inhibitory. What do I mean by that? Well when one network's activity is prominent, the other two networks actually have lower amounts of activity. So, let's say that you are engaged in a highly selective task— your laser like focus is being used for something you're trying to do. In that sense, your central executive network is going to be more active but you're noticing network and your mind wandering networks are going to be less active. And the opposite is also true if you're engaged in a lot of mind wandering. Your capacity to select and direct your attention may become compromised.

So, the reason that these three networks are quite important from my point of view is that they give us a clue into the brain regions that may be involved in brain training involving mindfulness. So, let's talk about the research that's been conducted on this topic of brain training and investigation of brain networks in people that are mindfulness practitioners, or are participating in brain training involving mindfulness training.

So, there are two research designs that we've described: the cross-sectional design and the longitudinal design. The cross-sectional design involves long term mindfulness practitioners, for example, versus other groups that don't have that as part of their life experience. The longitudinal design would be more of a training design that involves the randomized control trial. So, in the context of mindfulness this could be a design in which people are randomly assigned to participate in an eight-week mindfulness based stress reduction course, for example, versus some other form of training. Or they may be involved and randomly assigned to participate in a multi-day mindfulness retreat. And the intention for those studies is to see if there are differences before and after engaging in the mindfulness training program.

So, what I'd like to tell you about next is what is known about these various research designs and the brain changes that may accompany mindfulness training. The first thing to say is that there are many different ways we can look at brain changes, but when we want to first look at structural changes in the brain, we might look at one of a couple of things.

The first is something called brain gyrification. And that's kind of a mouthful of a term, but all its referring to is sort of how tightly packed and condensed the brain is. So, to put it more simply, we could think of the brain as a series of tissues, kind of like stacked pieces of paper. Gyrification has to do with crumpling up those pieces of paper as tightly as possible so that we can house the brain inside our skull. As we age, as we experience stress, as we might encounter brain related disorders, the brain becomes un-crumpled, it becomes smoother. So, a smoother brain, a less gyrified brain, is a less healthy brain. But a more gyrified brain, a more densely packed brain, is a healthier brain.

So, one of the questions researchers were looking at is to see if those individuals that engage in long term mindfulness practice may have better gyrification—a more efficient looking brain. And that's in fact what's been found. It looks to be the case that long-term mindfulness practitioners have cortical gyrification in networks that are tied to the brain's attention systems. Which is very interesting, because what it suggests is not only do certain parts of mindfulness practitioners brains look healthier, but those same regions are those that are tied to what we hypothesized: mindfulness exercises are actually training: attention, noticing, control over mind wandering.

So, now let's turn our attention to functional brain changes that may also be present in long term mindfulness practitioners. One research study was interested in seeing if a particular brain network, known as the default mode, might actually have less activity in those individuals who are long term mindfulness practitioners.

Now why would they have this prediction, that the default mode may be less active? Recall back to what we were talking about a few moments ago: That the default mode is a brain network tied to mind wandering.

And if the central practice of a mindfulness of breathing exercise, for example, is intending to have better control over mind wandering, such that it happens less frequently, you might predict that individuals that have been doing this for years on end may be better able to control the activity of this network. And in fact, that's what was found. It was found that two important nodes of the default mode, the medial prefrontal cortex, as well as the posterior simulate cortex, had less activity in mindfulness practitioners relative to control age and education matched control participants. This was very exciting, because what it suggests is that not only do we see structural changes, but that the functional brain activity profiles also look in line with better performance and better brain health.

Now let's move to thinking about not just this cross-sectional designs, which as I mentioned previously have their limitations. For example, we don't know—though it seems very promising—we don't know if long term practitioners might have had brains that just happened to be more gyrified, even before they decided to start practicing mindfulness. In fact, it may be that there's a causal relationship the other way. People that have gyrified brains may end up choosing to meditate or practice mindfulness, and it has nothing to do with the mindfulness actually instantiating those changes. It's an important possibility to consider.

So, a stronger test of this notion that brains can become healthier looking and function more efficiently as a function of mindfulness training requires us to really test this out with a randomized control trial. And that's what many different studies have been looking at now. Individuals are recruited into a mindfulness training study and then they're randomly assigned to receive mindfulness training over let's say eight weeks, or some other condition. And what we do is look to see at the structure and function of the brain before and after participation in that multi-week training program.

So far, we take our hypotheses from what's been found and long term practitioners. Maybe the brains will be looking healthier, their brains will be more gyrified, they'll be more densely packed with grey matter for example, maybe certain networks would be more efficiently functioning.

And in fact, that is what it looks like is happening in what are now an aggregate set of studies, something called a meta-analysis, that allows us to put together not one or two studies but dozens of studies to see what the pattern of research looks like. Meta-analyses now reveal that the kinds of structural and functional changes that are seen in randomized trials of mindfulness training look very much in line with what's seen in long term practitioners. There are beneficial changes to the brain structure as well as to the brain's functioning. It's very exciting.

Of course, we have to remember that though many research studies have been done, we are nowhere near the number that we now have for research investigating physical activity and physical health. Right? That number was 300,000. We're probably at a tenth of that. So, it's exciting times, but much more research is needed.

One final area that I'd like to share with you is work that's very close to the work that I hold near and dear in my own laboratory: looking at performance changes. Because of course all of us want to have healthy brains, but really we want that brain health to translate into the way we perform and act in the world. So, we're going to now talk about some of the recent research studies we've done on cognitive effects of mindfulness training conducted in my own lab.

Recall that I mentioned we look at many different groups, all of whom experienced some type of demanding interval. And for these individuals, in many cases, their attention can be the difference between success and failure, for example, for a student, or unfortunately life and death when you think about a firefighter or a military service member. Attention really matters. So, the question now is if it is the case, as the brain data suggests, the networks of the brain supporting attention are stronger and healthier. Is it the case that performance on tasks of attention looks like it's better in those engaging in mindfulness training?

And for the groups that I've looked at, unfortunately attention is not staying stable over these high stress intervals. What we find is that actually, if you index attention using simple computer based behavioral tasks, if you look at how well people perform, you see that over multiple weeks of high demand and high stress, attentional performance declines.

And this is true for even elementary, middle, and high school students. Over the course of the semester, we see that attention gets compromised. And this is quite unfortunate because at the end of the semester they have to take final exams, and that's where the performance will really matter. Unfortunately, they may have the most compromised attention at that point. Or think about the pre-deployment soldier who is preparing him or herself to be ready for deployment. But that training interval is leading up to deployment itself may degrade attention. So, they're not in peak shape as they leave.

Our interest for these types of groups is to promote something called cognitive resilience. This ability to maintain or regain cognitive capacities, in particular capacities like attention and working memory that are at risk for declining, we want to keep those protected against that, we want to keep them functioning well, even in the course of experiencing high demand as they're going through the academic semester or pre-deployment training. Our prediction is that if they engage in some form of mental training, for example mindfulness training, over this high demand period, they may stay stable in their performance over time. Whereas individuals going through high demand who aren't participating in such training decline over time.

And if you want to be very optimistic about this, we might predict that beyond simply staying stable over time, if you really commit to the exercises in these mindfulness training programs, you might be able to actually improve your performance from where you started, even if you're undergoing a high demand period of time.

So, let me bring you into the laboratory and give you a sense of how we're going to test attention: How do we see if attentional performance is better? How do we ask if mind wandering is less? And one way we do this is by giving people like I said very simple tasks. I'll give you a sense of one experiment that we did. This experiment was interested in seeing attentional performance, in particular sustained attentional performance, over a 20-minute period of time. We wanted to see if people could maintain their focus and we also wanted to know if their mind wandered and got internally distracted away from the task.

This is a little bit of a tricky thing to do, because of course if we asked them to mind wander, then they're not actually doing anything wrong—they're following our task instructions. So, we had to design an experiment that promoted mind wandering without ever telling them to mind wander.

So, we designed an attention experiment that might be considered one of the world's most boring experiments. It's called the sustained attention response task. What happens in this experiment is the part participant is seated in a room in front of a computer screen, and they see a number on the screen. Every time they see a number, they're to press a button and we're looking at the accuracy with which they're pressing and the speed with which they're pressing that button. Sounds simple enough. The only slightly interesting aspect of this experiment is that when that digit is 3, they are to withhold the responses. So, you'd see a series of numbers, you press the button over and over again, infrequently five percent of the time, a three would appear and you'd have to withhold.

Now as you can imagine this is kind of a boring experiment and pretty soon people though they can plainly see the numbers on the screen will press the button to the 3. And when you ask them what happened, why did you press the button? Usually it'll be a response such as, "Oh I wandered away from the task. My mind was not on the task anymore. I kind of was in autopilot just pressing the buttons." It's unfortunate, but it happens reliably. And it may be of no consequence in the context of this experiment, but you can imagine that a student missing content in lecture or a soldier on patrol or a firefighter really standing watch having their mind wander away can be quite problematic.

So, the study I'd like to tell you about, and many of the others that we've done kind of follow the same pattern, offered individuals a mindfulness training program. These were undergraduates that came into our lab, participated in a seven-hour, seven-week mindfulness training course in which they learned these foundational mindfulness practices with us. And we were interested in seeing what their attention looked like on this sustained attention task at the beginning of that interval and again at the end of that interval. We randomly assigned individuals to either get mindfulness training, or we had a control group that did not receive this training.

Now there's one important thing to keep in mind: When we recruited students into this study we did it during two time intervals. Once was during the academic semester, when the stresses and strains of a semester are high, and another time was during summer break. Our prediction is that over summer break, students may have stable attention because they don't have the academic demands, but over the semester their attention may decline because of the pressures and demands of the semester.

Indeed, over summer break attention is stable. There are no costs to your attention over a seven-week period of time if you're an undergraduate. But this is the unfortunate part. When we look at those same types of students over the semester and they're not offered mindfulness training, their attention significantly declined. So, they were compromised in their ability to pay attention. And remember, again, that we tested them right before final season, and that's the point at which their attention was the lowest.

So now let's ask the key question, which is, what happened in individuals that weren't just involved in taking our experiments, but actually performed the mindfulness training intervention. The news there is quite promising. What we found is that unlike their counterparts who didn't get the training and declined in their attention, those who received mindfulness training were able to stay stable in their attention, and actually slightly improve in their attention over the seven-week period of time.

So, this is just one example in the education context. But the same pattern is seen over and over again, and now there are many studies from my research lab as well as many others, in which there are reliable improvements found with mindfulness training in different aspects of cognitive functioning. Selective attention improvements, working memory improvements, and reductions in mind wandering. Which is quite promising from our point of view in thinking about mindfulness training as brain training.

Just to remind you what most people said were their motivations for training the brain had to do with either wanting to feel better, meaning they wanted to be more psychologically healthy; perform better, meaning they wanted their cognitive functioning to be improved; or to age better, they wanted to be better protected from age related brain changes and brain diseases.

And I want to say broadly speaking, mindfulness training may be a successful strategy by which to train the brain. In our time together a mostly focused on the performance aspects and the brain aging aspects that have to do with better gyrification for example. But I'd like to broaden out for just a second to give you a sense of what we know even about psychological health and mindfulness training. And as you recall, psychological health may be very much intertwined with our attentional capacity to protect us from depression or hypervigilance or even ADHD, when our attention systems and working memory systems aren't performing at optimal levels.

So, one recent meta-analysis actually involved 47 studies. And I want to give you a sense of what they said with regard to the benefits of mindfulness training and psychological health. This was a study published in *The Journal of the American Medical Association*, one of the premier journals of the field of medicine. What they said is that the effects were small—modest 10 to 20 percent improvements—but I really think it's interesting to think about how they translated how those effects work. They said, "(The) effects are comparable with what would be expected from the use of an antidepressant in a primary care population, but without associated toxicities."

What does that mean? Essentially, allowing people to, in a daily fashion, engage in mindfulness training had effects comparable to a pharmacologic solution they may take to improve their psychological health. But in this sense the improvement was in their own hands, the more they practiced, the more they benefited with regard to their psychological health. This is very exciting as a promising route by which we may think of mindfulness training as brain training even for psychological health improvement.

When it comes to that next feature of improving our performance or performing better as a motivation for brain training, as I recently reviewed with you, there are many examples now of improvements in cognitive functioning that happen with mindfulness training: working memory, selective attention, mind wandering reductions.

So, the third pillar of why people say they'd like to engage in brain training has to do with better aging and better protection for their brains as we age. One thing to know about aging is that our brains do change over the course of our lifetime, and there is such a thing as normal healthy aging.

One feature of that is that brain density in specific regions of the brain actually is reduced. It's like the brain becomes less gyrified and almost thinner in its cortical density as we age, and that's normal. But what recent studies have found is that mindfulness practitioners actually seem better protected against that normal age related decline. Their brains don't look like they're showing that trajectory of decline. It's as if mindfulness training is protecting against normal aging, which is also quite exciting.

The research evidence with regard to physical health and physical well-being is expansive—300,000 articles. And of course, we have to keep in mind that we're nowhere near that number with regard to mindfulness training. But yet, as we've reviewed, there's a lot of exciting promising evidence that suggests that the brain can be structurally, functionally healthier when people engage in mindfulness training. And there may be routes by which mindfulness training can protect against performance declines, performance vulnerabilities, under high stress, and even improved performance.

So, there is hope and there's a lot more work yet to be done.

THE SCIENCE OF MINDFUL AGING

LESSON 13

Aging is inevitable, but our rate of aging is partly under our control. Aging is a product of our genetics, our life experience, and our lifestyle. This lesson is about mindful aging, including how our cells age and what slows down and speed ups our aging.

MINDFULNESS EXERCISE: LONGEVITY

Reflect on your stage of life and write down your responses to these questions: What are your concerns about the future? What is your view of the future?

Reflect on your future and make conscious choices about how you want to spend the rest of your life. Think about and write down your answers to these questions:

How long do you want to live?

What do you look forward to?

How do you want to spend your time?

Who do you want to spend your time with?

HOW OUR CELLS AGE

There are four ways that our cells age.

Systemic inflammation. The inflammation in our blood, called systemic inflammation, rises with age—but at variable rates—causing the aging of body tissue and resulting in a fertile ground for diseases such as cancer.

Telomere shortening. Telomeres are the caps that protect the ends of our chromosomes, which contain our genes. When our genes get damaged by chemicals such as free radicals, bad cells, such as cancer cells, result. Telomeres shorten as we age, but not at the same rate in everyone. When we have a lot of inflammation, this shortens our telomeres, and when our telomeres are short, this causes the cell environment to be pro-inflammatory.

Mitochondrial impairment. Mitochondria are the energy-making machines in the cell that keep us feeling vital. They wear out with aging at a variable rate, and when they get worn out, they start leaking free radicals, which can damage the telomeres, which are near the mitochondria in the cell.

Epigenetic changes. Although we're born with one set of genes that can't change, genes can turn on and off based on signals. Some signals are ones that we tell our genes, such as if we're under chronic stress or feel danger. These signals will be more pro-inflammatory. Epigenetics involves turning genes on and off in a way that is more long term and permanent. The pattern of our epigenetics roughly matches our age, but some people are epigenetically older or younger than their chronological age. Epigenetics is also roughly correlated with telomeres.

One thing all of these pathways of aging have in common is that if we're under chronic or traumatic stress, we tend to age ourselves more in these four ways.

Stress and aging are closely related because our aging biology listens to all the chemical signals from stress. Research shows that caregiving parents, people who are under chronic stress, tend to have shorter telomeres.

Studies show that taking up a mind-body activity—such as mindfulness, qi gong, or different forms of meditation—and committing to it for several months can result in reduced inflammation and telomere stabilization compared to people who do not engage in a mind-body activity.

MINDFULNESS EXERCISE: STEREOTYPES OF AGING

Write down the negative thoughts that you have when you think about aging as well as any positive associations you have with aging. What are your stereotypes? When you think of aging, what does it remind you of?

You might think of pain, suffering, fear of dependency, fear of dementia, or fear of leaving people behind. But research shows that many of these are myths.

POSITIVE AND NEGATIVE ASPECTS OF AGING

Some aspects of aging, such as the physical part, are inevitable. But there's a richness and growth that comes with aging that has been shown in many studies. Some of the benefits of aging include wisdom, more positive emotions, a better balance in your daily life between negative and positive emotions, and having a more positive social network.

When we're young, we might think that we want a big sprawling social network and lots of connections, but those relationships tend to be more superficial and have more negative aspects. These connections don't necessarily make us feel supported or even make us feel insecure or criticized. But older people in general tend to prune their social network to have a more positive emotional tone—people whom they feel good around.

If we let our negative views of aging, which we all have unconsciously, fester, then the more negative views of aging we have, the more likely we're going to have early aging, memory loss, hearing loss, and slower healing. We are also more likely to have dementia and earlier mortality.

Becca Levy, a pioneer in the area of aging stereotypes, has found that countries who believe as a culture that people have much lower status in society when they age and view aging as very negative have a much higher rate of dementia. She has also found that individuals who hold more negative views of aging are more likely to get Alzheimer's dementia.

CONSCIENTIOUSNESS

Conscientious personalities are one of the strongest personality predictors of healthy longevity. Conscientious means governed by conscience, and it's when we are mindful of others. There are many traits that go along with conscientiousness, including being responsible, careful, reliable, and meticulous. Conscientious people tend to plan ahead more and be less impulsive.

When researchers study longevity to determine the common factors that lead people to live long, healthy lives, one of the factors is love. This is about relationships— having a social network and being with other people.

There has been a tremendous amount of research on conscientiousness and longevity, particularly by Howard Friedman, who followed a large sample of young men in a long-term study and found that when personality is measured young in life, it's those who are mindful and conscientious that live longer.

HEALTH BEHAVIORS THAT SLOW AGING

An easy way to think about what will slow aging is to consider what is most anti-inflammatory and antioxidant. What's going to soak up free radicals and reduce inflammation?

For example, whole foods and fiber create an anti-inflammatory diet. Conversely, refined sugars and meat create more of a pro-inflammatory diet. And these are the two diet patterns that are related to telomere length. Consuming more vegetables is related to longer telomeres and less inflammation, while consuming more meat and soda is related to shorter telomeres and more inflammation. In general, processed foods are pro-aging.

Hundreds of studies have found that moderate physical activity is enough for maintaining telomere length. Specifically, if you're running ultramarathons, you won't get much longer telomeres than you would if you were running a moderate amount a week.

STRESS RESILIENCE AND POSITIVE STRESSORS

Toxic stress—very severe or traumatic stress or stress that goes on for a long time, such as job strain or caregiving—can lead to speedier cell aging. You might think the answer is to avoid stress, such as work or social or physical activities. But we actually should pursue moderate doses of stressful things. This is what makes our body more resilient to aging as well as more resilient psychologically.

The biology of stress and the biology of aging are intricately intertwined. Extreme stress in large doses speeds up aging, but small doses of stress actually slow aging.

Positive stressors help you grow and are anti-aging. They are things that will put you on the edge of, or just out of, your comfort zone. This is particularly important for us as we age, because we need new challenges to keep our cognitive functions sharp.

There are not many things that get us stressed out that we think are good for us, but one is exercise, which is a physiological stressor. Getting a moderate amount of exercise is anti-aging. It seems that high-intensity interval training, which involves short bursts of effort, is just as good as longer-endurance, slower sports.

When we stress out our bodies, we are causing more anti-aging mechanisms—more scavengers to soak up free radicals, for example. When the stress is over, we turn on mechanisms that cause the clean-up of cells. Autophagy, the clean-up process, is more active after we exercise.

In our nervous system, once we have had a lot of sympathetic activity, then the antisympathetic system turns on the parasympathetic system. The vagus nerve, which is part of the parasympathetic system, turns on very strongly after we've had a bout of stress. We want to have vagal time; we want to relax when we can relax. We want to have a strong peak stress response when we're dealing with a stressor and then a quick recovery.

When you're safe, notice that you're safe. Tell yourself, "I can fully relax. There's nothing that is wrong in this moment." And let that be true if it's true. The reason why it's often not true is because of our thoughts. We're keeping threats alive in our mind by ruminating and wishing things were different or worrying about the future. So, if we can be present and let our bodies respond to those feelings of safety, that is a restorative state. Let yourself be in a restorative state when you are safe. And you're safe more often than your mind thinks you are.

When we want to face a challenge, a big stress response is good for us. Then, we want to have a big recovery. And part of that big recovery means that we stop ruminating over negative aspects, such as wishing we performed better. Catching those thoughts is critical. But we can only do this when we become aware and look at our thoughts.

Stressors can be viewed in a positive way using a challenge orientation or mentality. When we're facing an uncomfortable situation, we can fill ourselves up with positive thoughts that may be true, such as "I can cope with this," "This is going to go well," "I'm going to be happy when it's over," "I have a lot to gain," or "I've got what it takes." Thinking these thoughts beforehand is not only going to help you do better, but it's also going to change your physiological stress response to be more of a positive response.

Visit http://www.amecenter.ucsf.edu/telomereeffect to learn more about telomere science and to take assessments that help you discover more about your personality.

THE SCIENCE OF MINDFUL AGING

LESSON 13 TRANSCRIPT

[Introduction by Shauna Shapiro]

Dr. Elissa Epel is an author, professor, internationally recognized expert in mindfulness stress and aging. Over 10 years ago, she discovered that severe stress can impact the cellular aging process. And since then she and her colleagues have been studying how mindfulness interventions can improve and slow the aging process. Alissa's probably the smartest human being I know and I'm delighted she's joining us on this journey.

[End of introduction]

Welcome. Thank you for joining me. It's my pleasure to talk to you today about mindful aging. And this is a fascinating topic because it involves most of what you've heard so far about mindfulness and different aspects of life. And I'm going to tell you about how our cells age, the things that slow down and speed up our aging, and how you can apply these to your own day and your own life. This takes some self-reflection on your part, if you're going to really use some of what this science points us to.

So, aging is inevitable, but our rate of aging is actually elastic and it's partly under our control. So, while aiding aging is a product of our genetics, it's also a product of our life experience, our lifestyle, and how we are experiencing each moment as it unfolds. So, I'm going to talk about the biology of aging, how our cells actually age, what causes our cells to either die early or to stop dividing and replenishing tissue. So, we know what the levers are. We know a lot of what slows down aging, what speeds it up. And as you'll see it has a lot to do with how well you know yourself.

So, I'm going to ask you to just pause here and grab a pad of paper and a pen. And by the end of this, you're going to have some very strong guiding principles that you can use for the rest of your life. So, that's a tall order, so let's get started.

I would like you to just reflect on your own stage of life, wherever you're at right now: What are your concerns? What is your view of the future? So, it doesn't matter how old you are, but I'm going to talk to you as if you're

50 or older, and that you've lived half your life and you may be starting to think more about aging and the experience of aging. We kind of ignore aging because it doesn't feel like anything until it starts happening. Then you start thinking about it when your body starts changing.

So, you have crossed some thresholds in life, important thresholds by now. You've chosen a career path, you've made a living, you may have chosen a life partner, or raised children. And those are huge challenges that are behind you at midlife. And so now it's a really important time to reflect on your future and actually make conscious choices about how you want to spend the rest of your life.

There are questions that we don't really typically ask ourselves about the future. So even just thinking about retirement, there's actually been studies showing that we spend more time planning a vacation, choosing a Netflix to see, choosing what to eat, than we spend planning on retirement, which is crazy right? Because that's decades of our life, important years of our life, that could be different or better.

So, think about these questions. How long do you want to live? When people ask me that, I can tell you that after studying aging my answer is not to 100 as it might have been, but rather I want to live as long as I am healthy, as long as I'm well and I can do things. And actually, that's I kind of copied that answer... the longest-lived human being Jeanne Calment, when she was about 120, she was asked why do you want to keep living? What is it that you look forward to? And her answer was, "I can still do stuff." She had this social network, she was riding her bike into town. She was fully living.

My next question for you is: What to look forward to when you think about your future? And how do you want to spend your time besides work? And even more important, who do you want to spend your time with? So, in many studies of aging, such as the Harvard Longitudinal Study of Aging, when they look at longevity to see what the common factors that lead people to live long healthy lives, one of the factors is love. It's social network. It's being with other people. So, at the end of life, if you think about what you'd want on your epitaph or on your tombstone—it's pretty a grim picture, but it really, even though we spend so much time thinking about our current goals, about making money, about work, it's never "I wish I spent more hours at the office." And it's usually about love and relationships.

Now that you have some answers to those big questions, I want to tell you more about what's happening inside of our cells and how our cells are responding to the way we live, to how much love we have in our lives, to how much purpose and meaning, and of course to our lifestyle. So, what do we know about how our cells age? I'm going to tell you about four ways that our cells age that we're just discovering so much about, and it's just fascinating.

So, the first is inflammation. As we age the inflammation our blood rises a bit over time, over the years, but not for everyone. So, there's variable rates of inflammation, and this inflammation in our blood, we call it systemic inflammation, causes aging of body tissue. It causes this kind of ripe fertile ground for diseases like cancer. So, we want to keep our inflammation low. We even call it inflaming aging because it's so tied up with aging. So, that's I think of as a main pathway or highway to how our bodies age. So, we want to think about what can we do? What do we do every day that reduces inflammation rather than increases it?

Now there's another way that our cells age that I've been studying for over 15 years, and that is how quickly our telomeres shorten. Telomeres are the caps at the ends of our chromosomes. They're made of DNA, but they're not genes. They're these strings of repeating base pairs that actually protect the ends of our chromosomes. So, our chromosomes contain our genes, our genes are what make us unique, they make us who we are. They encode every single protein in our body in every cell. And it's very important that our genes are protected throughout life and not damaged, because when they get damaged by chemicals, like free radicals, that's when we get problems. That's when we get bad cells, cancer cells, cells that die. So, telomeres protect the cells, protect the genome, but they also shortened as we age. And then of course here's the catch: They don't shorten the same rate in everyone. Their rate of shortening is elastic. And so, we can do things in our daily life that protect our telomeres and keep them longer and stable.

Now inflammation and telomeres are very close. When we have a lot of inflammation, it shortens our telomeres. When our telomeres are short, it creates the cells environment to be pro-inflammatory.

Now there is a third player in the cell, and that is the mitochondria. So, these are little energy-making machines. These are the little batteries in our cells, and we need these mitochondria to be fully powered throughout life because they give us energy, they make ATP. They keep us feeling vital. And so of course they wear out, as most things do, wear out with aging out at a variable rate, and when they get a little bit worn, they start leaking free radicals and that creates oxidative stress. And these free radicals can damage the telomeres, which are right near the mitochondria. They are all kind of lived together in the cell. That's a problem. So, we want telomeres and mitochondria to be supporting each other.

But what happens if the telomeres get too short? They send signals to the mitochondria, mitochondria wear out, and vice versa. When the mitochondria start wearing out and spewing these free radicals, it shortens the telomeres. So, it's all kind of one family system in there.

And then the last thing I'm going to tell you is that we're learning so much about how our DNA is turned on and off. So, we can't change our genes, we're born with one set of genes at birth, for our whole life. But they do turn on and off based on signals. Some of the signals are ones that we tell our genes, like if we're under chronic stress and feel danger, are going to have our genes express a different pattern. It's going to be more pro-inflammatory.

Now there is a way that we turn genes on and off that is a little bit more long term and permanent, and that is through methylation bonds. So, that epigenome, the proteins around or above the genome, can turn genes on and off. And we now know that we can measure the pattern of our epigenetics. It matches our age roughly, but some of us are a bit older, some of us are a bit younger, than our chronological age. So, this is a new way we can look into our cells and determine our age. It's roughly correlated with telomeres in a small way, so they're kind of different pathways of aging.

Now one thing all of these pathways have in common is that if we're under chronic stress or traumatic stress, if we experience a lot of trauma, we tend to have aged ourselves more in these four ways. So, what I'm going to talk to you about today is how we can slow our cell aging, and stress is a big part of that.

Stress and aging are really closely related because our aging biology listens to signals from stress, all the chemical signals from stress. Now you've heard a lot of about mindfulness in this Great Course, and you might be wondering what about meditation? So, when I first published a paper on telomeres around 15 years ago and we showed that care-giving parents, people are under chronic stress, tended to have shorter telomeres. The question that emerged immediately, both from people as well as in my mind, was well can you slow telomere shortening process with meditation or mind-body interventions?

So, now over a decade later, I can tell you that there have been many studies. Some are big controlled randomized trials; most are smaller studies. But they tend to show that if you take up a mind-body activity, not just mindfulness but could be qi gong or different types of meditation, and you commit to that for several months, these studies mostly tend to show we can reduce our inflammation, our levels of CRP—C-reactive protein—and we can stabilize our telomeres. And so, the rate of shortening is slower if we're doing a regular mind-body practice like that, than the rate of telomere shortening in people who are not.

And I could just end there, right? So, the message is take up a mind-body practice and be committed to it, but I'm not going to end there because that's just one piece. It's a way to learn about your mind, your mind-body and be intimate with understanding yourself and how you affect other people in the world and how you are affected. So, it's a really wonderful, critical tool, but what I'm going to talk to you about is how mindfulness and awareness, attitudes, tendencies, personality styles we have, how these are shaping the rate of our cell aging.

We all carry around these stereotypes of people and we don't really, we're not really aware of them. But actually, most of us have developed a pretty negative stereotype of aging, while we're young when we don't worry about aging. So just take a minute and write down the negative thoughts that you have when you think about aging and any positive associations you have with aging. So, what are your stereotypes? When you think of aging, what does it remind you of? You might think of pain, suffering, fear of dependency, fear of dementia, fear of leaving people behind.

So, let's face it, we have pretty negative views of aging. But actually, if you look closely at the research, many of these myths. And well some of aging and the physical part is inevitable, there are benefits, and there's a richness and a growth that comes with aging that has been shown in study after study. So, some of the things are wisdom, more positive emotions, a better balance in your daily life between negative and positive emotions, having a more positive social network.

So, when we're young, we might think that we want a big sprawling social network and lots of connections, and those relationships actually tend to be more superficial and have more negative aspects. People who don't necessarily make us feel supported or they actually make us feel insecure or criticized. But older people in general tend to prune their social network to have a more positive emotional tone—people who they feel good around.

So, there's a lot of positive psychological states and wisdom that comes with aging. So, I want you to think of someone who is a role model in aging for you. It could be someone famous, could be someone you know, and write down that name. Because it turns out that if you keep these negative views of aging, which we all have unconsciously, if we just let them fester, the more negative views of aging the more likely we're going to have early aging, memory loss, hearing loss, slower healing when we have a hip fracture, more likely to have dementia, and earlier mortality. That's a big list. That's a pretty bad list.

So, a pioneer in this area about aging stereotypes is a colleague of mine, her name is Becca Levy at Yale and she has done some amazing studies. Some have been countrywide showing for example countries who believe as a culture that people when they age have much lower status in society and view aging as very negative have a much higher rate of dementia. So, that's at the country level. But then in an individual level, in big surveys studies like the health and retirement study, individuals who hold more negative views of aging are more likely to get Alzheimer's dementia. So, that's enough in my book for us to take this quite seriously.

There have been lots of studies trying to ask what kind of personality is most resistant to aging? And if there was a mindful personality it would probably be conscientiousness. Conscientious personalities are one of the strongest personality predictors of longevity, of healthy longevity.

So, what is conscientious mean? Governed by conscience is the literal definition. So, it's when we are aware of our impact on other people and we're mindful of other people and we try to be very conscientious, responsible, careful, reliable, meticulous, so there's a lot of traits that go along with conscientiousness. Conscientious people tend to plan ahead more and be less impulsive.

So, there's been a tremendous amount of research on conscientiousness and longevity, particularly by Howard Friedman at UC Irvine. He followed a large sample of young men, the Terman study and found that when you measure personality young in life it's not the cheery kids who live longer like you'd think, it's that it's those who are much more mindful and conscientious.

So, what are the health behaviors that slow aging? Well, there is an easy way to think about what is going to slow aging, and that is to think about what is most anti-inflammatory and antioxidant stress? What's going to soak up free radicals and reduce inflammation? So, if we think about diet, for example, it is whole foods and fiber that create an anti-inflammatory diet. And conversely, it's the refined sugars and the meat that create more of this kind of pro-inflammatory diet. And as we would expect, these are the two diet patterns that are related to telomere length. So, having more vegetables is related to longer telomeres, having more meat and soda is related to shorter telomeres. Same with inflammation.

So, when we think about what we eat it's good to think in terms of just... rather than super foods and what's going to be the most antioxidant thing I can eat, is really just processed foods are going to be completely pro-aging whereas whole foods are you...it's hard to eat too many vegetables, for example. And having unprocessed meat is much better than processed meat, particularly for cell aging and for telomeres.

So, I actually wrote a book a couple of years ago on all of the different levers that slow down and speed up telomere aging. And I did this with my colleague Elizabeth Blackburn, who is a molecular biologist who discovered the telomere telomerase system. She discovered how these cells age by having telomeres shorten too much and by having this enzyme called telomerase be slowing and repairing telomeres.

And so, this book is called *The Telomere Effect* and it focuses a lot on these lifestyle factors. I'm not going to go too into them except for to say that we did learn some good news as we were discovering what, out of all of the hundreds of studies, are related to long telomere length or stable telomere length. And it's not necessarily running marathons and doing extreme sports and activity, but rather moderate activity is enough. You don't get much longer telomeres than you do if you're just running a moderate amount a week than if you're running ultra-marathons.

Now for the rest of our time together, I'm going to focus on, rather than on the health behaviors, which you already know what you should be doing and what's good for the heart and what's good for the brain is also good for cell aging. So, there are not too many surprises there. I want to talk about a few invisible factors that we don't typically think of as important to our aging. And one is stress resilience, another is love and support, and finding meaning and purpose.

So, we talked about toxic stress, how very severe or traumatic stress or stress that goes on for years and years like job strain or caregiving, how those can lead to speedier cell aging. The answer you would think is avoid stress. Maybe I shouldn't go back to work. Maybe I shouldn't go out and do this activity that has all these social risks or physical risks. And that natural tendency to kind of avoid stress and life is actually the opposite of what we should be doing, which is we should be pursuing moderate doses of stressful things. That that is actually what makes our body more resilient to aging and makes us actually more resilient psychologically, too.

So, one key point here is that the biology of stress and the biology of aging are intricately intertwined. So, on one hand, extreme stress in too big of a dose speeds up aging, but on the other hand small doses of stress actually slow aging. So, let me give you a dramatic example from the animal world.

So, this has been discovered over and over in cells and in lower species, in worms and in rodents. And for example, if you take worms and you heat them up, you fry them up in a pan just a little bit, they actually live longer. You're turning on anti-aging mechanisms called hormesis. If you keep frying them, turn up the heat too high, of course they die. So, this hormesis is this kind of fine balance, like a moderate dose of stress that the organism can deal with.

What is that to you? What is that in your life that promotes positive stress? Positive stressors help you grow and are anti-aging. So, you want to think about some things that will put you on the edge a little bit out of your comfort zone. Now this is really important, particularly for us as we age, because we need new challenges, and that keeps our cognitive function sharp as well.

Now I'm going to give you an example of a positive stressor. There is a beautiful, natural experiment called the Experience Corps. The Experience Corps, it's an experiment where these this group of researchers and socially oriented activists decided to really see how can we help both elderly people age well and also help all of these at-risk school children, underprivileged children who aren't getting their social needs or their tutoring needs met. So, they matched up retired people. They came to their doors and their homes and they asked them, "Are you interested in trying to be a tutor in this local school and being matched up with a child?"

Now, how would you feel about that? You have not been working for years, you're comfortable and safe at home. Now you're being asked to go into a school and do something you've never done. And it might even be a bit of a low income or dangerous environment.

The beauty of the Experience Corps is that not only did the kids benefit, but the elderly people who said yes and who volunteered and took on this new role in life, their health got better too. Their mental function got better. Their hippocampus, the part of their brain that controls memory in the men who did this, actually grew in volume. And so, it's this example where it was stressful for them, and they had to deal with a lot of issues that were happening in the child's life, things like not having enough food or not having their basic needs met. And so, it wasn't an easy job, but they grew from it psychologically, and they grew in what we called generativity—they felt more purpose and meaning in their life as an Experience Corps volunteer. So, this is an example, in my mind, of both doing something that makes your life more meaningful and also is a positive stressor. So, this idea of positive stress just hasn't been explored enough in humans, but I believe that there are some very safe forms of this to suggest to you.

Now what do you do in your own life that's positive stress? There's not that many things that we do that get us really stressed out that we think are good for us, but one is exercise—that's a physiological stressor. Getting a moderate amount of exercise is of course anti-aging, and we know that in many different ways, having it in terms of a little burst, the high intensity interval training is something that's just starting to be more steady. But it looks like that is just as good as the longer endurance slower sport and that makes a lot of sense physiologically, that when we stress out our bodies, we actually are causing more of these anti-aging mechanisms, scavengers to soak up free radicals, for example. And that is because when the stressor is over we turn on all of these mechanisms that caused us to clean up cells. So, autophagy, the little Pac-Man clean up machines in our cells, are much higher and more active after we've exercised for example.

And then in terms of our nervous system, once we have had a lot of sympathetic activity, then the anti-sympathetic system turns on the parasympathetic system. We call this the vagus nerve and that turns on very strongly after we've had a bout of stress. And that is a really important way to think about our nervous system. We want to have vagal time. We want to relax when we can relax. We want to be really have a good strong peak stress response when we're dealing with a stressor, and then we want to have a quick recovery.

So, think of it like this: When you're safe, notice that you're safe, tell yourself right now I can fully relax. There's nothing that is wrong in this moment. And let that be true if it's true. The reason why it's often not true is because our thoughts, because we're keeping threat alive in our mind, we're ruminating and we're worrying about things. We're either ruminating about wishing things were different or we're worrying about the future. So, if we can be present and let our bodies respond to that, those feelings of safety, that is what we think of as a restorative state. Let yourself be in restorative state when you are safe. You're safe more than you your mind thinks it is.

When we want to mount a...face a challenge, you want to have a big stress response. Stress is good for us. And then we want to have a big recovery. Now part of that big recovery means that we stop ruminating and thinking over negative aspects. I wish I did better, etc. Things like that. So, catching those thoughts is really critical. And what skill does that take?

You've been hearing about different forms of mindfulness, but it's only if we can actually become aware and look at our thoughts that we can catch that type of vigilance that we carry with us, those negative thoughts that keep us vigilant.

So, I've been in some positive stress. I'm getting to do a very interesting study right now in my lab where we're just comparing different types of positive stress. So, we're comparing an extreme form of breathing, you might have heard of Wim Hof breathing. So, we're comparing the practice of just doing hyperventilation and hypoxia and exposure to cold. So, you know how relaxed you might feel after you do hot-cold baths? So, that's an example of how we condition the nervous systems works. So, we're looking at these short term physical stressors, high intensity exercise. So, these are two ways to activate our bodies in the short burst and then get that recovery, that restorative effect, that anti-aging effect, and then we're comparing that to meditation, which is going to be more of a what we call top-down, more of a mental way of putting us into a restorative mode. So, we'll see. You'll have to look out for that on my website and see what we find.

So, we've talked about some ways we can recognize our attitudes about aging and notice how conscientious we are. We can always change. We used to think personality was fixed and rigid throughout life, but we can always become more mindful, more conscientious. And I've also talked about how we can respond to stress in this positive way. So, I've talked about positive stress situations, where you stretch yourself and you put yourself in situations that are just a bit uncomfortable so you can cope with them and grow in that way—grow physiologically, turn on anti-aging mechanisms grow psychologically.

There is a way that we can view stressors in this positive way as well. We call this a challenge orientation or challenge mentality. And that is when we're facing one of these uncomfortable situations, we think this whole set of positive thoughts that may be true—I can cope with this, this is going to go well, I'm going to be happy when it's over, I have a lot to gain, I've got what it takes, a bring it on mentality, so that's what we call a challenge mentality. So, filling yourself with those thoughts beforehand is not only going to help you do better, it's going to change your physiological stress response to be more of this positive response.

So, you can actually assess some of your tendencies, some of these traits we've been talking about. I put some quizzes up on my lab website for you, and we use these in our book. And so, if you go to my lab website and you see *The Telomere Effect*, you click on that and it gives you the quizzes that are in the book, the ones that we can make public. So, you can take your, take a self-assessment quiz to see how conscientious you are, how hostile you are, how much you're likely to feel cynical and distrustful—that's associated with telomere shortening and inflammation. You can take a quiz to look at your stress response style and just notice what is your automatic tendency? Are you more threatened? Do you immediately think that you're going to be ashamed or do badly? Or do you tend to have more of a positive challenge orientation?

So, the website is amecenter—that's one word—.ucsf.edu. AME stands for aging metabolism emotions. So, it's amecenter.ucsf.edu. And all of this is just to learn about your own tendencies. Because we're so used to ourself, we're often on automatic mode and we don't have a sense of how our habitual responses are maybe hurting or handicapping us. And once we're aware of them, that can change everything. That mindfulness of how we tend to react is the first and most essential step. And then softening our response so that we can surf the waves of life and the stressors that come to us in a more graceful way.

POSITIVE BEHAVIORS THAT SLOW AGING

LESSON 14

We are social mammals, and the things that stress us out the most are interpersonal stress and conflict in relationships. This lesson includes research that shows how important your social world is.

POSITIVE CONNECTIONS

Think about your social landscape. Who do you feel most connected to? Do you talk to or see this person as much as you'd like to? If you see this person once a year and you can roughly project how many years you have left to live, this gives you a startling sense of how many more times you'll be together.

Our social connectivity is so important that it's not just how much time we spend physically together, but also what our schema—our model in our head—is of how alone versus connected we are.

Studies have shown that people who feel like they have more social support in their life have healthier stress responses. Overall, these people have less secretion of cortisol, a hormone that is released in stressful situations.

One thing that mindfulness teaches us is that we are intricately connected to each other—to this earth. It's just difficult to see. Especially if we're feeling stressed or down, we become very focused on ourselves. Alternatively, when we can see the interconnections that are truly there and how we are connected, that is one of the most freeing and important realizations that can come from a compassionate or mindful practice.

Studies have shown that loving-kindness, feeling positive toward other people, and feeling compassionate toward ourselves and toward other people is related to better health. In some cases, it's related to longer telomeres, at least in a study related to telomere lengthening and meditation practice that makes us feel connected to other people.

On the opposite side is loneliness—which is, in part, a state of mind. Feeling alone, whether you see people or not on a daily basis, is as big of a risk factor for early death as smoking.

It's particularly difficult when older people are so isolated. There are 13 million older people living alone, and they rarely see others. Loneliness is a huge predictor of early mortality.

There are many things we can do—either for ourselves or to encourage people we care about who live alone—to connect socially, including taking a class, finding a hobby, volunteering, scheduling a phone call each day with someone, or sharing a meal with someone.

It is extremely important for us to be socially connected in positive ways to each other. Without social connections, people suffer emotionally and physiologically.

EMOTION CONTAGION

Research shows that we transmit emotions to others through a phenomenon called emotion contagion. If one member of a couple tends to have more positive emotions, the other member of the couple does, too. If one of the people in a couple tends to have higher cortisol, the other partner does, too.

Our mood and physiology change depending on the people we're with. This happens somewhat with families, and it may happen with people you work with. You influence the mood of the people you are close to, the people you care about, and they influence yours. The fact that we set the tone for others around us, not just for ourselves, is something to take note of so that we can harness this to positively affect the world.

In families who are taking care of a child with autism or a developmental disorder, some caregivers feel that they're very influenced by their family's emotions. For example, if their child has a bad day, they're much more likely to have negative feelings themselves.

Other caregivers have more independence so that when they notice the negative mood of their family, they're less influenced by it. This doesn't mean they're less compassionate or caring, but it doesn't cause them to adopt that negative mood.

And that takes mindfulness—remembering that you can be compassionate and empathetic without going down that same rabbit hole or entering that same blue state of mind.

People who report that they are more independent of others' emotions have much better mental and physical health.

It takes mindfulness and awareness to be compassionate but not to let yourself have empathic distress, which is when you take on emotions and feel distress, which can lead to burnout. When teachers and therapists easily adopt the emotions of the person that they're caring for, they tend to get much more burnt out and feel numbness, demoralization, and lack of ability to keep empathizing.

PURPOSE IN LIFE

Purpose in life is something that has just arisen in the field of aging and longevity, and it is such an important factor for our healthy aging and our happiness or good mental health. In a study of US populations, researchers found that people who feel more purpose tend to live longer and are healthier, regardless of whether they're retired or not—and regardless of depression or positive or negative mood.

Having a purpose in life is buffers against stress. It's related to having less overall cortisol in our hair (one way to measure cortisol) as well as less inflammation in our blood. It's also related to having less buildup of chronic disease risk factors over the course of 10 years. In other words, if you have high purpose in life, you're going to age less over 10 years, and that's partly because you feel more control over your health, according to some studies.

MINDFULNESS EXERCISE: MEASURING PURPOSE IN LIFE

If you want to measure your purpose in life, you can ask yourself these questions:

> What is it when I wake up that matters to me about my day?
>
> Do I feel like my plans are important and what I do is important?
>
> Do I have things to look forward to?

To more formally assess your purpose in life, visit:
http://www.amecenter.ucsf.edu/purpose-in-life.

GAINING CONTROL OF YOUR DAY

You determine your day and how you're going to view events. And while you do have some automatic reactions, you could gain control of your secondary reactions.

Rather than thinking of a big change in your health—such as a big shift in diet or suddenly going to the gym every day—think about small changes that you know you can implement into your day. For example, think about a time of day, such as right when you wake up or during a lunch break or walk with someone, when you might be able to be active for 10 minutes more than on a typical day. You can add small pieces of wellness to your day in a structural way that you can sustain and keep.

Research shows that doing a mind-body activity right when you wake up is important. When people wake up, whether they feel joy or stressed sets a different trajectory for their day.

For people who wake up feeling joy, their cortisol level right after waking does not rise as high and their cell aging looks better than those who wake up feeling stressed, out of control, or full of dread—which is related to the opposite effects.

We're habitual creatures. You might tend to be the type of person who wakes up with dread, but when you're mindful of that and notice it, that's when you take control. You can spend a few minutes in bed thinking about something you're looking forward to that day or thinking about something you're grateful for.

These are strong, potent, positive exercises that you can build into your day. You can develop realistic daily rituals that you can maintain.

MINDFULNESS EXERCISE:

Starting tomorrow morning, what can you add to your day in terms of health behaviors, social connections, and positive stress that keeps your cells from aging as quickly as they would normally?

>**POSITIZE YOUR ATTITUDE ABOUT AGING.** Think about someone older who is inspiring to you and realize he or she walks on a path that is possible for you. Catch and notice your negative stereotypes of aging when you have them. Build in more conscientious behavior.

>**BUILD IN POSITIVE STRESS.** Where's the positive stress in your life? What are you going to add that is going to be a short-term positive stressor for your body or mind, or both? Notice when you have these threat responses. Be mindful of how you carry around stress with you. Even when you're not in the middle of dealing with a stressor, you might be planning around it or worrying about it. Once you can develop the habit of getting intimate with your mind, you notice this, giving you the ability to build in spaciousness, let your body go into restorative mode, or laugh at your thoughts when they're self-critical.

>>Write down a time of day tomorrow when you're going to work on turning something that's typically stressful into a positive stressor. Where in the landscape of your day are the stressful events? Thinking about this gives you the opportunity to plan ahead and to practice a different way of approaching stressful moments, viewing them as challenges and positive stressors.

>**THINK ABOUT YOUR RELATIONSHIPS.** Are there ones that stress you out, that you don't need, or that you don't need to have exposure to as much? Are there people that you haven't connected with that you feel particularly grateful for that you can express that to? Showing gratitude is not automatic.

It's not something we're typically raised to think about, and we often don't realize how important it is. But you can become better at being grateful—for example, by writing someone a card describing how much they mean to you or how much what they did meant to you.

In general, think about how you want to be tomorrow—how you want to show up to other people and to yourself—and try to align your intentions with your day. Starting from right when you wake up, notice your automatic thoughts. Then, shift the trajectory toward more positive thoughts. What's right in your life? What are you grateful for? Finally, have the kind of day that's more restorative than stressful.

POSITIVE BEHAVIORS THAT SLOW AGING

LESSON 14 TRANSCRIPT

Our next topic is going to be about your social world. We are social mammals, and it turns out that the things that stress us out the most are about relationships—their interpersonal stress or conflict. I'm going to point out some things we've learned from research that show you how important your social world is.

We've talked a little bit about attitudes, stress responses, and some health behaviors. Now I want you to think about your social landscape. Who do you feel most connected to? And do you talk to or see this person as much as you'd like to? If you see them once a year and you can project how many years roughly you have left, it gives you a startling sense of how many more times you'll be together. Now our social connectivity is so important that it's not just how much time we spend physically together, but also how are our schema, our model in our head is of how alone versus connected we are.

So, let me tell you a couple pieces of what I mean by that. When we did a study to see how stressed people got when they just did a lab stressor, we wanted to see if so if their feelings of social support would buffer that. Whatever, however connected people felt to others in their lives they weren't in the room with them, they might've lived across the country, but if they felt like they had more social support their stress responses were healthier. They followed that positive stress response curve more. It would go up; it would come down quickly. They had less cortisol secretion overall.

So, it's kind of the concept that we carry around with us: How alone are we? How separated are we? One thing that mindfulness teaches us is that we are intricately connected to each other, to this earth, it's just hard to see. And especially if we're feeling stressed, if we're feeling down, we get very focused, so focused, the world closes in and we think about our favorite topic: ourself.

And so, when we become more mindful and we can see the interconnections that are truly there and how we are connected, that is one of the most freeing and important realizations that can come from a compassionate or mindful practice.

And we have now seen some very interesting studies, for example, that loving kindness, that feeling positive toward other people, and feeling compassionate toward ourself and toward other people is related to better health. It's related in some cases, to longer telomeres—at least a new study related to telomere lengthening with this kind of meditation practice that makes us feel connected to other people.

On the opposite side is loneliness. And loneliness is, in part, a state of mind. Feeling alone, whether you see people or not on a daily basis, this loneliness is actually as big of a risk factor for early death as smoking. We can never remind ourselves enough how important it is for us to be socially connected in positive ways to each other. So, it's particularly hard when older people are so isolated. There are 13 million older people living alone, and they rarely see each other. So, when we're older, we know that loneliness is a really big predictor of earlier mortality. And so there are these things we can do, either for us self or encouraging people we care about who live alone, and that is really connecting socially in some way. It might be taking a class, finding a hobby, volunteering, scheduling a phone call each day or a meal together. So, these are really important social connections and without them we know that people suffer emotionally and physiologically.

One of the most interesting areas in understanding us as social beings and our health is that we transmit emotions to others. We have emotion contagion happening all the time around us. So, we've been studying this pretty carefully because we're interested in how people stay resilient to stress. So, when they're living, for example, with someone with a chronic condition, if they're a caregiver, how do they stay positive? Now we know that when couples are studied, if they tend to have more positive emotions, the other member of the couple does too. If one of the couples tends to have higher cortisol, the other partner does too. And so, we see these correlations; we move around in our mood and are physiology with the people that we're with.

So, we know this happens with couples, we know this happens somewhat with families, and it may happen with people you work with. People you are close to, people you care about, you are influencing their mood and they're influencing yours. So, that's really something for us to take respond, take note of and take responsibility of because we can use that for positive effects in the world. And certainly, I've tried to not bring in as much stress to my workplace and to my staff after really realizing how we really set the tone for others around us, not just for ourselves.

So, this emotion contagion is something we've been studying in our families who are caregiving, who are taking care of a child with autism or a developmental disorder. And what we found is super interesting. We found that the mothers who feel that that they're very influenced by their family's emotions—so if their husband comes home in a bad mood, they're more likely to get in a bad mood. If their child has had a bad day, they're much more likely to have rubbed off, to have negative feelings themselves.

So, what we see is that some people have more independence, that when they notice the negative mood of their family, they're less influenced by it. So, it doesn't mean they're less compassionate or caring, but it doesn't actually cause them to, just like a pinball, to adopt that negative mood. And that takes mindfulness, that takes remembering that you can be compassionate, that you can be there for someone and hold their suffering and empathize and listen without you going down that same rabbit hole or that are entering that same blue state of mind.

So, the people who report that they are more independent of others emotions have much better mental health and physical health. So, this is something that I believe is probably takes some mindfulness and awareness to be compassionate, but to not let yourself have empathic distress when you take on emotions and you feel distress and that can lead also to burnout. We see that professionally with teachers and therapists, that when they are easily adopting the emotions of the person that they're trying to care for, they tend to get much more burnt out and feel numbness, demoralization, and really just lack of ability to keep empathizing.

One of the questions that we started with is: What you want the rest of your life to be like? How do you want to spend your time? Who do you want to spend your time with? So, that leads us to this big question of what is your mission here on earth? It doesn't have to be some grandiose thing, but what matters to you? How do you want to be living now that you have more wisdom, more control over your life, hopefully have some more time or at least can create more time to reflect on these important questions?

Purpose in life is something that has just arisen in this aging and longevity field, and it is such an important factor for our healthy aging and our happiness or good mental health. In one of these big studies of US populations, they found that people who feel more purpose tend to live longer, healthier, regardless of whether they're retired or not. And that's regardless of depression or positive or negative mood. So, there's something about meaning and purpose, that transcends feelings and mood, that really does directly impact our health. Purpose in life is stress buffering. It's related to less having less overall cortisol in our hair—that's one way we measure it. It's related to having less inflammation in our blood. It's related to having less just buildup of kind of chronic disease risk factors over the next 10 years. So, if you have high purpose in life you're going to age less over 10 years, and that's partly because you feel more control over your health. At least that's what some of the studies show. We can measure control over health, but it's probably much more profound than that.

So, if you want to measure your purpose in life, you can ask yourself: What is it when I wake up that matters to me about my day? Do I feel like my plans are important and what I do is important? Do I have things to look forward to? So, the scales ask things like that. It's more on a daily basis. So, you can take a scale to assess your own purpose in life and get your score if you'd like, and again that's on my lab website, amecenter.ucsf.edu.

So, I want to end with having you really take stock of your day. So, we've talked a lot about big trajectories and thinking about new things to try and how we want to maybe shift priorities. But what it really comes down to, in the biology of aging, is also the little things we do every day. They add up and they are the levers on cell aging. The little habits we do add up over decades and predict, for example, how long our telomeres are when we're older, how much inflammation we have.

So, when you think of these health behaviors rather than thinking of a big change, a big shift in diet or all of a sudden going to the gym every day, think about small changes that you know you can do, that you can implement into your day. So, for example, think about a time of day where you might be able to be active for 10 minutes more than your typical day. That might be right when you get up, that might be during a lunch break, that might be taking a walk with someone. So, those little built-in pieces of wellness that you can add to your day in a structural way are what matter. And those are what we can sustain and keep.

I tend to think of them as stapling—let's staple in a little burst of activity for you. And so, stapling means you want to say what is it going to come after my day already has, for example, a lunch break or it already has a commute in it. So, you staple this activity right after something that you know is going to happen so that you remember, so that becomes a habit. It becomes the landscape of your day.

A mind-body activity is just like that too. So being able to do that right when you wake up is important. We found that when people wake up, if they feel joy, that sets a different trajectory for their day; that their cortisol rise right after waking is not as high, that their cell aging looks better. Whereas if you wake up feeling stressed, feeling like you don't have control, dreading the day, that is related to the opposite. And so, you know we have, we're habitual creatures. We may wake up, we may be, tend to be the type who just wakes up with dread. But, when you're mindful of that and you notice that, that's when you take control and you say and now I'm going to spend a few minutes, in bed still, thinking about something I'm looking forward to today, thinking about something I'm grateful for. These are strong, potent, positive little exercises that you can build into your day. You can develop realistic daily rituals that you can maintain.

And in our book, we go on and on about things like sleep. How to get better quality sleep? And all the different rituals that you might add. How do you influence sleep? You influence the time before sleep. Those few hours right before sleep, like having a curfew on screens, not dealing with stressful discussions or activities, things like that. So now we're getting into the nitty gritty, and these are things you can read about on the web or in our book, or you may already have these types of small behaviors.

But it's these that that add up to create these restorative periods. We've been talking about, restorative sleep, or periods of relaxation when you're not having to cope with things.

So, your rate of aging, the amount of inflammation you have in your blood, and how quickly your telomeres will shorten, how long your mitochondria are going to stay like Energizer bunnies, these are partly under your control. You determine your day and how you're going to view events. And while we have our automatic reactions, you get get to control your secondary reaction.

So, I'd like to end by having you take out your pad and your pen again. And I'm just going to go through some of these main points about mindful aging and have you decide what you're going to do, what fits for you. What you're going to do starting tomorrow morning. So, one thing we talked about is "positizing" your attitudes about aging. Thinking about someone who's inspiring to you, who is older, and realizing that is a path and a possibility for you. Catching and noticing your negative stereotypes of aging when you do have them.

Building more conscientious behavior. And so, for me, for example, I'm just, you know, a late person. I'm doomed to always be late, right? Well, no. So, when I can actually be planful and mindful of how much that stresses me out and stresses out people around me, I actually change my day dramatically by arriving early. By building ahead that kind of mindful, planful, conscientious behavior that makes everyone happier.

We also talked about not just positive attitudes but positive stress. Where's the positive stress in your life? What are you going to add that is going to be a short term positive stressor for your body, or your mind, or both? And noticing when you do have these kind of threat responses. So being mindful of how we carry around stress with us. Even when we're not in the middle of dealing with a stressor we might be planning on it, worrying about it, just this kind of repetitive, we called perseverative thinking. It's just so common. And once you can develop the habit of looking in and getting intimate with your mind, you notice this and that gives you the ability to build in spaciousness, to let your body go into restorative mode, to laugh at your thoughts when you notice you're having self-critical thoughts again.

So, write down a time of day that you're going to spend tomorrow, where you're going to work on turning something that's typically stressful into a positive stressor. Where in your day, in the landscape of your day, are the stressful events? So, for a lot of people it's morning, it's commuting, dealing with certain meetings. You know that's going to happen, it's just so predictable, right? So, this gives you the opportunity to plan ahead and to practice a different way of approaching those moments and viewing them as challenges and positive stressors. It certainly helps if you've done a mind-body activity if you built up your mind-body reserve. If you have more "vagal town," you know, and this kind of restorative base that you're coming from.

Think about now your relationships: Are there ones that stress you out, that you don't need, or that you don't need to have exposure to as much? Are there people that you haven't connected with, that you feel particularly grateful for, that you can express that to? Showing gratitude is something that is not automatic. It's not something we're typically raised to think about and realize how important it is. But I've become much better. For example, in my post-50-years of doing things like writing a card and telling someone how much what they did meant to you, or how much they mean to you.

So, in general, tomorrow, think about how you want to be, how you want to show up to other people and to yourself, and try to align your intentions with your day. So, starting from right when you wake up, noticing your automatic thoughts. Then shifting the trajectory toward more positive thoughts. What's right in your life? What are you grateful for? And then having that kind of day that's more restorative than stressful.

So, every day I like to think of base pairs. Now we want to maintain our telomeres. We can have a day that's wearing, where we're having more toxic stress than positive stress, where we're eating more pro-inflammatory and oxidative meals, and those are wearing us out sooner. So, you want to think of balancing that and what can you add to your day in terms of the health behaviors, in terms of the social connections, in terms of positive stress that actually balances you and keeps your cells from aging as quickly.

So, I hope that at least one of these points will stay with you and that you'll staple something, and that you'll bring one of these positive attitudes with you after you finish this lecture. Thank you so much for your attention, your reflection, and your commitment to your own life and your own mindful aging.

MINDFUL SEX: BEING PRESENT IN YOUR BODY

LESSON 15

This lesson offers some techniques to bring mindfulness into your sex life. Studies have shown that you can become more aware of pleasure in your body, address issues around sexual dysfunction and erectile dysfunction, and have more connection with your partner.

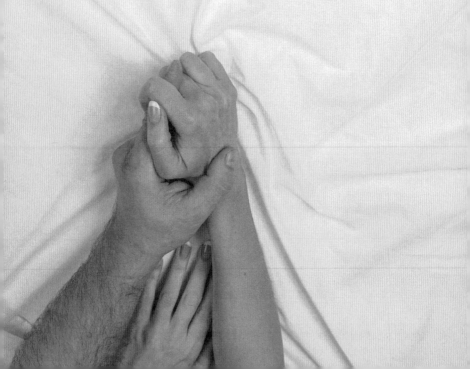

REASONS TO BRING MINDFULNESS INTO SEX

There are many good reasons for bringing mindfulness into sex.

Increase pleasure. If you're more in touch with your body, you're going to be more in touch with pleasure.

Reduce stress and anxiety. Meditation, specifically mindfulness meditation, has been shown to lower stress and anxiety, meaning that the anxiety and stress that many people experience during sex can disappear and you can just be present and enjoy the experience.

Create a deep connection and intimacy with partners. When you're really able to connect, really seeing and feeling that other person in this deep way, sex becomes a completely different experience.

MINDFULNESS EXERCISE: A TOUR THROUGH THE BODY

During sex, many people are in their minds—thinking about how they look, their performance, and whether they're going to have an orgasm too soon or too late or at all—so they're not actually having the experience of being in the body and in the pleasure that's available in the body. This exercise takes you on a tour through the body, getting in touch with physical sensations and then encouraging, cultivating, and noticing pleasure in the body.

Take a moment to bring some attention to your body. And if you like, you can close your eyes.

Begin by paying attention to the sensations in your face. Notice your eyes. Notice the sensations in your mouth and jaw. How does your neck feel? What about your shoulders?

As you continue to move down the body, don't try to get rid of anything; if there are a lot of thoughts coming up for you, don't worry about that. Just gently come back to the body whenever you find yourself pulled away. You might come in contact with sensations that don't feel so good, and that's all right—just greet them with as much acceptance as you can.

Keeping a curious attitude, bring your attention to your arms and feel any sensations there. Notice sensations in your hands. Feel into the chest the area around the heart and the lungs, using your physical awareness to really explore these sensations in your body.

Move your attention into your stomach. Now move your attention to your back, feeling any sensations along the spine and in the muscles of the back. Continue down into your hips and your seat and your pelvic area, noticing any sensations there. Move down both of your legs and into your feet. Now just get a sense of your whole body.

Start tuning your attention into pleasure in the body, beginning by intentionally relaxing. Release the muscles of your jaw and release any tension in your shoulders. Relax your chest and your stomach. Relax your hips and your seat. Release the pelvic floor muscles, those you would use to clench if you wanted to stop urinating midstream. Relaxing down your legs and into your feet.

Now smile. Start to notice the sensation of that smile and the sensation of relaxation through your body. Focus on what feels good; focus on pleasure in your body. Any time you're pulled into a thought, gently bring your attention back to any sensation in the body that feels good. Open your eyes.

MINDFULNESS EXERCISE: MINDFUL MASTURBATION

During sex, there's a lot of pleasure. The simplest way to think about mindful sex is actually being in your body while you're having sex, feeling the sensations of sex. This could be with a partner or with yourself. You can do this exercise on your own as a practice.

Create a comfortable space to lie down in, maybe with cushions and blankets surrounding you. Set a timer for 10 to 15 minutes, putting away any toys, video content, books of erotica, or other tools that you might use to masturbate normally. You're just going to take some time to be with your body and do your pleasure.

Once the timer begins, start by gently touching your face. This might feel silly or embarrassing at first, but that's okay. Just notice that there are some feelings of embarrassment, or maybe resistance, in your body and then come back to the exercise.

Touch your shoulders and your arms. Touch your chest, the sides of your body, and your stomach. Try different pressures and different strokes on your thighs, even on your calves and feet. Do all of this before bringing attention to the genitals.

Once you've really had an opportunity to feel into what it's like to touch your own body, then move to masturbation, letting go of what you would normally do. Just start to get to know your genitals using your hands. Explore sensation. Find out what feels good as well as what doesn't feel so good—that's important, too.

During this 10- to 15-minute period, you may or may not have an orgasm. Either way is fine. Put orgasm to the side rather than striving for it during the exercise.

When the timer rings, take a moment to check out your body. How are you feeling? Are there any emotions? What's going on in the mind? For some people, a lot of emotion can come up, even some sadness or grief or anger. And for some people, this is a liberating experience, and one that is really fun.

Then, if you like, do some stream-of-consciousness writing. Write about the experience, including how it made you feel and what you discovered about yourself.

Finally, if you want to go back to it, you're welcome to masturbate however you like until you orgasm. But see how you feel. Maybe you won't even need to do that; you might feel completely satisfied already.

You can bring these techniques of basic body and pleasure awareness and mindfulness during sexual activity into sex with your partner. Ideally, you have a partner who is on board, and you can share the experience before, during, and after.

While having sex with your partner, the main idea is to keep coming back to your body. When you get pulled off into thoughts, or maybe just lost in the moment in a way that's not present or conscious, come back to the sensations in your body. Start to notice how good it actually feels to be engaging sexually with your partner. Take orgasm off the table; maybe it happens but maybe it doesn't. Let it be more about sensation and exploration of pleasure in your body.

MINDFUL SEX

Mindful sex isn't just one thing. It's whatever your sexuality looks like, but being more present. Mindful sex doesn't have to be spiritual and doesn't have to involve burning candles and sprinkled rose petals. It could be just a quickie.

There is no right way to do this. Have fun, be curious, and let go of any perfectionism.

In many sexual relationships, people are afraid to express their desires, fantasies, and needs. People are also not always expressing what they don't want. This is why communication is so important when it comes to truly consensual sex. Bringing mindfulness into sex increases the odds that your sex is going to be more pleasurable and 100 percent consensual.

When thinking about talking to their partner about sex, people feel afraid, embarrassed, and shy. They think that their partner might not like what they say, or that their feelings will be hurt, or that they'll be turned off. Mindfulness can help us to get in touch with these thoughts that come up when we're considering talking to our partners about sex. Observing thought, witnessing thought, and recognizing that it's just a flutter of activity helps us to not be so afraid to speak our mind, because we realize that thoughts are just thoughts.

MEDITATION EXERCISE: CONNECTING WITH YOUR SEXUALITY

Close your eyes and bring your attention to the area where mental talk arises for you. For most people, this is around the head, but it could be somewhere else for you.

Start to notice if any thoughts are arising. There may not be any thoughts, and that's okay. But if there are, simply witness that activity—the coming and going of thought. Some of these thoughts may be auditory, and some may be visual. Any time you get pulled in and start taking the thoughts personally, try to pop back out to a broader perspective. Keep coming back to witnessing the activity of the mind.

Bring to mind something about your sexuality that you've been hiding—something that you could share with your partner or a potential partner—such as a fantasy or a certain sexual position. Bring this to mind and just honor it in this moment. This fantasy or sexual desire is true for you.

Imagine sharing this information with your partner or a potential partner. You might notice that some part of the body tightens up. You might feel the chest tighten or a knot in your stomach—or you might feel great about it. Either way, just notice the emotional reaction in the body.

Now take a moment to relax the body, letting go of the exercise. And if your eyes were closed, you can open them.

Now that you've had a chance to explore the mind and check out some of your fantasies and desires and what it might be like to share them with someone else, try this writing exercise: Write a list of all your fantasies and desires without censoring yourself. Some may be things you've already played out or would like to play out, while others may be things you never want to do but still bring up a sexual charge for you. There's no need to judge or censor yourself when it comes to your sexual desires and fantasies. This is about you exploring you. No one else is ever going to read this list, unless you decide that you'd like to turn it into a sexy letter for your partner.

MINDFUL COMMUNICATION ABOUT SEX

In our culture, we don't really have mindful communication about sex—about pleasure, consent, desires, and actual connection with each other.

If we start talking to our partners about what's going on for us sexually, not only are we going to have better sex, but we're going to have better relationships and deeper intimacy. It might feel scary and radical to start talking about what you like and don't like, but this is the key to a wonderful relationship.

This idea of bringing mindfulness into communication about sex is a powerful thing—not just for your relationship and sexuality, but for our culture in general. Especially these days, as we start to lean more into issues of consent, mindful sexual communication becomes incredibly important.

Consent is the first ingredient for good sex. And along with that comes safe sex. Many people are afraid to have the safe sex conversation, but it's actually quite simple. You just need to say, "Hey, I've been tested. Have you?" If you need to disclose a sexually transmitted disease or infection, you share that information, then you take in any information the other person is giving you, and then you move forward. When we incorporate mindfulness, conversations about consent and safe sex can be fun and easy.

If you are having anxiety around having a safe sex talk or negotiating consent, take some time to observe and witness the thoughts and emotions associated with this. Just sit down and bring it to mind. Consider sitting down with a partner and sharing openly about your sexual history and notice what comes up inside you. Maybe there's fear, anxiety, or a big cluster of thoughts. Use your mindfulness practice to simply observe, in a kind and accepting way, this arising and passing of emotion and thought.

You can continue to practice this way until it's time to have the talk, and then bring your mindfulness practice with you. As you're discussing safe sex or consent, notice what's happening in your body. How are you feeling? Notice what's happening in your mind. Stay present. Be honest with yourself. Be honest with your partner. This kind of mindful communication is so important and will add to the wonders that can be had in mindful sex.

If your partner brings up something with you, try to receive it with as much kindness and acceptance as possible. Try to let go of any judgment, even if what he or she is suggesting isn't really your style. Maybe make another suggestion.

If you bring a desire, fantasy, or sexual need to your partner and you aren't received with kindness, this can be difficult. Take a moment to comfort and soothe yourself. Check in with any thoughts or emotions that are arising. Maybe think about coming back to the conversation when you're not feeling upset.

Mindfulness can help you navigate anything that comes up in these conversations, whether it's excitement or heartbreak. So, keep leaning on your practice and remembering that coming back to observing thoughts and emotions is a great way to get some space, especially when you're having an overwhelming experience.

Another way that communication comes in handy with sex is when you're having a dip in libido—when there's not as much sex happening as you might like. Take some time to talk about sex every day. It might be as simple as letting your partner know how beautiful or sexy he or she looks before leaving for work, or maybe it's sending a sexy text. It could be just having some kind of sexual interaction every day, even if it's not actual sex. Have a longer kiss instead of a peck on the cheek; maybe give your partner a stroke down the back rather than a pat on the shoulder.

If you bring sexual communication, both verbal and nonverbal, into your relationship, it will usually generate more of a sense of sexual energy between you and your partner and potentially create a more exciting sexual relationship.

MINDFUL SEX:
BEING PRESENT IN YOUR BODY

LESSON 15 TRANSCRIPT

[Introduction by Shauna Shapiro]

Jessica Graham is one of the most courageous, authentic, and wise meditation teachers I've met. Her boldness in diving into the topic of mindfulness and sexuality is unparalleled. Her philosophy is accessible to all of us and doesn't require any particular spiritual belief sets or ideologies.

[End of introduction]

Hi, I'm Jessica Graham, and I'm going to be teaching you some techniques to bring mindfulness into your sex life. Now I've come across some people who aren't so sure about this mindful sex thing, but there are a lot of really good reasons for bringing mindfulness into sex. One of them is studies have shown that you can actually become more aware of pleasure in your body, you can address issues around sexual dysfunction and erectile dysfunction, and you can have more connection with your partner.

When I started meditating, my life really changed very quickly. I started practicing mindfulness meditation and everything changed. Food tasted better, the sky looked more beautiful, massages were more enjoyable. Everything started to take on a kind of shine, a kind of aliveness. And at some point, after a meditation retreat I thought, wouldn't mindfulness be a good combination with sex? If it makes everything feel so good, wouldn't it make sex feel amazing?

So, I began down this path of bringing mindfulness into my sex life, and pretty quickly I had what I call a sexual awakening. It really became a whole different thing, and now I feel super passionate about sharing mindfulness in terms of sexuality with everyone else. Because if I'm having a good time I want you to have a good time too! So recently I wrote a book called *Good Sex: Getting Off Without Checking Out*, and it tells my story of going from kind of shut down and checked out around sex to really awake and present and enjoying it so much more. So, the book goes through that and also teaches you meditation techniques, like the ones we'll be doing in this lesson.

So here are some of my favorite reasons for bringing mindfulness into sex: One, more pleasure. If you're more in touch with your body, you're going to be more in touch with pleasure. Two, meditation, specifically mindfulness meditation, has been shown to lower stress and anxiety. That means the anxiety and stress that many people experience during sex drops out and you can actually just be present and enjoy the experience. Another reason I love bringing mindfulness into sex is that it creates a deep connection and intimacy with partners. When you're really able to connect, and see that other person, and feel that other person in this deep way, sex becomes a completely different experience. And you deserve to have really good sex.

So, we're going to start with this first lesson on embodied sex. So, makes sense that you'd want to be in your body during sex, right? But a lot of people aren't. A lot of people are in their minds, thinking about how they look, thinking about their performance, thinking about if they're going to have an orgasm too fast or too slow, or at all. And so, they're not actually having the experience of being in the body and in the pleasure that's available in the body. So, let's start there.

Just take a moment to bring some attention to your body. And if you like, you can close your eyes. Good. Begin by just paying attention to the sensations in your face. Notice your eyes, sensations in your mouth and your jaw. How does your neck feel? And what about your shoulders? As we continue to move down the body, I don't want you to try to get rid of anything, so if there's a lot of thoughts coming up, don't worry about that. Just gently come back to the body whenever you find yourself pulled away. And you might come in contact with sensations that don't feel so good, and that's alright; just greet them with as much acceptance as you can. Keeping a curious attitude.

Bring your attention to your arms. Feel any sensations in your arms. Noticing sensations in your hands. Feel into the chest, the area around the heart and the lungs. Using your physical awareness to really explore these sensations in your body. Moving your attention into your stomach. And now your back, feeling any sensations along the spine, in the muscles of the back. Continue down into your hips and your seat and your pelvic area, noticing any sensations there. Now moving down both of your legs and into your feet.

Now just get a sense of your whole body. Good. Now the great thing about sex is that it's really, really pleasurable. And so, let's start tuning our attention into pleasure in the body. We can begin by intentionally relaxing. So, release the muscles of your jaw, release any tension in your shoulders. Relax your chest and your stomach. Relax your hips and your seat and release the pelvic floor muscles. So, these are the muscles you would use to clench if you wanted to stop pee midstream, so we're going to release those muscles. Good. Relaxing down your legs and into your feet.

So now I'd like you to smile—just a little smile. And start to notice the sensation of that smile and the sensation of relaxation through your body. Focus on what feels good. Focusing on pleasure in your body. Any time you're pulled into a thought, gently bring your attention back to any sensation in the body that feels good. Great. You can go ahead and open your eyes.

So, we've just taken a little tour through the body, getting in touch with physical sensations, and then encouraging, cultivating, and noticing pleasure in the body. So, during sex there's a lot of pleasure. So, the most simple way to think about mindful sex is actually being in your body while you're having sex, feeling the sensations of sex. This could be with a partner, and it could also be with yourself.

So, I'd like to talk you through mindful masturbation. This is something you can do on your own as a practice. Here's how you start. Create a comfortable space to lie down in. Have cushions and blankets—you want to be really comfortable. And then you're going to set a timer for 10 to 15 minutes, putting away any toys, any video content, any books of erotica or any other tools that you might use to masturbate normally. All of those go to the side. You're just going to take some time to be with your body and do your pleasure.

So, once the timer begins, start by gently touching your face. And this might feel silly at first, you might be embarrassed, it's okay. Just notice, oh there's some feelings of embarrassment in my body, maybe some feelings and resistance, and then come back to the exercise.

So, touch your face. Try touching your face gently, maybe with more pressure. Touch your shoulders and your arms. Touch your chest, the sides of your body, your stomach. Try different pressures, different strokes on your thighs, even on your calves and feet. Do all of this before bringing attention to the genitals. Once you've really had an opportunity to feel into what it's like to touch your own body, then move to masturbation.

What I'll invite you to do here is let go of what you would normally do. So, whatever your style of masturbation is, for this exercise, put it to the side. Just start to get to know your genitals, using your hands. Explore sensation. Really find out what feels good, and maybe what doesn't feel so good. That's important too.

So, during this 10 to 15-minute period, you may or may not have an orgasm. Either way is totally fine. I'd like you to put orgasm to the side rather than striving for it during the exercise. And then as the timer rings, take a moment, pause, check out your body. How are you feeling? Are there any emotions? What's going on in the mind? For some people a lot of emotion can come up, even some sadness or some grief or even anger. And for some people, this is a totally liberating experience. And really fun. So how do you feel?

And then if you like, do a little writing. I highly recommend stream of consciousness writing. Just write about the experience, how it made you feel, what you discovered about yourself. And then if you want to go back to it, you're welcome to masturbate however you like until you orgasm. But see how you feel. Maybe you won't even need to do that. You might feel completely satisfied already.

So of course, you can bring these techniques of basic body awareness, pleasure awareness, and mindfulness during sexual activity into sex with your partner. Ideally you have a partner who's on board and you can share the experience before, during, and after. The main idea here will be to keep coming back to your body. So, when you get pulled off into thoughts, or maybe just lost in the moment in a way that's not present, not conscious, come back to the sensations in your body. Start to notice how good it actually feels to be engaging sexually with your partner. And maybe take orgasm off the table. Maybe it happens, maybe it doesn't. Let it be more about sensation and exploration of pleasure in your body.

Before we move on to talking about communication and mindful sex, I'd like to mention a few more things about mindful sex. One, mindful sex doesn't necessarily mean spiritual, candles burning, rose petals sprinkled.

It could be just a quickie. So, mindful sex isn't just one thing. It's whatever your sexuality looks like, but being more present. Another thing I want to put out there is that there is no right way to do this. All of my teachings on mindful sex are invitations, ways that you might start to explore bringing mindfulness into your sex life. But there's no one right way. So, have fun, be curious, and let go of any perfectionism.

One of the number one things that couples come to me with as an issue in their relationship is communication. And there's this quote from Madonna that I love. It goes "A lot of people don't ask for what they want, that's why they don't get what they want." This is absolutely the case in a lot of the sexual relationships I see. People are afraid to actually express their desires, their fantasies, their needs, and people are not always expressing what they don't want. This is why communication is so very important when it comes to truly consensual sex. Bringing mindfulness into sex absolutely increases the odds that your sex is going to be more pleasurable and 100 percent consensual.

So, what comes up for people when thinking about talking to their partner about sex? People feel afraid, they feel embarrassed, they feel shy. They think their partner might not like what they say, or their feelings will be hurt, or they'll be turned off. Mindfulness can absolutely help us to get in touch with these thoughts that come up when we're considering talking to our partners about sex. Observing thought, witnessing thought, recognizing that it's just a flutter of activity. It's just thought is really, really helpful. This way we're not so afraid to speak our mind, because we realize that thoughts are just thoughts.

So, let's explore this a little bit in a meditation exercise. You can go ahead and close your eyes, and bring your attention to the area where mental talk arises for you. For most people this is around the head. It could be somewhere else for you. Start to notice if any thoughts are arising. There may not be any thoughts, and that's okay. But if there are, simply witness that activity—the coming and going of thought. Some of these thoughts may be auditory, and some may be visual. Just witness. Any time you get pulled in and you start taking the thoughts personally, see if you can pop back out to a broader perspective. Witnessing. Witnessing the activity of the mind. Keep coming back to witnessing. Good.

Now I'd like you to bring to mind something about your sexuality that you've been hiding. Something that you could share with your partner or your potential partner. Maybe it's a fantasy, maybe it's just the way you want to be kissed, maybe it's a certain sexual position. Bring this to mind. Just honor, that in this moment, this fantasy or this sexual desire is true for you.

Now I want you to imagine sharing this information with a partner. You might notice that some part of the body tightens up. You might feel the chest tighten, or a little knot in your stomach, or you might feel great about it. But either way, just notice the emotional reaction in the body. To thinking about sharing this with your partner or a potential partner. Okay good. Now you can let that go, and take a moment just to relax the body, letting go of the exercise. And if your eyes were closed, you can go ahead and open them.

Now that you've had a chance to explore the mind and check out some of your fantasies and desires and what it might be like to share them with someone else, I'd like to offer you a writing exercise. So, you can do this after the lesson, or you can push pause and do it right now. What you'll do is get a pad of paper and a pen, or you can do it on your computer. And just write out all of your fantasies. Some of these fantasies may be things you've already played out, some of them may be things you'd like to play out, and some of them may be things you never want to do but still bring up a sort of sexual charge for you. So, write out your fantasies and desires without censoring yourself. There's no need to judge yourself or censor yourself when it comes to your sexual desires and fantasies. This is about you exploring you. No one else is ever going to read it, unless you decide that you'd like to turn it into a sexy letter for your partner, which I completely invite you to do.

In our culture, we don't really talk about sex that much. We'd like to think that we do, and if you look at our advertising it has a lot of sex in it. But I'm talking about actual mindful communication about sex. Talking about pleasure, talking about consent, talking about our desires, talking about actual connection with each other.

If we start talking to our partners about what's going on for us sexually, not only are we going to have better sex, we're going to have better relationships, deeper intimacy. And so, it might feel scary and might feel radical to start talking about your fantasies with your partner, to start talking about what you like and don't like. But this is absolutely the key to a wonderful relationship. The relationships that I see flourish and really have amazing connection are the ones where partners are talking and actually talking about sex.

So, this idea of bringing mindfulness into communication about sex is a really, really powerful thing not just for your relationship and for your own sexuality, but for our culture in general. Especially these days, as we start to lean more into issues of consent, mindful sexual communication becomes incredibly important. I think of consent as the first ingredient for good sex. And along with that is safe sex.

I've met so many people who are afraid to have the safe sex conversation and it's actually quite simple. We just need to say "Hey I've been tested. Have you been tested?" If you actually need to disclose something about STI you share that information, you take in any information the other person is giving you, and then you move forward. The thing about talking about safe sex is that it means you might be having sex, which is a really good thing. So, consent and safe sex, when we bring mindfulness in, can actually be a really fun and easy conversation.

I recommend that if you are having any kind of anxiety around having a safe sex talk or negotiating consent that you take some time to observe and witness the thoughts and the emotions associated with this. Just sit down and bring it to mind. Consider sitting down with a partner and sharing openly about your sexual history and notice what comes up inside you. Maybe there's some fear, some anxiety, maybe a big cluster of thoughts. Use your mindfulness practice to simply observe in a kind and accepting way this arising and passing of emotion and thought. You can continue to practice this way until it's time to have the talk, and then bring your mindfulness practice with you. As you're having a discussion about safe sex, as you're negotiating consent, notice what's happening in your body. How are you feeling? Notice what's happening in your mind. Stay present.

Be honest with yourself. Be honest with your partner. This kind of mindful communication is so important and will absolutely add to the wonders that can be had in mindful sex.

If your partner brings something up with you, try to receive it with as much kindness and acceptance as possible. Try to let go of any judgment, even if what they're suggesting isn't really your style. Maybe make another suggestion. If you bring a desire or a fantasy or sexual need to your partner and you aren't received with kindness, this can be hard. So, take a moment to just comfort yourself, soothe yourself. Check in with any thoughts or emotions that are arising and maybe take some time to think about coming back to the conversation when you're not feeling upset.

Mindfulness can help you navigate anything that comes up in these conversations, whether it's excitement or heartbreak. So, keep leaning on your practice and remembering that coming back to observing thoughts and emotions is a really great way to get some space, especially when you're having an overwhelming experience.

Another way that communication really comes in handy with sex is when you're having a dip in libido, when there's not as much sex happening as you might like. And so, I suggest to clients to take some time to talk about sex every day. It might be as simple as letting your partner know how beautiful or sexy they look before they leave for work. Or maybe it's sending a sexy text. It could be just having some kind of sexual interaction every day, even if it's not actual sex. Have a longer kiss instead of a peck on the cheek, maybe a stroke down the back rather than a little pat on the shoulder. Bring sexual communication, both verbal and nonverbal, into your relationship, and usually that will generate more of a sense of sexual energy between the two of you and create potentially a more exciting sexual relationship.

Thank you so much for joining me for this first lesson in mindful sex, and I hope you try it out soon.

BEYOND THE ORGASM: COMMUNICATE AND FLOW

LESSON 16

Orgasms can bring up anxiety for many people. Some people are worried that they're taking too long; other people are worried that it's happening too soon or that it's not happening at all. Mindfulness can help us get space from the thoughts around orgasm anxiety and get into the pleasure of sex. As we move through mindful sex, we repeatedly come back to focusing attention on the body— on pleasure. In this way, instead of spending the entire time you're having sex thinking about the orgasm, you can focus on feeling the sensations.

MINDFULNESS EXERCISE: BRINGING RELAXING INTO SEX

What would it be like to connect with your partner without the orgasm being the focus? A big piece of this is relaxation—learning to relax into sex and into pleasure. The idea behind this relaxation practice is to bring it into sex.

Begin by closing your eyes. Bring your attention to your forehead. Start to soften and relax all the muscles in the forehead. Now move your attention to your eyebrows and the space between your eyebrows. Relax and soften the eyebrows. Now relax the eyes and all those little muscles around your eyes.

Moving your attention to your jaw, invite the jaw to release and relax. Let the mouth drop open a little, letting go. Now relax into your neck and over your shoulders. Let your shoulders release. Relax down both of your arms and into your hands.

As you continue to move down the body relaxing, you might run into some spots that don't want to relax, and that's okay. Just relax around those areas, letting go of resistance. If you get pulled into thoughts, that's also okay. It's normal. When that happens, just gently bring your attention back to your body and back to relaxing.

Continue to relax into your chest and into the solar plexus area at the pit of the stomach. And continue down into the rest of your abdomen, relaxing, softening, and letting go.

Now start to relax your back. If you're sitting up, only use the muscles you need to and release and relax the rest of those muscles. Now bring your attention to your hips, relaxing the them and allowing them to widen. Bring attention to your seat, relaxing all around the tailbone.

Now bring your attention to the pelvic area—to the muscles of the pelvic floor and to the genitals. Relax and release, letting go. Invite that relaxation to continue to move down both of your legs and into your feet.

Take a moment and scan through your body and notice anywhere that might have tightened back up. This could be one of the spots where you personally hold tension and stress in the body. Pay attention to this area and try to sit and relax it a little more. This might also be a spot that tends to tighten up during sex, so while having sex, you can practice this exercise of releasing and relaxing. When you're ready, open your eyes.

Many people have a lot of tension going on while they're having sex, and that reduces the possibility for pleasure. More relaxation means more blood flow, which means more pleasure. So, bringing in this exercise while you're having any kind of sexual activity, including sex with yourself, can make sex feel so much better.

This is also an antidote to the anxiety that can come up around orgasm. Practice relaxation with your partner before having sex. And as you're doing this, if you become aware of thoughts and emotions, you can acknowledge and notice them and then return to relaxation. Of course, relaxation is very pleasurable, so this will also continue to tune into pleasure in your body.

If you have a partner, sit down with him or her before sex and go through this exercise of relaxing from your head to your toes, paying special attention to those areas you've identified in which you personally hold tension and stress and also remembering to relax in the pelvic area. Bringing this kind of relaxation into sex is a way that mindfulness can increase the pleasure and lower the anxiety.

TIPS FOR COMMON ORGASM ISSUES

Men are often worried about orgasming too quickly. If you experience this anxiety, try this method on your own.

> Play around with the start-stop method. Begin pleasuring yourself, and right before you think you're about to orgasm, stop and breathe. Feel the sensations in your body. Notice the thoughts; notice the emotions. There might be some frustration, and that's okay. Just acknowledge it, notice it, and then you can begin to pleasure yourself again.
>
> Try this for 10 to 15 minutes, really getting in touch with what it's like to go to the brink and pause and feel the body and then come back to pleasure. Try this on your own first and then bring it into sex with your partner.

Women often have anxiety about not orgasming quickly enough. If you tend to experience anxiety in this way, here are some tips.

Let go of the idea that there's a right way or time to orgasm. This is your sexual pleasure. It doesn't belong to anybody else, and it shouldn't be compared to anybody else. Start with some self-love and acceptance.

If you'd like to work with this, as you're having sex and receiving any kind of pleasure, when you find yourself caught in the mind—caught in thoughts about not orgasming quickly enough—use that tool of coming back to pleasure and to your body.

This will take a lot of practice at first, but after a while, just like with a regular mindfulness practice, you'll become more and more capable of returning to your body and to pleasure. It doesn't mean you need to quiet the thoughts; you don't need to turn them off. Just notice that they're there and come back to the body. Ideally, you can share with a partner that you're having this anxiety.

Some women have trouble having orgasms at all during sex with a partner. If you're having this challenge, let go of the idea that there is anything wrong with you. You're great just the way you are. If you'd like to work on orgasm with a partner, here are some tools.

Start by bringing attention to the genital area while having sex or receiving any kind of sexual pleasure. Communicate what feels good. How much pressure? What pace? All of these things matter. And the more you can communicate about what feels good, the easier it will be for you to move toward climax. You can use the tools of communication from the previous lesson if you're shy or embarrassed about talking about what you want.

Once you've been clear about what feels good for you, keep your attention on the genitals. One way to sensitize yourself to this part of the body is to squeeze the pelvic floor muscles and then release them (also called a Kegel), staying in touch with the sensations of pleasure in the genitals.

Don't put any pressure on yourself to have an orgasm or to have an orgasm right away—just start this as a practice. Over time, you'll start to notice that you get more tuned into pleasure and less caught up in anxiety and worry. And most likely, you can work toward having orgasms with a partner. It's also acceptable to use toys and different ways of having an orgasm. Do what works for you. We all have unique bodies, so pay attention to what yours likes.

It's really important that we share our anxieties with our partners. If you're having anxiety about orgasming or about any other part of sex, let your partner know. Sit down and share it with him or her. And if you're feeling nervous about talking, use the practice of focusing on thoughts and emotions and of relaxation. And then come back to communicating, connecting, and sharing your anxieties. As you do this, the anxieties will lessen. Just talking about it will help.

DEEPER INTIMACY AND CONNECTION

You've probably heard the term "becoming one" as it relates to sex, and that's actually possible. It's possible to truly feel connected on that deep level with your partner.

Take a moment and think about what kind of connection you'd like to have with a partner, whether a long-term partner or a partner for the night. How would you like to be connected? What's meaningful for you? This is what makes the connection: your values, what's meaningful for you, what excites you, and what turns you on. It's up to you to dive into your sexual creativity and imagination and find out what you want.

A meditation called flow can help you feel a deep sense of unity during sex. Flow is simply anything that's moving or changing, such as your breath or the sounds around you. You can notice how these are moving and changing. You can do the same thing with thoughts, emotions, sensations, and sights.

You can also bring this into sex. The tastes, smells, sensations, and sights are constantly moving and changing. When you get in touch with these aspects of flow while you're having sex, you can start to really feel connected to your partner.

MINDFULNESS EXERCISE: FLOW MEDITATION

You can bring the concept of flow into sex to improve how it feels.

Start by closing your eyes. Bring your attention to your body, noticing the sensations in your face, your neck, and your shoulders. Notice the sensations in your arms and hands. Notice how your chest feels. Feel into any sensations in the abdomen. Notice any sensations in your back.

Bring your attention to your hips and your seat and your pelvic area, just feeling any sensations that are there. You don't have to create anything, and you don't have to get rid of anything. Just pay attention to what's present. Now feel into any sensations in your legs, all the way down to your feet.

Now get a sense of your whole body. From this embodied place, bring your attention to your breath. Start to pay attention to the movement and change that's occurring in the body as you breathe, feeling the expansion and the contraction of each inhale and each exhale. Get interested in that flow sensation. If it's helpful, as you feel the sensation, in your mind label it "flow." This can help facilitate mindfulness.

Begin to move your attention around the body, noticing any other areas where flow is present. There might be a tingle, a wave of sensation, or an undulation somewhere in the body. There might be a big burst of sensation somewhere. There might be a contraction or an expansion. There's flow in pleasant sensations, neutral sensations, and unpleasant sensations, so you can explore any of these. Keep being curious about the way this movement and change in your body feels.

Begin to bring your attention to sound, such as the sounds in the next room or sounds outside. In particular, pay attention to the movement and change of these sounds—the way sound flows. Let yourself deeply encounter this flow of sound.

As you're practicing this flow meditation, you may have noticed some thought. Bring your attention to this mental activity—it could be auditory or visual—and pay attention to the flow of it. You're not trying to stop the thinking; instead, you're getting interested in how the thoughts bubble up, spread out, and vanish. You're getting curious about how the images move and change or how the pitch, pace, and volume of mental talk shifts. Get really interested in the flow of mental activity.

If you'd like, open your eyes just a little. Start to let in some light and start to become aware of any flow in sight. You might be aware of a tree out the window, leaves moving in the wind, or some other kind of flow in the visual field. Take a moment to experience that.

Close your eyes again. Let go into the flow of sensation, sound, and thought without directing your attention anywhere in particular. Just drop in to that constant movement and change in the body, in the mind, and in the sounds of your environment, diving into flow.

As you do this practice, if you need to use other techniques, you're always welcome to do that. Maybe you get really pulled into thoughts and need to just observe them for a moment and give them some acknowledgement. Or maybe you start to feel some pain in the body or an intense emotion. You can notice that, give that some space, or turn to relaxation and take a moment to settle the system. All of these tools work together.

When you're ready, come back to flow, noticing that even your awareness gathers around something and then moves and gathers around something else—a sensation, a sound, a thought. Even your awareness is flowing.

Take another moment to drop into flow, but this time notice flow that's pleasurable in the body, in the mind, or in the sounds around you, relaxing into the flow and going with the flow.

If at any time you're doing this technique and you get confused or lose track of what you're doing, you can always come back to the simple flow of your breathing. Your breathing is always flowing, moving, and changing with every inhale and every exhale.

You can now open your eyes.

Imagine how good sex will feel if you bring in this technique. You could start by simply feeling the sensation of your partner's body moving against yours, the sensation of his or her fingertips touching your body, or the sensation of his or her skin under your fingertips. However you have sex, there's always going to be some movement and change, and you can start to pay attention to that.

Before sex, you can even synchronize your breathing with your partner. Just sit down and breathe in and out together, maybe looking into each other's eyes. As you begin to move into sexual activity, keep your breathing synced up. Then, notice the flow in all the waves and spikes of pleasure. As you do this, you might become tuned in to the flow occurring in your partner's body, and this is where you might experience the mystical feeling of oneness and unity.

BEYOND THE ORGASM: COMMUNICATE AND FLOW

Let's talk about orgasms. Now, everybody loves orgasms, but most people are so focused on the orgasm that they miss out on a lot of the other pleasure available during sex. So, all I'm all about the journey, not just the destination.

Orgasms can bring up a lot of anxiety for people. Some folks are worried that they're taking too long. Other folks are worried that it's happening too fast, or that it's not happening at all. Mindfulness can help us to get space from the thoughts around our orgasm anxiety and actually get into the pleasure. So, you'll see that as we move through mindful sex, again and again, we come back to focusing attention on the body, on pleasure. The mind is there as a tool. We don't want the mind to drag us around, making us feel anxious and stressed out. We want to use the mind to increase the pleasure. So instead of spending the entire time you're having sex thinking about that orgasm, feel the sensations.

In tantric sex, all of the emphasis is off of orgasm. Now I'm a fan of orgasm, so I'm not saying take all the emphasis off orgasms, but let's take a little bit of it off. What would it be like to just connect with your partner without that being the focus? A big piece of this is relaxation—learning to relax into sex, learning to relax into pleasure. And of course, relaxation will help you relax around anxious thoughts. So, let's do a little bit of this relaxing together.

Begin by closing your eyes. Bring your attention to your forehead. Start to soften and relax all the muscles in the forehead. Now, move your attention to your eyebrows and the space between your eyebrows. Relax and soften the eyebrows. Now relax the eyes and all those little muscles around your eyes. Moving your attention to your jaw, invite the jaw to release and relax. Let the mouth drop open a little, letting go. Now relax into your neck, and over your shoulders. Let those shoulders release. Relax down both of your arms, and into your hands.

As we continue to move down the body relaxing, you might run into some spots that don't want to relax, and that's okay. Just relax around those areas, letting go of resistance. If you get pulled into thoughts, that's also okay. It's totally normal. When that happens, just gently bring your attention back to your body and back to relaxing. Continuing to relax into your chest and relaxing the solar plexus area. And continuing down into the rest of your abdomen, relaxing, softening, letting go.

You can now start to relax your back. If you're sitting up, just use the muscles you need to, and then by all the rest of those muscles to release and relax. Now bring your attention to your hips, relaxing the hips, allowing the hips to widen. Bringing attention to your seat, relaxing all around the tailbone. And now, very important, bring your attention to the pelvic area—to the muscles of the pelvic floor and to the genitals. Relax and release. Letting go. Now, invite that relaxation to continue to move down both of your legs and into your feet.

Now take a moment and scan through your body and notice anywhere that might have tightened back up. This could be one of the spots where you personally hold a lot of tension and stress in the body. So, paying attention to this area and see if you can release it and relax it a little bit more. This might also be a spot that tends to tighten up during sex. So, while having sex, you can be practicing this exercise, releasing and relaxing. Good. As you're ready, you can open your eyes as we come to the end of this meditation.

So, the idea here is that you bring this relaxation practice into sex. So many people have a lot of tension going on while they're having sex, and that actually reduces the possibility for pleasure. More relaxation means more blood flow, means more pleasure. So, bringing this in while you're having any kind of sexual activity, including sex with yourself, can make sex feel so much better. This is also an antidote to some of that anxiety that can come up around orgasm. I sometimes recommend to clients practicing relaxation together before having sex. And of course, as you're doing this, if you become aware of thoughts and emotions, you can acknowledge them and notice, oh, there are some thoughts, there's some emotions, and then return to relaxation. And of course, relaxation is very pleasurable, so this will also continue to tune into pleasure in your body.

So, try it out. If you have a partner, sit down with them before sex and go through this exercise of relaxing from your head to your toes, paying special attention to those areas you've identified that you personally hold tension and stress, and also remembering to relax in the pelvic area. Bringing this kind of relaxation into sex is a way that mindfulness can really increase the pleasure and lower the anxiety.

Here are a few tips for orgasm issues that I hear about.

Oftentimes, I hear from men that they're worried about orgasming too quickly. And so, something you can play around with on your own is the start-stop method. And you can bring your meditation and mindfulness practice into this. So, you'll begin pleasuring yourself, and right before you think you're about to orgasm, you'll stop and you'll take a moment and breathe. Feel the sensations in your body. Notice the thoughts. Notice the emotions. There might be some frustration. That's okay, just acknowledge it, notice it, and then you can begin to pleasure yourself again. And I would suggest that you try this for 10 to 15 minutes, really getting in touch with what it's like to go to the brink and pause and feel the body and then come back to pleasure. Now while you can do this with a partner as well, I often suggest trying it on your own first, and then bringing it into sex with your partner.

What I hear most often from women is that they have anxiety about not orgasming fast enough. Well, first of all, let go of the idea that there's a right way or time to orgasm. This is your sexual pleasure. It doesn't belong to anybody else, and it shouldn't be compared to anybody else. So, start with that: just some self-love and some acceptance.

Then, if you'd like to start to work with this, one of the tools I recommend is as you're having sex and you're receiving pleasure, when you find yourself caught in the mind, caught in thoughts about not orgasming fast enough, just use that tool of coming back to pleasure, coming back to your body. And this is going to take a lot of practice at first, but after a while, just like with a regular mindfulness practice, you'll become more and more capable of returning to your body, returning to pleasure. It doesn't mean you need to quiet the thoughts, you don't need to turn them off. Just notice that they're there and come back to the body. Now ideally, with a partner you can share that you're having this anxiety.

Some women I've met have trouble having orgasms at all during sex with a partner and I want to offer a technique that you could play around with and see if it works for you, if you're having this challenge. First of all, let go of the idea that there is anything wrong with you. You're great just the way you are.

If you like to work on orgasm with a partner, here's some tools. Start by bringing attention to the genital area while having sex or receiving any kind of sexual pleasure. Communicate what feels good—how much pressure, what pace. All of these things matter. And the more you can communicate about what feels good, the easier it will be free to move towards climax. Remember, you can use the tools of communication from earlier in the lesson if you're feeling shy or embarrassed about talking about what you want.

Once you've been clear about what feels good for you, keep your attention on the genitals. One way to sensitize yourself to this part of the body is to squeeze the pelvic floor muscles and then release them. This is also called a Kegel, which you may have heard of. So, you'll just squeeze and release, squeeze and release, staying in touch with the sensations of pleasure in the genitals.

Don't put any pressure on yourself to have an orgasm or have an orgasm right away; just start this as a practice. Over time you'll start to notice that you get more tuned into pleasure, less caught up in anxiety and worry, and most likely you can work towards having orgasms with a partner. It's also completely acceptable to use toys and to use different ways of having an orgasm. Do what works for you. We all have unique bodies, so pay attention to what yours likes.

It's really important that we share our anxieties with our partners. So, if you're having a lot of anxiety about orgasming or about any other part of sex, let your partner know. Sit down and share it with them. And again, if you're feeling nervous about talking, use the practice of focusing on thoughts and emotions. Use the practice of relaxation. And then come back, come back to communicating, to connecting, and to sharing your anxieties. As you do this the anxieties will lessen. Just talking about it will help. So, relax and enjoy.

During this exploration of mindful sex, you've heard me mention deeper intimacy and connection a few times. And in this lesson, I'd like to explore that more deeply. You've heard the term "becoming one" during sex, and that's actually possible. It's actually possible to truly feel connected on that deep of a level with your partner. It requires all the tools we've been exploring so far, and there are ways to enhance it even more. And I'll be guiding you into meditation for that.

But first, just take a moment and think about what kind of connection you'd like to have with a partner, whether this is a long-term partner or a partner for the night. How would you like to be connected? What's meaningful for you? This is what makes the connection: your values, what's meaningful for you, what excites you, what turns you on? Anything that I share with you is just an invitation. It's up to you to dive in to your sexual creativity, your sexual imagination, and find out what you want.

My favorite way to help people feel a deep sense of unity during sex is a meditation called flow. Flow is simply anything that's moving or changing. And so right now, you can just notice your breath. As you breathe in there's movement in the body, and as you exhale there's movement in the body. The lungs expand and contracts the diaphragm expands and contracts. Maybe the shoulders lift and release. There's the movement of air through your nostrils. All of that would be considered flow.

You can take a moment now and notice sounds around you. The sound of my voice, maybe the sounds of someone in the next room, sounds of the street outside or a dog barking. All of that is also moving and changing. You can do the same thing with thoughts, with emotional sensations, and with sights as well. You go out into nature and you just watch the trees moving in the breeze and the birds flying around, that's a version of flow too.

So, we can bring this into sex: the tastes, the smells, the sensations, the sights—they're all constantly moving and changing. When you get in touch with that while you're having sex, you can start to really feel connected to your partner. So, I'd like to guide you through this flow meditation, and then we'll talk a little more about bringing into sex.

You can start by closing your eyes. And bring your attention to your body, just like we did all the way back in the beginning. Just noticing the sensations of your face. Sensations in your neck, your shoulders. Any sensations in your arms or your hands. Notice how your chest feels. Feel into any sensations in the abdomen. Notice any sensation in your back.

Now bringing your attention to your hips and your seat and your pelvic area, just feeling any sensations that are there. You don't have to create anything, and you don't have to get rid of anything. Just paying attention to what's present. Now feeling into any sensations in your legs, and all the way down to your feet.

And then zooming out and getting a sense of your whole body. From this embodied place, I'd like you to bring your attention to your breath. Start to pay attention to the movement and change that's occurring in the body as you breathe. Get really interested in that flow sensation. If it's helpful, as you feel the sensation you can just quietly in your mind label "flow." That's just to help facilitate mindfulness—if it's not helpful for you, you don't have to do it.

Feeling the expansion and the contraction of each inhale and each exhale. Now, begin to move your attention around the body, noticing any other areas where there's flow present. There might be a tingle somewhere, a wave of sensation somewhere, an undulation somewhere in the body. There might be a big burst of sensation somewhere. A contraction, an expansion. There's flow in pleasant sensations, neutral sensations, and unpleasant sensations. So, you can explore any of these. Keep getting really curious about the way it feels, this movement and change in your body.

Now you can begin to bring your attention to sound: the sound of my voice, sounds in the next room, sounds outside. And I want you to, in particular, pay attention to the movement and change of these sounds. The way sound flows. Let yourself deeply encounter this flow of sound.

As we're practicing this flow meditation, you may have noticed some thoughts. I'd like you now to bring your attention to thought. This could be auditory or visual, and what I want you to pay attention to is the flow of this mental activity. So, we're not trying to stop the thinking.

Instead we're getting really interested in how the thoughts bubble up, spread out, and vanish. How the images move and change. How the pitch and pace and volume of mental talk is always shifting just a little. Get really interested, really curious in the flow of mental activity.

And now if you'd like, open your eyes just a little. Start to let in some light, and start to become aware of any flow in sight. So, if you're looking at me, my mouth is moving, parts of my body are moving a little bit. That's flow. You also might be aware of a tree out the window, leaves moving in the wind, or some other kind of flow in the visual field. So just take a moment to experience that.

Now you can go ahead and close your eyes again. And I want to invite you to let go into the flow of sensation, sound, and thought, without directing your attention anywhere in particular. Just drop in to that constant movement and change in the body, in the mind, and in the sounds of your environment. Diving into flow.

And as you do this practice, if you need to go back to one of the other techniques, you're always welcome to do that. Maybe you get really pulled into thoughts and you need to just observe them for a moment, give them some acknowledgement. Or maybe you start to feel some pain in the body or an intense emotion. You can notice that, give that some space, or you could turn to relaxation and just take a moment to settle the system. All of these tools work together.

And as you're ready, you come right back to flow. Noticing even your awareness—it gathers around something and then it moves and gathers around something else. A sensation, a sound, a thought. Even your awareness is flowing.

Take another moment to really drop into flow, but I want to invite you to notice flow that's pleasurable, since ultimately you'll be trying this out during sex. Take a moment now to notice pleasurable flow in the body, mind, or in the sounds around you. Relaxing into the flow. Going with the flow. If at any time you're doing this technique and you get confused or lose track of what you're doing, you can always come back to this simple flow of your breathing. Your breathing is always flowing, moving, and changing with every inhale and every exhale.

Okay, you can now open your eyes as we come to the end of this flow meditation.

You can probably imagine how good sex will feel if you bring in this technique. You could start by simply feeling the sensation of your partner's body moving against yours. The sensation of their fingertips touching your body, or their skin under your fingertips. However you have sex, there's always going to be some movement and change, and you can start to pay attention to that.

Another thing you can do is start to synchronize your breathing with your partner. You can start this before sex. Just sit together and breathe in and out together, synchronizing your breathing. Maybe even looking into each other's eyes as you do this. And then as you begin to move into sexual activity, keep your breathing synced up. It's a really easy way to be in touch with flow during sex.

And then all those waves and spikes of pleasure; you can really notice the flow in that. And as you do this, you just may become tuned in to the flow occurring in your partner's body. And this is where things get really, really interesting. This is where you might start to experience that mystical experience of oneness, unity. Ultimately, sex and sexuality can be a spiritual path. Or if you're not interested in the word spiritual it can just be an adventure. So, dive into the flow and check it out for yourself.

Thank you so much for joining me for this exploration of mindful sex. I want to let you know that there is no graduation date here. There's no getting it right. This is an exploration. It's an adventure! So, pay attention to the journey, don't get too caught up on the destination, and enjoy yourself.

Everything in my lessons for *Masters of Mindfulness* is also in my book, along with lots of other techniques and exercises to improve your sex life. My book is called *Good Sex: Getting Off Without Checking Out*, and it's available wherever books are sold. You can also find out more about me and my work at yourwildawakening.com. I offer virtual sessions for couples as well as individuals in areas of sexuality, spirituality, and creativity. Feel free to get in touch if I can be of any help to you.

AWE: A DEFINING HUMAN EMOTION
LESSON 17

What is awe? This lesson answers this question first by differentiating awe from related emotional states, such as beauty, wonder, and epiphany. Then, the lesson traces its cultural history to determine where it came from. Finally, the lesson considers sources of awe as another way to get insight into the nature of this emotion.

DIFFERENTIATING AWE FROM RELATED EMOTIONAL STATES

When we define awe, it's important, given the complexity of the emotion, to differentiate it from related phenomena. Awe is the feeling of being in the presence of something vast that challenges your understanding of the world.

We differentiate awe from related emotional states, such as astonishment, which is less intense.

Awe is different from beauty, which is less powerful.

Wonder is the state of curiosity and amazement that motivates the search for understanding. It's more of a knowledge-seeking state than awe is.

We also differentiate awe from elevation, where you feel inspired by the moral goodness of other people.

Finally, we differentiate awe from epiphany, which is the sudden realization of something really deep and meaningful about your life or the world. Epiphany doesn't necessarily have to be vast like awe.

A CULTURAL HISTORY OF AWE

Awe, like all of the human emotions, has a phenomenally rich and interesting cultural history. In the written record of early human history, awe was an emotion that was intertwined with religious experience. It was filled with the dread, wonder, uncertainty, and deep humbleness people felt thousands of years ago when they encountered God.

Then, awe transformed dramatically in the era of the Enlightenment in the 18th century—in large part thanks to the dramatic, radical writing of the Irish philosopher Edmund Burke. In 1757, he published *A Philosophical Enquiry into the Origin of Our Ideas of the Sublime and Beautiful*, in which he contends that awe arises when perceiving power that is obscure. He writes about how awe is triggered by thunder, clouds, and the sky. He differentiates awe from beauty, which he writes as being a softer emotional response. Through his writing, Burke takes awe out of the purely religious realm and brings it into our everyday perceptual experience.

Ralph Waldo Emerson, one of the great writers in the American transcendentalist movement, advocated for nature as a source of awe. Emerson wrote about the experience of getting out into our favorite part of nature and feeling our sense of self start to fade. We feel an expansion of who we are, and we no longer care about the more egotistical concerns of life.

We also learned about awe from psychologist William James, who wrote *The Varieties of Religious Experience*, published in 1802. He surveyed Puritan preachers, Buddhists, and Hindus, and wrote about the mystical core to experiences of awe, such as visions, enlightenment, and transitional states, in which you lose the sense of the boundaries between self and other, as well as the sense of time, and feel deeply interconnected.

SOURCES OF AWE

Researchers surveyed thousands of people in 26 different countries, including countries of all the great religious traditions, countries of different degrees of economic wealth, countries that range from collective to individualistic, and countries that vary in their degree of education. In this study, participants were asked to write about an experience of awe.

The researchers found that the most common source of awe worldwide is other people; the second most common source of awe is nature; the third most common source of awe is spirituality; and less common sources of awe include art, music, and architecture.

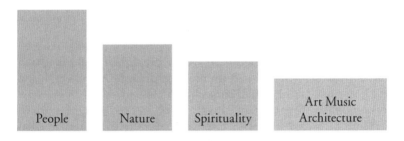

The researchers were struck by the fact that other people are an underappreciated and most common source of awe.

They discovered that we are awestruck by people's kindness.

We are also awestruck by people's virtuosity. For example, if we hear a child play the piano, we might be struck by how good he or she is.

We are awestruck by size. For example, a person who is seven feet tall makes us feel awestruck.

We're awestruck by people's heroism—for example, people who overcome challenging life circumstances to do good in the world.

Unexpectedly, researchers found that childbirth (the spectacular aspects of the process and the fact that life comes out of it) was a common source of awe across countries.

The second source of awe, nature, is intuitive to people. We are awestruck by sunsets, waves, trees, vistas, tornadoes, and other natural patterns.

Spirituality is the third source of awe, which is found in prayer contemplation. When people meditate or engage in mindful practices, they will often be struck by a sense of awe about what it can bring to them and what the qualities of their mind are like.

These are also other, less common sources of awe.

People very commonly feel awe when engaging in collective activities, such as dances, festivals, celebrations, weddings, and even funerals. People feel awe at political rallies and at sporting events.

There's a sense of awe that people commonly feel when encountering remarkable architectural structures, paintings, and poetry.

People feel awe about ideas. For example, a person feels awe when first learning about how DNA or evolution works.

People feel awe about technology, such as rockets and spacecraft.

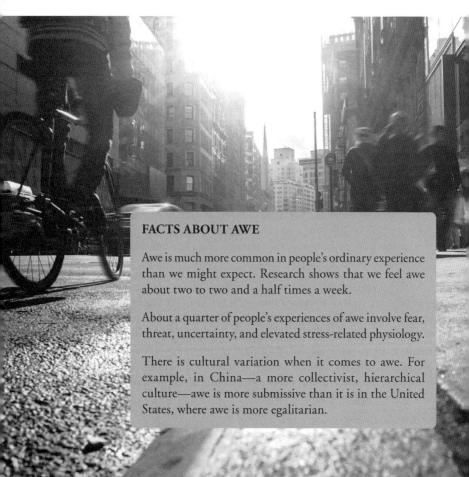

FACTS ABOUT AWE

Awe is much more common in people's ordinary experience than we might expect. Research shows that we feel awe about two to two and a half times a week.

About a quarter of people's experiences of awe involve fear, threat, uncertainty, and elevated stress-related physiology.

There is cultural variation when it comes to awe. For example, in China—a more collectivist, hierarchical culture—awe is more submissive than it is in the United States, where awe is more egalitarian.

AWE: A DEFINING HUMAN EMOTION

LESSON 17 TRANSCRIPT

[Introduction by Shauna Shapiro]

Dr. Dacher Keltner is a professor of psychology at University of California Berkeley, and faculty director of the Greater Good Science Center. His research focuses on the biological and evolutionary origins of compassion, awe, love, beauty, power, social class, and inequality. Dacher is the professor you always wish you had. He is truly dedicated to knowledge as a means of bringing the greater good to this world.

[End of introduction]

It's a real privilege to take you on a tour of the science and practice of awe today. Awe is a defining emotion and a really important property of the human mind in our social culture. The great Greek philosopher Pythagoras told a really interesting origin story about the origin of the human species that resembles a lot of the origin stories. Which is as God was giving out the different skills and traits to the different species, he gave away all the physical characteristics like strength and speed and ferocity. And when it came to humans there weren't that many skills left over and so what was endowed into human beings was this defining quality or strength called awe, or reverence, or our capacity to find things to be sacred and meaningful.

This idea, that awe is a defining human emotion, is seen across time. The great physicist Einstein said that "The most beautiful thing that we can experience is the mysterious. It is the source (and I think he was talking about awe) of all true art and science."

So, I'm going to be approaching awe largely as an emotional state that's part of our repertoire of emotions that make humans what humans are. And we think in the field of emotions as really brief multi-component responses that involve physiology, and experience, and expressive behavior, that really help humans navigate the immediate environment that they're in—most typically a social environment—in ways that benefits their goals and concerns. So, emotions are these ways of interacting with the environment.

So, as we define awe, what's first important, given the complexity of this emotion and this phenomenon, is really to differentiate awe from related phenomenon so that you have a kind of a clear idea of what we're talking about as we move through the science and practice of awe. So, awe is the feeling of being in the presence of things that are vast and that you don't have knowledge to immediately understand, and they require that you revise your beliefs and knowledge about the world. So, awe has vastness in it temporal, or physical, or psychological. And then it challenges your knowledge structure so you don't really know how to make sense of what you're perceiving.

We differentiate awe, for example from related states like astonishment, where you're astonished by the beauty of a sunset. But it's less intense than awe and it doesn't kind of sort of subvert your knowledge structures. You'll see there's a lot of thinking about how awe is really different from beauty. A beautiful sunset, or a beautiful field of flowers, or a beautiful face, or the beauty of a laugh of a young child—most typically we think of beauty as being less powerful, involving for the person, more agency, you have more control. You don't feel like you're losing control as you do with awe.

Philosophers have been interested in a state called wonder. Wonder, in fact, fueled Newton and Descartes to try to figure out the physics of the rainbow. Why is it that when water, light moves through water it bends in particular ways it produces rainbows? This sort of state of wonder, which we define as the curiosity and amazement you feel about things and a search for understanding, is really different from awe. It's more of a knowledge seeking state.

And then finally, we differentiate awe from something that Thomas Jefferson was really interested in, as well as John Hyde, which is elevation—where you just feel elevated or inspired by the moral goodness of other people. You may see a teenager help an elderly woman get her cat out of the tree, as I did one day, and get a rush of tears and goose bumps, and that's really elevation as opposed to awe.

And then finally we differentiate awe from epiphanies. The poet T. S. Eliot was really interested in epiphanies, which is the sudden realization of something really deep and meaningful about your life or about the world.

Right? It doesn't necessarily have to be vast like awe, but it's a sudden realization of a truth. And T. S. Eliot wrote beautifully about how sometimes you might see a natural event like a leaf falling and it makes you realize some truth about your life—that your parents are getting older and perhaps heading into the end of life. So, we differentiate awe from things like astonishment and beauty and wonder and elevation and then intellectual epiphany.

Awe, like all of the emotions and like every human construct, has a phenomenally rich and interesting cultural history, if you will, that really charts how it has a core to it, but changes over time. Awe early in human history in the written record was really an emotion that was intertwined with religious experience. It was filled with sort of the dread and uncertainty and deep humbleness you might feel, or people felt 2,500 years ago when they encountered God. It is filled with wonder.

So, there are famous stories for example the prophet Ezekiel feels God, feels awe and has a sense of God, when looking at lightning in the clouds, in these dramatic clouds. In Hinduism, Djuna one of the great figures in the legends of Hinduism, has this experience of awe or *vismaya* in looking out in the world through God's eye. And then there's the famous story—very typical of these sort of accounts of awe, a sort of feeling dread and wonder and fear in relationship to God—of St. Paul on the road to Damascus, where he had this conversion experience and through the encountering of a bright light and the voice of God. So early in its history, when you study how humans were writing about awe in religious texts across different religions, it really is an emotion of dread and wonder, vis-a-vis a sort of a supernatural force.

Then awe really transforms dramatically in the era of Enlightenment in the 18th century, and in large part thanks to the dramatic writing—I would even call it radical writing—of the Irish philosopher Edmund Burke. In 1757, he published a book *A Philosophical Inquiry into the Origin of Our Ideas of the Sublime and Beautiful*. So, you see this pulling apart that Immanuel Kant was interested in as well, of what is awe-inspiring, or the sublime, versus what is beautiful. And what Burke does is he takes this experience and he secularizes it. He brings it into our everyday perceptual experience that you might have as you move through the day. It's not just a religious experience, it's really a particular kind of psychological, perceptual experience.

And what Burke contends is that the two key qualities of awe are that the thing is powerful vis-a-vis you, and it's obscure. You can't make it out, you can't figure it out, your knowledge can't sort of make sense of it, and has to come up with an explanation. And that's why we define awe involving vastness and the need to revise your knowledge structures.

So, Burke writes incredibly about how awe is triggered by shadows and loud sounds like thunder and large powerful animals like the ox, right? And clouds in the sky. All natural events, not necessarily religious events, that trigger this feeling of the sublime or what you might call awe in human beings. Burke does a lot of really creative work in differentiating awe from beauty. And beauty he really writes as being a softer emotional response. It's more about soft features of things you see, sort of rolling hills, soft curves to a baby's face, smoothness. The more kind of pleasing qualities to what you're perceiving as a source of beauty. So, Burke, very importantly, takes awe out of the purely religious realm and brings it into our everyday experience.

And then a final awe revolutionary, if you will, or an awe pioneer, of course, was Ralph Waldo Emerson, one of the great writers in the American transcendentalist movement. And does, again, a lot of contemporary thinking for us in taking awe and taking it into our experience in nature. And we're going to be returning to this theme throughout our discussion today. So, I love this quote of Ralph Waldo Emerson, writing in his essay "On Nature" from 1836 where he says:

> In the woods, we return to reason and faith. There I feel that nothing can befall me in life—no disgrace no calamity (leaving me my eyes), which nature cannot repair. Standing on the bare ground—my head bathed by the blithe air and uplifted into infinite space—all mean egotism vanishes.

So, Emerson's talking here about this experience many of you probably have had, which is we get out into our favorite part of nature, we may be on a walk that we particularly enjoy, and a sense of self starts to fade. We feel an expansion of who we are, and we no longer care about the more egotistical concerns of life. And Emerson did a lot to kind of advocate for nature, a theme that was picked up in the environmentalist movement for example as a source of awe.

We also learn a lot about awe from the very important psychologist William James, who wrote this very important book *The Varieties of Religious Experience*, and in 1902 published the book. And what he was making the case for and he surveyed was what Puritan preachers' visions were like, and what enlightenment was like, in Buddhist traditions and what kind of transcendent states felt like in Hinduism and what happens when people do yoga. James himself experimented with laughing gas—brought all of these first-person narratives and accounts of experiences into this remarkable book *The Varieties of Religious Experience*. And what he said is that there's this mystical core to these experiences where you lose a sense of the boundaries between self and other. You lose that sense of time. You feel deeply interconnected, that has awe at its core as an important part of the religious experience across religions. A very radical and important idea.

So, the first way that we answer the question of like what is awe is we differentiate it from related states, which we've done, like beauty and wonder and epiphany, and then we trace its cultural history. And then another way in which we get insight into the nature of an emotion is we think about what where does it come from? Right? What does the context of that that I'm in that makes me feel this particular emotion? Where does awe come from? Where do we feel it?

You know when you consult your own experience it comes from many different things. So, when I think about my life in Berkeley, I think about how I felt awe in reading Mahatma Gandhi in his thinking about sort of the kind of commonalities of human beings. I feel awe when I'm lucky enough to go travel to a beautiful cathedral and see the stained glass of San Chapelle. I feel awe when I travel to, up in the mountains and see the peaks of the Himalayas or travel into the Sierras like John Muir did. I feel awe when I contemplate how wonderful food can be, or go to great cultural artifacts like the Chichen Itza pyramids. I feel awe when I think about the Free Speech Movement in 1964 where students kind of advocated for free speech that led to various protests against war and the like. And this is a personal bias, but I feel awe, like many young people about rock n' roll figures, Iggy Pop being my favorite.

So, to get a handle on this deep question of how do humans feel awe, what do they feel awe about? Where are they? What's happening? What are the psychological themes that trigger awe? Right? And that tells us what this important emotion is. My colleagues at Berkeley and I have actually surveyed thousands of people in 26 different countries. And this is countries of all the great religious traditions, countries of different degrees of economic wealth, countries that vary in their sense of being more collective like China, or more individualistic like the United States, countries that vary in their degree of education. We've surveyed 26 different countries and the people there, and we just ask them to write about an experience of awe. What was going on?

And here's what we find: We find that the most common source of awe is other people, and I'm going to talk about that in just a second. So, in a sense, Burke was right—awe comes from the marvels of other people in our social lives. A second most prominent source of awe is nature. And around the world, whether you're in a desert in parts of Africa or you're in the mountains of upper Scandinavia, nature is a common source of awe. A third common source of awe worldwide is spirituality; contemplative practice; religion, the rituals, for example, going to a Catholic service and then there are other less common sources of all that are really important like art and music and architecture and the like.

So, let's drill down a bit just to give you some specifics about what causes awe as a way to think about what awe is. We were struck in surveying 2,600 people in 26 countries that other people are an underappreciated and most common source of awe. We are awestruck by people's kindness and their virtuosity. You might hear a little child play the piano and just be awestruck by how good they are. We are awestruck by big people, right? If they are seven feet tall, it makes us feel awestruck. We're awestruck by people's heroism. Somebody who overcomes really challenging life circumstances to do good in the world.

Unexpectedly, we found that childbirth and kind of the spectacular qualities of that process and the fact that life comes out of it was a very common source of awe across countries. So, other people, their magnanimity, their kindness, their virtuosity, their strength really give our common source of awe.

A second source is nature. That should be really intuitive to you. You know, people write about… one of our Chinese participants was—their village was flooded and just watching the waters rise. People are awestruck by sunsets and waves and trees and vast trees that I live nearby that are 360 feet tall. Vistas, tornadoes, lightning, earthquakes. This idea that awe and the mysteries are intertwined with nature finds its way in various philosophies. In Taoism, which is 2,500 years old, that comes from Chinese thought, there is Lao Tzu, who's the great first practitioner of Taoism and he really writes about and I love this quote about Tao: The mysterious force of life, the deep meaning of life, Lao Tzu writes, is like water and in that it in its own interconnected way interacts and benefits many different things around it but doesn't compete or contest with those things. And Lao Tzu really thought that that kind of sense of the vital life force in us, or what you might think of as a feeling of awe, has these properties of water.

Drilling down again, what is awe? It's found in… we'll return to the neuroscience of this in prayer, contemplation.

People when they do meditation or mindful practices will very often sort of be struck by a sense of awe about what it can bring to them, what their qualities of their mind are like. And then as I've noted, there are these other sorts of sources of awe that we shouldn't lose sight of. People feel awe at political rallies, at sporting events, people tell us from their 26 different countries study.

People feel very commonly in collective activities that Barbara Ehrenreich has written about that dances and festivals and celebrations and weddings and even funerals. There's a sense of awe and the transcendent. People commonly feel awe in encountering remarkable architectural structures, paintings, poetry, and then it's really interesting and gives me reason for my own career which is that people feel awe about ideas.

You know when a person first hears of how DNA works or how evolution works or you know when Charles Darwin was in the Amazonian rain forest and he was looking at this multiplicity of species and he started to get a sense a very vague sense in the 1830s and in a young man about how natural selection may be creating all this incredible beauty in the South American Amazonian reinforced his feet felt the awe and wonder and he had to figure it out. And people feel about technology. They'll you know, rocket ship or whatever the case may be, will be a source of awe.

So just to wrap up our thinking about, what is awe? There are a few other things that we've learned that I think are really important for you to know. First of all, is awe is much more common in people's ordinary experience than you might imagine. The word awe very often makes you think, you know, I had it once in my life, it was when you know I met Bono in an ice-cream store and he gave me his ice cream cone or whatever the case may be. But, in point of fact, when we do rigorous research figuring out how often people feel awe they feel it about two to two-and-a-half times a week. It's subtler forms of awe, but still important.

A second point is awe… I've given you a sort of a positive version of awe, and we're going to delve into that in more detail, but about a quarter of people's experiences are fearful and they feel threatening and they have a layer of uncertainty and they elevate, our research shows, your stress related physiology, your heart rate goes up and you have higher blood pressure. You know a young child may, when they first hear about the universe and that we're… the role we have in the universe and how small it is and how short and fleeting life is, often they'll have this form of awe that is almost imbued, that's imbued with anxiety. And so, that's about a quarter of the experiences that people have, has this fear layer to awe.

And then a third issue that I think you should be thinking about is how awe shifts from one culture to another. Right? This science is young so we're just starting to learn this. But what we're learning, for example, is that awe in China, more collectivist hierarchical culture, tends to involve more hierarchy and you feel a little bit more submissive when you're feeling awe, as opposed to if you feel awe in many parts of the United States. And in fact, when you look at the Chinese ideograms that map onto awe, they translate to fearful respect. So, awe is really deferential or submissive. So, we should be attentive and thought and mindful to cultural differences in awe as well.

So, when we wrap this up—what is awe? —as you can see awe is this complicated family of states, it's about other people, it's about spirituality, it's about nature, ideas, art, architecture, music, great technology. It is many different things. And important to bear that in mind.

HOW CAN YOU FIND MORE AWE?

LESSON 18

What does awe do for us? This lesson answers this question by explaining what functions awe serves in human interactions and why we evolved the emotion of awe. The lesson also addresses how to find more awe in life.

SURVIVAL: SELF-INTEREST VERSUS SOCIAL GROUPS

Emotions help humans adapt to problems and opportunities that are important to our survival.

In his book *The Social Conquest of Earth*, biologist E. O. Wilson wrote about ultrasociality, which he said is the defining strength of the human species. We defended ourselves, took care of vulnerable young, and got food for our survival in tight social groups.

This idea that our collective tendencies are a deep part of our evolution traces back to Charles Darwin, who in *The Descent of Man* wrote about how sympathy, as well as many of the prosocial emotions—such as awe and gratitude—are increased through natural selection. He argued that to survive as a species, we need to survive in strong communities.

One of the implications of this analysis is that if we're going to survive as an ultrasocial species in strong social groups, we have to have mechanisms that help us move away from gratifying our self-interests to acting in ways that benefit the interests of others.

Various intellectuals, from economist Robert Frank to philosopher Elliott Sober, have grappled with the complicated concept that we're not just self-interest machines. We have to have particular emotions, tendencies, and ways of interacting with each other that benefit others first and often sacrifice self-interest. That is at the heart of being an ultrasocial species.

In light of the concept of ultrasociality and transcending self-interest in the service of others, a variety of scholars, from David Hume to Martha Nussbaum, have made the case that there are certain emotions—such as compassion and gratitude—that motivate behaviors that help us act in the service of other people and momentarily ignore our own self-interest.

Research has shown that this amazing experience of awe does a few important things that help us form strong social groups:

It shifts our attention away from our own self-interest to focus on other people's interests.

It helps us form strong ultrasocial groups by motivating and producing more altruistic, cooperative behavior—a foundation of human social living.

In a study conducted over two weeks in China and the United States, one group of participants was asked to write every night about whether they experienced awe on that day, while another group was asked to write about whether they experienced another positive emotion, joy.

Researchers found that if participants had an experience of awe during the day, their sense of self was smaller than the sense of self of participants had who experienced joy.

Research shows that as people's sense of self becomes smaller and starts to vanish, they are aware of the much stronger connections that they have to other people in their social network.

Another benefit to the diminishing or vanishing of the self is the ethic of humility, which has two different attributes: You have a realistic view of yourself, including your faults, and you are open to the strengths of other people. A variety of studies show that momentary experiences of awe make people humbler, which helps us fold into social collectives.

This vanishing of the self has been traced into the human brain.

One of the functions of a region of your brain called the default mode network is that it keeps you on task and helps you achieve your goals. Scientists now think of the default mode network as part of the self, keeping track of things in the present environment. Research shows that awe experienced through nature, contemplation, mindfulness, and even psychedelics reduces activation in the default mode network, meaning that the sense of self starts to be diminished.

As self-focus fades, we become more curious about other people. Research shows that when people feel awe, they ask more questions of other people during social interactions. Some studies even show that we have an expanded sense of time.

We also feel less everyday stress. Research shows that as we feel awe and experience less self-focus, the body's stress-related inflammation response—which produces cells that attack pathogens in your body and is problematic to have chronically activated—lowers bodily inflammation.

One of the implications of the idea that awe helps us fold into strong social collectives is that awe should increase the likelihood of prosocial tendencies, such as sharing, being cooperative, sacrificing for another person, and various forms of kindness. And research supports this thesis.

Studies have shown that awe makes us feel connected to others and makes us kinder and more prosocial. Studies have also shown that brief experiences of awe make us share more, cooperate more, give to strangers more, and act in a more altruistic fashion.

WHY WE EVOLVED THE EMOTION OF AWE

In 1872, Charles Darwin was facing a lot of criticism about how evolution would account for the emergence of particular human tendencies, such as emotions. In response to his critics, Darwin published *The Expression of Emotions in Man and Animals*, in which he laid out a few ways of answering the questions of why we have awe and where it comes from in our human and mammalian evolution.

> The first thing that he pushed was the idea of universality—that the characteristics of humans that are produced by evolution should be genetically encoded and have physiological structures. They should be part of the universal human as it has been crafted by evolution.

> The second thing that he captivated people with was mammalian origins. He wrote about the emotions of cats, dogs, nonhuman primates, and other species as a way of saying that perhaps there is a precursor in mammalian evolution that we could trace back to help us understand why we have awe.

Paul Ekman, a founding figure in the study of emotion, was a pioneer in translating these two criteria—universality and mammalian origins—to the study of human emotion by studying facial expressions and their universality.

Based on research in this area, what do we know is universal in awe? What might be some of the behaviors that are precursors in other mammals to human awe?

The human vocal apparatus is a spectacular system of communication. Anatomically, the brain sends signals down to the muscles that surround your lungs, which contract, sending bursts of air particles to your vocal cords. The vocal chords start to vibrate and produce sound waves of different frequencies, which then move through your mouth into your nasal passage. Finally, a sound comes out. And sounds come in very diverse forms, including laughs and words.

> Depending on dozens of different factors, it takes more than 100 muscles to produce a single sound.

Vocal bursts are sounds that we make to communicate emotion to other people (without words). It is believed that vocal bursts predate language; some linguists even believe that early vocal bursts are millions of years old. In fact, in combination with things like pointing and gesturing, vocal bursts may have given rise to words and other linguistic structures. Cross-cultural studies have shown that vocal bursts are very old universal characteristics of human communication.

Remarkable work has been done on the bodily response of awe, which is colloquially called the chills and involves a rise of sensations and the body shaking in response. Research in this area has found that the feeling of the chills breaks into two distinct sensations: goose bumps and the cold shiver.

> Goose bumps, which are related to awe, describe a pattern of response that goes up your arms and the back of your neck.

> The cold shiver results when you shiver and shudder when you feel something is scary or worthy of wariness.

Research has shown that goose bumps map onto feelings of awe and elevated joy, whereas the cold shiver maps onto a much different response, which is social disgust.

Research conducted in 26 different countries found that the goose bumps of awe are a universal response, and when we feel them, they make us feel part of a social collective or community. We feel like we have a common cause with people, and this is at the heart of our motivation to fold into social collectives.

There is speculation about the mammalian origins of this response. The idea is that many different species of mammals, such as rats and certain dogs, will fluff up their fur—which is the same anatomical response as human goose bumps—to get warm and to get close to each other when they face collective threats. This may tell us about the deep origins of awe, because it is a response that we feel in the chills, when we're trying to get warm and bond to each other to handle circumstances in the environment.

HOW TO FIND MORE AWE

Awe gives us a sense of more time, reduces stress in our life, makes us more prosocial, and quiets the inflammation response in our nervous system, so there is increasing active literature on finding awe.

Get out in nature. Research has shown that just getting out in nature gives you awe. Find a place of awe that strikes you, that gives you goose bumps, that makes you feel a sense of deep meaning. When we immerse ourselves in nature, we feel more purpose and more content and we concentrate better.

> South Korea and Japan have a rich tradition of healing forests, in which you can experience awe by partaking in rituals as a form of health care.

Study nature to get a sense of awe in the sacred. Early thinkers and philosophers wrote about how to find things that transcend our understanding of the world, make us find deeper meaning, and endow life with a sense of the sacred. Humans in different parts of history and different cultures have studied nature to get a sense of awe in the sacred by looking to the clouds, the sky, the tides of the ocean, or the changing colors of leaves on trees.

Engage in contemplative practices. Many great contemplative practices, such as mindfulness and collective rituals, give us a sense of awe.

Find texts that resonate with you. For example, find a great novel or film that you can return to over time. Specifically, historical studies of great people and how they inspire us give us awe.

Take an awe walk. This is a walk you can do once a week that takes you to a place that makes you appreciate something vast, such as a tree or a beautiful pattern on a building, that has special meaning to you. You can do this in urban or suburban settings, near parks or green spaces. Awe walks are a great way to reduce levels of stress, create a sense of connection to others, and take a more mindful approach to cultivating this very powerful emotion.

HOW CAN YOU FIND MORE AWE?

So, now that we know a little bit more about what awe is let's ask the question: What does awe do for us? What functions does awe serve in human interactions?

This is actually something that we use to think about the nature of emotion, which is to think about how do emotions help us solve problems in our social interactions and sort of help us capitalize upon opportunities that are really important to our survival. To help make sense of awe we're going to rely on this concept of ultrasociality which E. O. Wilson, the great biologist, wrote about in his book *The Social Conquest of Earth*, which is he said that the defining strength of the human species and how we defended ourselves and took care of vulnerable young and got food for our survival and so forth was we did this socially in really tight social groups.

Now you may be surprised to learn that this idea that our communal tendencies, our collective tendencies, are really a deep part of our evolution, actually traces back to Charles Darwin and Darwin in the *The Descent of Man* wrote about how sympathy and a lot of the prosocial emotions like awe, and I'll talk about gratitude really briefly, "will actually have been increased through natural selection; (and I'm quoting Darwin here) for those communities which included the greatest number of the most sympathetic members will flourish the best, and rear the greatest number of offspring."

So, what Darwin is arguing before E. O. Wilson is that to survive as a species we really need to survive in strong communities. So, what does this really mean in more specific terms? Well, one of the sort of implications of this analysis is that if we're going to survive as an ultrasocial species in strong social groups what we have to do, or what we have to have, are mechanisms that help us move away from gratifying our self-interest to really honoring and acting in ways that benefit the interests of others.

And various people from economists Robert Frank to philosopher Elliott Sober have really grappled with this complicated question which is, we're not just self-interest machines, we really have to have particular emotions and tendencies and ways of interacting with each other that benefit others first and often sacrifice self-interest. That is really at the heart of being an ultrasocial species.

So, in light of this concept of ultrasociality and sort of transcending self-interest in the service of others, a variety of different scholars from David Hume to Adam Smith to Charles Darwin to Martha Nussbaum more recently have really been making the case that there are certain emotions that capture our physiology, that direct attention, that motivate behaviors that help us act in the service of other people and momentarily ignore our own self-interest. So, you could think about for example, compassion, the feeling of concern for an individual in need and the motivation to help, as being one form of an emotion that helps us benefit others even if it costs ourselves.

A lot of people have written about gratitude. Another moral emotion where you really feel reverential for things that people give to you and you will sacrifice in the future to kind of balance out that gift as another kind of moral emotion that helps us serve others and so that raises this question of what does awe do within this conceptual framework?

And so, what I'm going to argue is that this amazing experience of awe that comes from nature and other people and social groups and contemplative practice and other kinds of sources like art and music, it does a couple of really important things that help us fold into social collectives to make for strong social groups.

First of all, we're going to see that it really shifts your attention and what you care about away from your own self-interest, what you desire and want, to a focus on other people's interests and their concerns. So, in a way, quiets the voice of self-interest and turns up the volume on your awareness of other people's interests. And then the second thing that we're going to see is that awe helps us fold into social collectives and makes for these ultrasocial strong groups by motivating and producing more altruistic cooperative behavior, a foundation of human social living.

So how does awe transform the self? In Japanese, they write about this interesting state called *kando* and kando is a state where it literally is the state where the self vanishes like light or wind on water. It's as if you see it for a minute and then it disappears. And so, we're going to ask the question of how in the world does awe produce this reduced sense of self.

Before we do, just think for a moment about what the psychology of the self tells us. So, when I think about the self Dacher Keltner and my goals and my characteristics and what I'm my intentions in the world, when I have this self-focus, what happens is I tend to be more self-critical, I tend to ruminate about what I'm doing, I'm more goal driven.

I'm a little bit more anxious which is something to worry about. I'm a little bit less attentive to other people's interests and less co-operative in social situations. So, self-focus has a place in human existence which is it's about making sure you gratify your self-interest in and do well in according ways.

Awe, we're going to argue, actually quiets that very loud voice of the self and opens up your mind to other people's interests and their characteristics. One of my favorite poetic reflections upon this was John Muir, the great naturalist who started the Sierra Club here in California. Muir, as many of you know, he used to take sheep out into the Sierras and go out there by himself and spend time and go to Yosemite and live out in the wild. And it really changed his life. And he has this wonderful quote where he writes:

> We are now in the mountains and they are in us, kindling enthusiasm, making every nerve quiver, filling every pore and cell of us. Our flesh-and-bone tabernacle (And when he's talking about there is our sense of self) seems transparent as glass to the beauty about us, as if truly an inseparable part of it, thrilling with the air and trees, streams and rocks, in the waves of the sun, —a part of nature...

So, what he's really talking about here is this fascinating process that people have written about with respect to awe which is the boundaries between the sense of self, the boundaries between self and others seem to disappear, our flesh and bone tabernacle is transparent to other things around it.

So, let me tell you what we've learned about this. In some research, we actually in China in the United States, every night for a couple of weeks people wrote about did they experience awe today. Right? Or did they experience other positive emotions like joy, where you feel really, like life's burdens have lifted and you feel joyful. We sort of keep track of people's narratives and then each day we take, gather a measure of how much are they thinking about themselves, how so focused are they, right? And what we find across these two weeks, both in China and the United States, is that if you've had an awe experience during the day— you go to a garden in Beijing and it's the flowers are blooming and you're struck with awe at the blooming of the flowers— your sense of self becomes smaller compared to the control condition which was joy.

We did another experiment, more dramatic, in this particular case our researchers stopped people from all over the world at Fisherman's Wharf in San Francisco. This highly visited place, lots of tourists go there, it's right on the bay it's beautiful, you ride on the trolley car, lot of fun, right? Or you go to Yosemite Valley and Yosemite is this incredible valley, glacially formed, gives people awe, and all we did, is we had them draw a picture of themselves on a piece of graph paper. Right? Really simple. Kind of fun they drew these pictures of themselves, and then sneakily, we sort of counted-up how many squares occupied that sense of self and what you find is that if you're in the wonders of Yosemite the sense of self is really small, compared to if you're at Fisherman's Wharf, even though it's just as pleasurable and fun when you're on vacation, it's, it's smaller.

What we also find in this research is as my sense of self sort of gets smaller and starts to vanish, I am aware of the much stronger connections that I have to other people in my social network as my mind is less attuned to the self,

I'm aware of how supportive and strongly connected other people are to me. So, a really nice benefit of this vanishing of the self.

Another benefit to the vanishing or the diminishing of the self is this ethic of humility that a lot of people have been interested in for quite some time. We think about humility really having two different attributes which is, you have a realistic view of yourself including your faults. Right? Well,

I tend to overstate things or whatever the case may be and then the second attribute of humility is that you really have this openness to the strengths of other people. Right?

You are aware of your own sense of self and you are appreciative or open to the strengths of other people.

So, here's what we did, and we've done a variety of studies showing that momentary experiences of awe make us more humble which should really help us fold into social collectives. In this study students went up to the top of this tower on the Berkeley campus, the high tower a couple hundred feet tall. They looked out at this this beautiful view of the Bay Area. The other condition, students sat on a beautiful part of campus. Right? It was pleasing, they were calm, had those qualities. And at the end of that experience we just had them kind of rate how humble they felt, right. Were they aware of their faults? Were they are aware of the strengths of other people around them and what we found is vistas and beautiful views make college students more humble, even those just a couple of minutes of the view, it makes them more humble.

This vanishing of the self that produces, which the Japanese describe as *kando,* actually has been traced all the way down into the human brain and its really remarkable research. There's a region of your brain that you've probably been hearing about called the default mode network and one way to think about one of the functions of the default mode network, which is a series of chunks of your cortex as you move in the middle of your brain from the front to the back, is that the default mode network kind of keeps you on task, it helps the self— me Dacher Keltner— achieve my goals. So, the default mode network is activated when I think about my present moment and my goals, what I'm going to do in the future? When I think about memories from my autobiographical past, this region of the brain is activated, and scientists now think of the default mode network as part of the self, right, keeping track of things in the present environment.

Quite remarkably, when people feel awe, through deep experiences in nature or contemplation or mindfulness or even psychedelics with the research of Roland Griffiths at Johns Hopkins University what we see across these awe-inspiring experiences is reduced activation in the default mode network. So, the sense of self is starting to be diminished all the way down to these networks of parts of your brain.

So, as the cell focus fades as we experience awe, there are other things that ensue. We become more curious about other people. Our research shows that when people feel awe they actually ask more questions of other people in the interactions that they're engaging in. You may really like this one. There are studies showing that when we feel awe, and our sense of self fades, we have an expanded sense of time. It's as if we have more time to get the things done in our lives. We feel less everyday stress. Research from my lab shows, very importantly, as we feel awe and we experience less self-focus, the body's stress related inflammation response, which produces cells that attack pathogens in your body and it feels like a fever really problematic to have chronically activated, awe lowers bodily inflammation.

So, the second question we can ask about, what are the benefits of awe? What does it do for us is, what does it do to our social relationships? And back to this broader argument that I'm making which is that awe helps us fold into strong social collectives. One of the implications of that is that awe should really enhance or increase the likelihood of pro-social tendencies; things like sharing being co-operative, sacrificing for another person, and various forms of kindness.

So, here are some studies that really support this thesis that enhances prosocial tendencies. A first study Lani Shiota did. She brought students to a part of the Berkeley campus. They stood next to this amazing T-Rex skeleton in our paleontology museum or they stood in the same place, but they looked down a hallway which wasn't so awe-inspiring. And what she found, she asked the participants in those two conditions— awe-inspired by the T-Rex, looking down the hallway—who are you as a person? Right? And what you found is if you're standing next to the T-Rex you really integrate yourself into humanity. Right, you define yourself as being part of a group and part of a university and part of a species and you're made of DNA and you're related to all sentient beings right. If you're looking at the hallway you're, I'm, I've got these pressures and personal goals and characteristics. Awe makes us feel connected to others.

Here's a great study demonstrating how awe actually makes us kinder and more pro-social as we fold into social collectives. It was carried out by Paul Piff down at UC Irvine, but this was always at UC Berkeley. So, what Paul and his colleagues did, and I was part of this study, is he very simply took undergraduates, and they're like "What are we doing?" You know, he brought them to this part of campus and they got to look up into this beautiful grove of eucalyptus trees, which smell wonderfully and reflect light, this beautiful presence. Or on another condition they're standing in the same place, same time of day, and they're looking up at this science building which is not so pretty or awe-inspiring.

Here's what Paul found. And it really is a remarkable testimony to the power of awe, even if it's just a minute or two. Paul surveyed people, when after looking up at the trees for a minute or two, or at the building, and he found those people who looked up into the trees felt less self-important, they felt less entitled. They kind of said the world doesn't owe them stuff. This is kind of funny. They actually needed less money to do this study. We paid them. We said, "We're going to pay you five dollars. How much you want?" And they're like, "I don't believe in money." You know whatever the case may be.

And then Paul very ingeniously, while they were doing this, this person walked by, who was actually part of the study, and kind of stumbled and dropped all these pens and people feeling awe actually reached out and picked up more pens. Right? And this complements other work Paul did showing brief experiences of awe make us share more, cooperate more, give to strangers more, and act in more altruistic fashion. So, awe enhances our pro-social tendencies.

So, we've tried to answer the first question which is—What is awe? —and differentiated it from related states. And then we've just thought about: What does awe do for us, right? How does it sort of help us diminish self-interest and connect to others? And now we're going to turn to a deeper question in a way which is— Why awe? In the deep story of the remarkable evolution of the human species, why in the world did we evolve this emotion awe?

We really owe a debt of gratitude to Charles Darwin for providing a conceptual framework for thinking about why did we evolve the particular emotions that we experience today. Darwin in 1872 was facing a lot of criticism as it, will actually before that, when he released his theory of evolution, and he was he was encountering criticism about how evolution would account for the emergence of particular human tendencies like the emotions and so in response to his critics, Darwin published this remarkable book *The Expression of Emotion in Man and Animals* in 1872 in which he laid out this argument and really a description of all the different emotions that make up the human species. And he really laid out a couple of ways of answering this question of, why do we have awe and where does it come from and our human and mammalian evolution?

The first thing that he really pushed was this idea of universality; that the characteristics of humans that are produced by evolution should really be genetically encoded and have physiological structures and they should be universal, right, they should really be part of what we call the universal human, as that's been crafted by evolution. And then the second thing that Darwin captivated people by or with is to really think hard about mammalian origins.

Right? And Darwin in writing about the emotions wrote about the emotions of cats and dogs and non-human primates and other species because what he was saying is that perhaps there is something in mammalian evolution that we could trace back that helps us understand why we have awe, are there precursors to the responses we experience of awe in other mammalian behaviors.

My mentor Paul Ekman was really a pioneer in translating these two criteria to the study of human emotion, the criteria of universality in mammalian origins, and really is a founding figure in the study of emotion. He studied facial expressions and their universality in New Guinea and other places. And now I'm going to talk to you about what we know is universal in awe and what might be some of the behaviors that are precursors in other mammals to human awe.

What I'm going to focus on is this remarkable modality of communication by which we communicate awe, which is through the human voice. Now the human vocal apparatus is one of the most spectacular systems of communication that you'll find in the universe. And I'm not exaggerating. You know when you think about the anatomy it really is remarkable, which is that brain the brain send signals down to the muscles that surround your lungs, those muscles contract up become these bursts of air particle that hit your vocal cords. Those vocal chords start to vibrate. They produce these sound waves of different frequencies, the sound waves then move through your mouth in your nasal passage, and depending on dozens of different factors (it takes over 100 muscles to produce a sound), the sound comes out and the sound can be a laugh or a sarcastic sound or a sound you'd make to a baby or a pet or words or poetry. It really is a spectacular system of communication.

Now, my lab studies these little sounds that we call "vocal bursts" and vocal bursts were first coined by Klaus Scherer in Switzerland in the 1990s. There are little sounds that don't have words by which we communicate a motion to other people. Currently people believe that these vocal bursts, and I'm going to give you a couple of examples, are actually they predate language and there are certain linguists who believe that these early vocal bursts, millions of years old in our communication, actually in combination with things like pointing and gesturing and orienting mutual gaze, may have given rise to words and other linguistic structures. These are very old universal human communication characteristics, vocal bursts.

So, here's one see if you know what it is and see if you can discern what emotion is I'm trying to communicate. This is a vocal burst sometimes I hear from teenagers around me right (vocal sound). When you hear that sound you're like, "Well, that feels kind of disgusted or socially disgusted or disdainful or maybe contemptuous, right? And there is a whole rich array of vocal bursts.

So, here's what we did to document the universality of awe and a first piece of universality. We had students in Berkeley and then subsequently in many different cultures we've been studying, we gave them descriptions of emotions and we said make a sound that that would really communicate this emotion. So, they would see the word anger and they go (vocal sound) okay, and we captured it. Or they would hear that, see the word sympathy, they go (vocal sound). Or they would see the word contentment, (vocal sound). And then they got the word awe and they're like (vocal sound), something like that. We had about 20 different emotions.

So, inspired by Charles Darwin and his thinking about the universality of human emotion and Paul Eichmann's early work on the face and its universality, Dan Cordaro travelled to 10 different countries and here's what he did. He took vocal bursts of about 20 different emotions and I've given you examples of about five. And then he played them to participants in 10 different countries as diverse as Pakistan and South Korea and Poland and West Germany and New Zealand and Japan and the like. And then a participant would hear the sound and just guess what emotion they just heard, right?

Chance guessing in this particular study, in this paradigm, was about 25 percent and what Dan found is that for about 17 emotions, people were way above chance in guessing what emotion was occurring in that vocal burst. Emotions like sympathy and anger and fear and interest and contentment and pain and then awe was the second most readily identified emotion in vocal bursts at about 85 percent accuracy. Very universal signal.

Now one of the concerns of this kind of research is that these are all people who have access to the internet, are reading magazines, have access to television. Maybe they're learning how to read vocal bursts through their immersion in a shared culture, through all the different media that we are exposed to today. So, what Dan did to handle that concern is he travelled in Bhutan, to eastern Bhutan, in the Himalayas and Bhutan is this incredible culture, but quite remarkably there are parts of Bhutan that are very remote and separate from all the influences of globalization and the like. Bhutan had no television until 1999.

The place that Dan went to, which was up in the Himalayas in eastern Bhutan, takes four or five days on a fairly narrow road to get there, had no electricity, no cars, no amenities from the West; these people whereas untouched by technology and the internet and television in the West as any people you could find in the world. So, what Dan did is he gave people a story that fitted emotion, like you stub your toe on a rock.

They listened to three vocal bursts and the target one of interest is pain (vocal sound) right and then they had to match a vocal burst to the story. And again, what he found is a lot of similarity in how people in this remote village in Bhutan label or match a story to a vocal burst as people do in the West. Awe did really well once again in this study, telling us in this radically different culture, no contact nor immersion in the internet, Buddhist tradition, they're interpreting a vocal burst of homage like we would. A lot of good data on universality.

Second way that we think about why is, why does an emotion emerge in mammalian evolution? Are there early bodily responses or behavioral reactions or patterns of physiology that you can find in other species with whom we share the mammalian nervous system and start to push emotions way back in mammalian evolution? So, when I studied human embarrassment, one of my favorite emotions, and we noticed that people when they get embarrassed kind of turn their head away and show their juggler vein and touch their face and smiled awkwardly and kind of shrink like that. It turned out a lot of different species, 23 in fact, show this kind of shrinking mortifying behavior responses when they want to pacify or appease other members of their group. So, it resembles human embarrassment.

What about awe? There is remarkable new work on the bodily response of awe which we colloquially call the chills. Right? When we think of the chills we kind of feel like this rise of sensations, and our body shakes in response to awe inspiring things like music and cathedrals and you see your child graduate or you go through a wedding and you have these chill responses. Really careful work by Laura Maruskin and Todd Thrash and others has found actually the chills breaks into two different distinct sensations. A first is really close to awe, which is the goose tingles. It's actually a little pattern of response that goes up your arms and your back, in the back of your neck. And what happens anatomically is those are little muscles that surround hot hair follicles. And when the sympathetic autonomic nervous system activates your body those muscles contract and they give you the sensation of goose-tingles or goose bumps and it goes up your arms and your back. That's one kind of chills.

The other kind of chills is what they call the cold shiver. It's kind of you shiver and shudder and almost as when you feel something is scary or worthy of wariness and that is what Laura Maruskin and Todd Thrash are finding is that goose-tingles really cope varies or maps onto feelings of awe and elevated joy whereas the shudder, the cold shiver, really maps onto a much different response, which is social disgust.

Other researchers found, 26 different countries once again, that the goose-tingles of awe really is a universal response and it makes us feel part of a social collective. When we feel these goose bumps, we feel like we're part of a community. We feel like we have a common cause with people and that really is at the heart of awe motivating us to fold into social collectives.

Very interestingly, there is now speculation about the mammalian origins of this sort of response and here's how the story goes. Which is that a lot of different species—rats, certain dogs, other kinds of species— will actually fluff up their fur, which is the same anatomical response as our goose-tingles, which is little muscles contract and the fur goes upright. And what that speculation is now is that mammals do this to get warm, to get close to each other, and what they tend to do is they tend to fluff up their fur (piloerection is the term in the literature) when they're facing threats collectively.

Now that tells us something really interesting about the deep mammalian origins of awe, which is it's a response that we have and we feel it in this piloerection or chills when we're trying to get warm and sort of bond to each other to handle circumstances in the environment; may tell us about the deep origins of awe.

So, finally, now that we thought about what is awe, what it does for us, why we have it and why it's part of human evolution, a really important question is, how can we find more awe, right? We've learned and you've learned that awe gives us a sense of more time; it reduces stress in our life; it makes us more pro-social. It actually quiets the inflammation response in your nervous system. So, there is this increasing active literature on finding awe. Let me just give you a few ideas that are going to be really intuitive to you.

Frances Kuo and her colleagues have found just getting out in nature gives you awe; find a place of awe that strikes you, that gives you goose-tingles, that makes you feel a sense of deep meaning and go find awe. And her studies show that when we immerse ourselves in nature, and this is seen in other countries, we feel more purpose, we feel more content. We concentrate better.

There's a rich tradition of healing forests in South Korea and Japan as part of their healthcare. They structure forests, the equivalent of our national parks in some sense, but in this particular case they have rituals in which you experience awe in forests and we know that there are health benefits to that.

A second way to find awe and early thinkers and philosophers writing about the sense of how do we find things that transcend or understanding of the world and make us find deeper meaning and start to endow life with a sense of the sacred and the philosopher Eliade, who has written about this in the 40s and 50s, is humans in different parts of history and different cultures have looked to nature and studied nature and they look to the clouds or sky or the tides of the oceans or changing colors of leaves on trees and when we study nature we often have a sense of awe in the sacred.

A third thing is what you're learning here, which is to engage in contemplative practices. A lot of the great contemplative practices, a deep mindfulness tradition, give us a sense of awe. As a fourth source and a lot of people are returning to this, is to think about collective rituals, right, ways of honoring a teen's development, ways of honoring a wedding or a graduation or a quinceañera or a funeral, as these places to house and really cultivate awe.

Obviously, there are many other sources of awe. I really encourage students to find texts that really resonate with them, be it Lao Tzu, the *Tao Te Ching*, or a great novel, a great film that they can return to over time. Historical studies of great people and how they inspire us, give us awe.

And then one of the things that we have developed at Berkeley, in collaboration with mindful.org is what we call the awe walk. And the awe walk is a walk that you can do, on say, once a week basis that takes you to a place that makes you appreciate something vast; could be a tree or a beautiful pattern on a building that has special meaning to you. And what we encourage with the awe walk is just to set your intention about going to feel awe, slow down, get into a nice breathing rhythm that the mindfulness traditions cultivate; kind of direct your attention to things that are really small and shift out to sort of expanses. And what we're finding, really remarkably, is that this awe walk, you can do it in urban settings, suburban settings, near parks, near green spaces.

There's a schoolteacher in the Bronx in a place where there's not a lot of parks to benefit the kids. She takes her kids out on an awe walk or they just go next to one tree and look up at the sky. And we're starting to find that these awe walks are actually a great way to cultivate awe and to kind of reduce levels of stress, to cultivate a sense of connection to others, and to build into a more mindful approach to cultivating this very powerful emotion.

In my own work, just to round this out, capitalizing on the benefits of awe in light of and how to cultivate it, what we've done in a couple of recent studies in partnership with the Sierra Club, and Stacy Bare who led the outdoors programs, is we took teens who are at risk in really poor neighborhoods in Oakland, California and Richmond, we took veterans who are really at risk and vulnerable to PTSD, we took them out on a whitewater rafting trip for a day.

Very awe inspiring and what we found is they felt less stress a week after the trip. They're getting along better with others, happier in life. Both the teens and the veterans, and remarkably, the veterans had a 28 percent drop in PTSD symptoms, sort of flashbacks and had sort of heightened fear and so forth. Just from a day out on the rivers and what we found is these benefits have less stress and the like were really produced by experiences of awe.

So, awe is one of the great emotions that Protagoras felt was our defining human strength. I wouldn't go so far. I would say we also need all of the emotions; from laughter, to compassion, to gratitude and the like, but awe certainly helps us fold into social collectives and find more meaning in life.

BLUE MIND:
THE HEALING
POWER OF WATER
LESSON 19

Being near, in, on, or even under water helps us be happier, healthier, more connected, and better at what we do. This connection between our mind and our water planet is called blue mind. Water is life. We are made primarily of water, and the planet we live on is covered mostly with water. Water is our oldest medicine for not only our physical health, but also for our mental and emotional health. Our brains and bodies are hardwired to respond positively to water of all kinds in ways that can improve our physical and emotional health. Water can also provide a universal tool for enhancing mindfulness.

THE VALUE OF WATER

We live on a small blue planet; it is mostly covered with water. Our bodies are mostly made of water, and whatever we do on this small blue planet matters—the big things, the little things, the good things, and the bad things.

> What's your water? What's the water that you dream about and long for?
>
> When did you fall in love with your water?
>
> Who took you there? Who was your guide? Who is the person—maybe a teacher or family member—who brought you to your water the first time?

Think about how much that water means to you and your life.

For some people, their water is simply a matter of hydration and hygiene—the water we drink and bathe in. For others, it's a more adventurous experience; it's the water we play in, from white-water rafting to paddling on flat water. For many people, it's the community and the family time we get when we spend time on the water together, sometimes just standing around having conversations in the water with the people we love.

For still other people, it's being in domestic water—being indoors in bathtubs and showers or even taking a sip of water from the tap. We get to luxuriate in the taste and feel the coolness, the hydration, and the refreshing sense that all is well when we connect with our water.

When we're out on our water, we pause and think. We ponder and dream. Water can help us sleep; it can help us slip away and calm our minds. When we learn new skills on or in the water, we feel more empowered and stronger. We feel like better versions of ourselves. We connect with ourselves and the people around us.

This water story is not just about oceans. It's also about lakes, rivers, and springs. Wherever we are in the world, we are never far away from water, even if we're in the desert.

We need to understand the true value of healthy waters cognitively, emotionally, psychologically, socially, and even spiritually in order to protect them, as well as ourselves, and take care of the planet we share.

MINDFULNESS AND WATER

There are a number of books related to applied neuroscience and neuropsychology in the realms of music, creativity, happiness, and even economics. There are many books about how we can change our mood and our minds by being more mindful.

Now there's a whole new generation of books exploring how nature—and, in particular, water—can help us reconnect with ourselves and with those around us.

The field of neuroconservation connects neuroscience and conservation biology and involves protecting the world around us in a more mindful way. In order to do good neuroconservation, we have to understand that people are human. And understanding how people react to the world around us is incredibly important to taking better care of that world.

Research on how our brains track nature has shown that when we're swimming in the water, we follow the eyes of animals as they swim with us. We are drawn to novelty.

The water around us also helps us relax. It switches our emotional state from a focused, prefrontal cortex, active, working state to a more distributed perspective involving the default network of the brain.

The value of water is ecological, economic, and educational. But it's also emotional, and the emotional value of water is important to our wellness and to understanding how to better take care of the water around us.

The emotional value needs to be the focus. Conceptually, emotion underlies all of our decisions. And as psychologists and neuroscientists have unpacked the science of emotion, we've learned that emotion is a physical, physiological response to the world around us.

RED MIND AND GRAY MIND

Around the world, people are experiencing increasingly higher levels of stress all the time. Many things are easier for modern humans, but we're still experiencing a high level of stress for a number of reasons.

The world seems to be more connected. We're ever more stimulated. We're always "on." And this takes its toll on our minds and bodies.

Social media is changing the way we interact with the world. Higher levels of anxiety and depression are occurring in people. Many people are self-medicating. They're taking care of the stress and anxiety in ways that only create more and more stress and anxiety.

About 60 percent of modern diseases and disorders relate to stress. They're either caused by stress directly or exacerbated by it.

There is a public health crisis as a result of the stress and anxiety that pervades our lives. At its most extreme—for people who have experienced acute or repetitive trauma—we refer to it as post-traumatic stress.

Sometimes the result of all this anxiety and stress is suicide. A number of people take their own lives and are unable to manage the anxiety that is occurring for them daily.

Taking all of this together, this state is called red mind, and it is increasingly the norm. It's a state of overstimulation and overconnection, but at the same time a disconnection that causes anxiety and stress in our lives.

Eventually, red mind leads to gray mind, which is a burned out, numbed out, indifferent, blasé perspective of the world. None of that is good for us.

Red mind is useful; we need it to get things done and to reach deadlines. But if it's all we have, then eventually it burns us down.

We often bring messages of fear and anger to try to motivate people to respond to the environmental crisis that the world faces today, even though research shows that anger creates a fight-or-flight response. We bring tools like shame and unload a lot of facts on people.

This combination of fear, anger, shame, and facts creates even more red mind. And in that red mind fight-or-flight state, we are less creative, less collaborative, and less likely to solve problems and find our way forward. We're more likely to run away or fight. And that doesn't solve our problems.

The message that we share about water is that we have a huge problem. Instead, we should lead with gratitude. What if we say thank you for what people are doing to help solve the problem? We begin with gratitude and build on that with love. We create connections, and respect builds up between people and allows us to communicate in a way that helps solve problems.

By bringing more positive emotions to the conversation about water, we have a better chance of solving our water problems.

GREEN SPACE AND BLUE MIND

There's an increasing amount of literature on how green space can help us take better care of ourselves and improve our health and wellness, both physically and mentally. And blue space is now entering the picture.

In this conversation about water and forest, green space refers to plants, forests, and trees. Blue space refers to lakes, rivers, and oceans.

When we add blue to the equation, the benefits increase. Even the sound of water allows us to relax and helps us become more mindful.

Recent reviews of all the studies on blue space indicate that from a mental health and emotional health perspective, water is a wonderful tool. In fact, water is medicine for our mental health.

These are important insights into understanding the world around us and how we communicate the need to protect and restore the lakes, rivers, and oceans of our planet.

Lab-based research is being conducted to determine how the brain responds to fields of green and fields of blue—to scenes related to a creek running through the mountains or a coast, an ocean, and waves. This research has shown that specific portions of the brain light up in response to nature. These new studies are giving us even more insight into the science behind blue mind.

BLUE MIND:
THE HEALING POWER OF WATER

[Introduction by Shauna Shapiro]

Wallace J. Nichols is a renowned marine biologist and wild-water advocate. In his critically acclaimed book *Blue Mind*, he shares the ecological, economic, emotional, physical, and social benefits of healthy oceans and water. Jay is revolutionizing our understanding of the power of water to impact our individual and collective lives.

[End of introduction]

In this section of the *Masters of Mindfulness* course, we're going to talk about water. We're going to talk about how being near, in, on, or even underwater helps us to be happier, healthier more connected and even better at what we do. And this is something I call blue mind. The connection between our mind and our water planet and the overview of this section, really, we're going to look at how water makes our lives worth living. We're going to talk about how when we undervalue water, bad things happen. We lose our waterways. We talk about how that water is our first medicine, both for our physical, but also our mental and emotional health. And remember that the emotional benefits of water are critical to our understanding of what the true value of water really is. And that how water can provide a universal tool that will enhance mindfulness for all people, all over the world, throughout all ages of our lives.

And are always remember that when you talk about water you should talk about blue mind and these emotional benefits. There's a great quote from the Japanese scholar Tanaka Shozo, and he says "The care of rivers is not a question of rivers, but of the human heart." And we can take that idea and extend it more broadly to waters; that the care of waters is not just a question of water, but a question of our hearts and our minds.

When I meet people around the world, I often give them a blue marble like this one, as a small gesture of gratitude and a way to say thank you for what they do to fix what's broken on the planet. And these blue marbles are a simple representation that we live on a small blue planet. Our planet is mostly covered with water. We ourselves are mostly made of water and whatever we do here on this small blue planet matters: the big things, the little things, the good things, and the bad things.

It's also a reminder that we never do anything alone. We always are working together. We're always collaborating on anything, even if we feel alone. We're never alone. And when I share these blue marbles with people I often follow up with a question and that is: What's your water? Now I ask you to consider that simple question: What's the water that you dream about? What's the water that you long for? And when did you fall in love with your water?

And finally, who took you there? Who was your guide? Who is the person or the people? The teacher? The family member who brought you to your water the first time?

Just take a moment and think about that. Think about your water and when you fell in love with it and who took you there and how much that water means to you and your life. For some people their water is a matter of hydration and hygiene, simply of the water we drink and bathe in. For some it's a more adventurous experience, it is the water we play in. It's the adrenaline rush we get from the whitewater or from paddling on flat water. For a lot of people, it's the community and the family time we get when we spend time on water together, sometimes just standing around having conversations in the water together with the people we love.

Bridges can even give us access to our water when you pass over your water, following from one side to the other using a bridge, you often get a short moment to ponder the water as you're crossing over it. A well-designed bridge will safely get you from point A to point B, but it will also give you a beautiful view of your water and especially in urban areas.

When we're at our water we pause, and think; we ponder, we dream. Water can help us sleep. It can help us slip away and calm our minds so that we have a restful evening and night. When we learn new skills on the water or in the water we feel more empowered, we feel stronger feel like a better version of ourselves. It's something that is pervasive throughout our lives that allows us to relax when we sit in our warm baths or hot tubs or hot springs. We connect with ourselves. We connect with whoever we're with, be it a fellow human or our pet, perhaps a water loving dog.

For me as a marine biologist, when I get in the water, meeting the fellow water dwellers is what lights me up: swimming with sea turtles or watching dolphins bow ride from the front of the boat or even being completely submerged under the ocean, eye to eye with a giant animal like a whale. Sometimes water reflects the mood around us, it reflects the seasons, it reminds us that time is passing, that the world is changing.

For some it's being in domestic water and inside in our bathtubs and our showers or even taking a sip of water from the tap. We get to luxuriate in the taste and the feel, the coolness, the hydration, the refreshing sense that all is well when we connect with our water.

Now this water story is not just about oceans, but it's also about lakes and rivers and wherever we are in our country or around the world we are never far away from water, even when we're in the deserts, we're never far away from a river, a lake, or a spring.

For me personally when I think about that question— what's your water? — I go back to my father. He was the person who introduced us to the water as kids. He taught us to swim, taught us to dive. He's synonymous with water for our family. I can recall a time spent in the Rocky Mountains by Deep Lake, just standing in the grass, breathing in the air, feeling the cold water when we jumped in it in the morning. It takes me right back to one of the best moments of my life.

But as a kid I was in love with sea turtles. I was just kind of obsessed with sea turtles and that desire to learn more about turtles led me to be a marine biologist and I've spent my career traveling the world learning about the ocean and working on behalf of sea turtles. I actually am quite obsessed with sea turtles to the point where I sometimes see them where sea turtles don't exist, like in the faces of rocks or patterns in clouds. I imagine sea turtles even in the faces of friends and colleagues, but I remember going home and telling my father that I was not going to be a doctor a lawyer, a businessman, or an engineer: that I was going to be a turtle guy. It felt a little bit like that scene in *Star Wars* where Luke Skywalker's face to face with his father, Darth Vader, and they have some explaining to do. My dad was very concerned I guess you could say, "What are you going to do with sea turtles?" he asked.

And what I told him is that I was going to follow my sea turtle dream to Mexico and begin to study the turtles of the Pacific coast of Mexico and the reason I bring that up is because the first sea turtle that we put a satellite transmitter on was a turtle named Adalita. She had been raised in captivity for 10 years in a tank and grew from a small size to an adult size. And when we got her back in the ocean, put a satellite transmitter on her shell, and released her. And what was so interesting is she swam from away from the boat, she swam underwater about the distance that the tank was wide, about 10 meters, and then she paused as if to say where's the wall, there's always been a wall. In her little turtle brain, she imagined a wall and that imaginary wall caused her to pause, caused her to stop swimming.

Now that is interesting biologically, but it's also a powerful metaphor for the things in our lives that stop us. that scare us, that cause us to shut down and maybe turn around and go the other way. The imaginary walls that only exist in our minds. So, here this turtle is teaching us a lesson about imaginary walls and the pause or the way they can stop us. For Adalita, this loggerhead sea turtle the other side of the wall represented the rest of her life. In fact, the other side of the wall represented a 7,000-mile journey that she took off on at that moment. She paused, she swam through the imaginary wall and then continued to swim 7,000 miles across the North Pacific Ocean. It took her 368 days but she made it all the way home to Japan, to the beaches in Japan where she was born.

So, on the other side of the walls that hold us in is the rest of our life. Sometimes it's a massive wide open beautiful blue ocean as is the case with Adalita. So, we need to better understand what's holding us back and consider what walls have we swum through. How did we do it? But more importantly, what walls do we still need to swim through?

And so, to round out the sea turtle story, I began to work with turtle hunters throughout Mexico, people like Jesus Lucero and Juan de la Cruz, the so-called "Enemies of Nature." They were the walls for the sea turtles. They were hunting them to extinction, but we began to collaborate and worked together to bring sea turtles back from the brink.

So, that was a wall that we swam through together. We defied status quo and began to collaborate. Scientists, conservationists, and former sea turtle hunters and now sea turtles are making a comeback in the eastern Pacific.

The reason for including a story about sea turtles in a course on mindfulness is that it took all of us that moment to pause to consider what our imaginary walls were that were stopping us and then to move through them. And as a result, we have protected millions of baby sea turtles and this population of sea turtles is making a tremendous comeback. It came from the understanding that we, the ocean, the sea turtles, the turtle hunters were all connected, were all part of the same fabric of life. We are made of the same stuff. There is no really disconnect between us.

The walls that that divide us are in fact imaginary. So, sea turtles are my teachers in this blue mindfulness conversation.

Another teacher is a woman named Barbara Daugherty. When I was an undergrad in college I was invited by our university chaplain to give guitar lessons to Barbara. She had been institutionalized for 15 years as a result of a car accident and when we started playing the guitar together every day, every afternoon on Wednesdays, it started to trigger some memories for her and she started to remember things about her childhood, about her young adulthood prior to her accident and that reminded me how powerful and interesting the human brain is and how music can unlock our seemingly lost memories and change us.

Our emotional connection to music is so incredibly important and as a lover of water I wondered whether water may play a similar role. So, Barbara Daugherty was one of my teachers, along with those sea turtles and turtle hunters.

There's a great passage from the Professor Gus Speth from Yale University where he describes how he once thought that if we just had enough science to understand how to fix the problems, people would respond and move in the right direction. But then he realized that that was not enough that we needed a personal, a spiritual and an emotional transformation and that science was not always equipped to do that; that we needed to widen our gaze and look beyond the narrow science that we had available and better understand the world around us. In the case of water, that holds true. We need to understand the true value of healthy waters: cognitively, emotionally, psychologically, socially, and even spiritually; in order to protect them, in order to protect ourselves and take care of the planet we share.

So, my journey to understand water took me to conversations with neuroscientists and psychologists, people who study the brain and even neurons at the cellular level. What I learned was that our understanding of the brain and the mind, the old model was limited due to the black box model where you could stimulate a person and see how they responded, but you couldn't see inside. Well, in reality you could, you could open up and look at the brain but only after people were done using it. And it wasn't until more recently that we began to acquire the tools, the technology, to look at the brain while it was still in use, to measure electricity, to measure oxygen using EEG and fMRI technology, and to ask questions about how the brain at rest is different from the active brain, the brain in motion, to ask questions about emotions such as love and to begin to understand that love has a neurochemical signature that involves chemicals like oxytocin, that are involved in building trust.

Now there are people who are very excited about neuropsychology and neurochemistry to the point where maybe they're enthusiastic and spend their lives studying it, just as people spend their lives studying water and some of us spend our lives studying sea turtles. But what we've seen is neurosciences has simply exploded onto the front covers of magazines, newspapers, radio reports. We are learning how to apply the understanding, the science of our brains, to everyday life in practical ways. Scientists are studying people who meditate and learning how they do it and how it benefits their health and the health of those around them. Neuroscientists are winning Nobel Prizes for their work to unlock the mysteries of the brain and we are literally living in what many refer to as the golden age of neuroscience.

So, you know that from all the other sections of this course that have been talking about our brain on mindfulness. But what I want to do is bring it into the water realm. Now, if you went a few years ago to the bookstore or the library you'd find a number of titles related to applied neuroscience and neuropsychology. Those relate to music, they relate to creativity, they relate to happiness, they even relate to economics and how we can change our mood and change our minds by being more mindful. But what you wouldn't find on the shelves were books about nature and water. You find all of these realms where neuroscience and neuropsychology connect to the world around us, but what was missing was this extra piece about nature. We even have a working owner's manual or a user's guide to our own brain.

So, I began to wonder about this gap between the science of mindfulness and water. And I notice that on many books about positive psychology about happiness, about mindfulness, water images graced the cover. The decision was made to put water on the cover, but rarely mention blue mindfulness in the text.

So, there is a book, it's called *Jaws*, that was I guess you say, about emotion and it really scared people out of the water. But now there's a whole other generation of books that is exploring how nature and in particular water can help us reconnect to ourselves, to the water, to nature, and to those around us. We're beginning to understand that behavior change involves small incremental steps; that we are human beings, that we are not cogs in a system. And this field that I called neuro-conservation connects neuroscience and conservation biology, protecting the world around us in a more mindful way.

Now, in order to do good neuro-conservation we do have to understand that people are human and to an understanding how people react to the world around us is incredibly important to taking better care of the world around us. So, we've done a few experiments to look at how our brains track nature and what we've learned is that when we're swimming in the water we follow the eyes of animals as they swim with us. We are drawn to novelty. The water around us helps us relax, it switches our emotional state from a focused sort of prefrontal cortex active working state to a more distributed perspective involving the default network as is referred to by neuroscientists.

We're understanding that the value of water is ecological, economic, educational, but also emotional, that the emotional value of water is incredibly important to our wellness and to understanding how to better take care of the water around us. I think the emotion needs to be put front and center and we need to lead with that conceptually.

Emotion underlies all of our decisions we've learned as psychologists and neuroscientists have unpacked the science of emotion and emotion is a physiological response to the world around us. Now to put this in context we can see that in our country and across the world we've had a higher level of stress. A lot of things are easier for modern humans but we're still experiencing a high level of stress for a number of reasons. And 60 percent of modern diseases and disorders relate to that stress. They're either caused by it directly or exacerbated by stress.

Now the world seems to be more connected. We are ever more stimulated. We're kind of always on. And that does take its toll on our minds and our bodies. As the dad of two daughters I pay particular attention to the research on adolescents and teens, particularly girls, and how social media is changing the way they interact with the world and the results are a bit frightening. Higher levels of anxiety and even depression are occurring in young women.

When I travel the country, I read headlines on local newspapers about drug addiction, about the war on drugs, about the problem with opioids. People are self-medicating. They're taking care of the stress and anxiety in ways that only create more and more stress and anxiety. We've got a public health crisis as a result of the stress and anxiety that pervades our lives and at its most extreme we refer to it as post-traumatic stress. So, people who have experienced some sort of acute trauma or repetitive trauma have what's called post-traumatic stress. Now the result of all this anxiety and stress sometimes is suicide. A number of people take their own lives and are unable to manage the anxiety that is occurring.

If you take this whole conversation and put it together I call this state red mind and it is increasingly the norm. This red mind state is one of overstimulation, over connection, but also a disconnection at the same time that causes anxiety and stress in our lives. This is our new normal. When we have too much red mind, eventually it leads to gray mind which is burnout. Gray mind is the numbed out, indifferent, completely blasé perspective on the world. None of that is good for us. Red mind is useful, we need red mind to get things done, to get across the finish line, to reach deadlines. But if it's all we have, eventually it burns us down.

Now if we could we would go to the doctor and say, "Hey I'd like this red mind removed," but that surgery is currently not available. So, from the perspective of the environment and communicating about the world around us, we show up and we often bring messages of fear and anger to try to motivate people to respond to the environmental crisis. Now we know from research that anger creates even more red mind, it creates a fight or flight response. We bring tools like shame and we unload a lot of facts on people. So, that combination of fear, anger, shame, and facts just creates even more red mind. And we know that in that red mind fight or flight state we are less creative, we are less collaborative, we're less likely to solve problems and be innovative and find our way forward. We're more likely to run away. We're more likely to fight and that doesn't solve our problems.

The basic idea, the message that we share, around water is that we've got a huge problem. It's your fault. But then we asked people, "Would you like to join our club?" And the answer is often no. So, what I like to lead with is gratitude. What if we say thank you for what people are doing? At first, we begin with gratitude and we build on that with love.

We create connections and respect. That builds trust between people and allows us to communicate in a way that helps to solve problems. So, by bringing more positive emotions to the conversation about water we have a better chance of solving those water problems.

Now there's an increasing amount of literature on how green space can help us take better care of ourselves and improve our health and wellness, both physically and mentally. But what's so interesting is that blue space is now entering the picture, this conversation about water and forest. So, green space refers to plants and forests and trees.

Blue space reform refers to lakes, rivers, and oceans. So, when we add blue to the equation those benefits go up. Even the sound of water allows us to relax, helps us to become more mindful. And recent reviews of all of the studies on blue space indicate that from a mental health and emotional health perspective water is a wonderful tool. In fact, water is medicine for our mental health. So, these are important insights into understanding the world around us and how we communicate the need to protect and restore the lakes and rivers and oceans of our planet.

Now even more lab based research is occurring that looks at how the brain responds to fields of green and fields of blue, to scenes related to a creek running through the mountains or a coast, an ocean and waves. And there are certain, specific portions of the brain that light up in response to natural beauty, response to nature, and these new studies are giving us even more insight into the science behind blue mind.

Now the reality is blue mind is not a new concept, it's an ancient concept. It goes all the way back to the beginning of recorded human history. Indigenous groups around the world know that water is life, that water is sacred, and they celebrate that. This is not a new idea. Artists around the world have depicted the emotion connected to water throughout the ages. The great works of art, many of them involve water. People once stood in line for hours in order to stand in front of paintings of the ocean. They paid money in order to witness the awe of the ocean brought to them through beautiful paintings, works of art.

The great Georgia O'Keeffe, before she became famous for painting in the desert, she painted lakes in New York. She painted water and did so beautifully. Modern Artists like Ran Ortner continue this tradition. They paint giant depictions of the surface of water using just pounds and pounds of paint to evoke the blue mind emotion. And my brother in law Jon Imber passed away a few years ago of ALS. He spent his career painting by the ocean with my sister, a fellow painter, and standing side by side they fell in love with each other. They fell in love with Stonington Harbor and the waters of Maine and they fell in love with their art and their art made the sense of awe portable that they experience, by putting paint on canvas. That feeling that they had for each other and for the ocean became portable so that others could experience it. That's what art does: it makes this sense of awe portable.

This idea of blue mind is depicted in art as well as music. The great Tom Waits also enjoined by Bruce Springsteen sang "Because down the shore everything's alright" in his song "Jersey Girl."

Carlos Argentino, *"En el mar la vida es mas sabrosa, En el mar te quiero mucho mas."* "At sea, life is sweeter. At sea, I love you more."

"When anxious, uneasy, and bad thoughts come, I go to the sea, and the sea drowns them out with its great wide sounds," wrote Rainer Rilke.

"Turn off your mind, relax and float downstream," sang John Lennon.

"Water is the softest thing, yet can penetrate mountains and earth. This shows clearly the principle of softness overcoming hardness," wrote Lao Tzu.

Advertisers have always known that water invokes feelings of calm and connects us. Throughout advertising history images of water have been used to sell products ranging from drinks from beer, even pharmaceuticals and automobiles. Emotion is used as a way to connect us to brands. A variety of companies have used emotion to connect us to happiness associated with their products. But the reality of that is that happiness is made by us, not by the product. Happiness is made internally through the production of dopamine. Dopamine gives us a feeling of happiness and water is one of the greatest sources of happiness.

Hollywood has understood this. Films like *Shawshank Redemption* ending with the character portrayed by Morgan Freeman on the beach, reminding himself that the dream of the ocean that he had been dreaming, from within his prison cell, of freedom. In fact, there it was, right at the end of the film.

We know that water is the oldest medicine, the first medicine, and that we in fact are made primarily of water and the planet we live on is covered mostly with water. It's important to remember that our brains and bodies are hardwired to respond positively to water of all kinds—our lakes, rivers, oceans, and even pools—in ways that can improve our physical and emotional health. That is fundamentally the message of this first section about blue mind and in the next session we'll describe how these ideas can be applied throughout our lives.

GO DEEPER: THE SEVEN AGES OF WATER

LESSON 20

Blue mind can be carried through our entire life history—
from birth through death—in what can be considered the
seven ages of water.

BIRTH

Each of us spent nine months in the womb—underwater in the dark in a sailing environment, just swimming around and relaxing, without a care in the world.

When we emerge into the world, suddenly there are bright lights, gravity, and air. Some people have a water birth that transitions from one watery environment to the next to make the experience less harsh for the baby. Our birth story is probably one of the most important stories that we carry with us, so when our birth involves water, that may set us up for a lifelong love of water.

It's important to consider the role of water in conception, gestation, and birth—but also in our early lives. Getting children into the water at an early age is good for their cognitive development. Moving in the water safely together and supervised is referred to as water parenting, and it's starting to catch on all over the world.

PLAY

As we become mobile, we begin to engage with the world around us, especially through play. Scientists have shown that play is not just for fun; it helps both our brain and body develop properly. We begin playing in three dimensions, interacting with the world, trying things, sometimes failing, and trying again until we succeed.

It's Just Science!
Play Fuels the Mind

Improves decision making

Clears out the cobwebs

Raises empathy

Increases speed of learning

Jump-starts imagination & creativity

Raises engagement & motivation

Learning new skills in the context of water allows us to fall and fail less painfully. Eventually, we learn to swim in water and to dive and jump into water—interacting with water in all of the many ways it allows—which is part and parcel to play.

Water helps us connect with the world around us in a hopeful way. Water can also help us deepen our trust in ourselves and in those around us, as well as the water itself. This is no small deal, considering that most of the planet is covered with water. We will all interact with water on purpose or otherwise throughout our lives, so building trust and respect for water is incredibly important.

Programs around the world are introducing children to water and helping them work through many of the disorders and dilemmas that may plague their young lives.

Children build confidence when they learn a new skill, and the water can be the vehicle that allows this. There are programs that teach children how to surf and swim as well as basic safety skills, and children leave those programs feeling empowered, stronger, and more connected to each other and to the planet we live on.

There's a sense of freedom that comes from being in the water that is hard to find anywhere else.

It's very important that we continue to play throughout our entire lives. As adults, we have a fear of letting go and finding that part of ourselves that is more open and more creative. But don't be afraid of that. Continue to get into the water and play. Splash around and let your mind open.

THE LOVER

This period is when we fall in love with ourselves, with big ideas, and with each other. It's when we begin to dream big dreams that become our future.

Research shows that mind wandering and daydreaming are incredibly important to creativity and solving problems. Disconnected time to let your mind wander is when we begin to dream, and those dreams become the ideas that will dictate our lives.

In many cases, taking time away from daily life, especially traffic and technology, and just walking on the beach with someone you love and having a moment of privacy to connect to each other is what falling in love is all about.

A sense of awe and wonder overcomes us when we experience nature, such as the large ocean or a sunset. Scientists have discovered that having a sense of awe and wonder sets us up for an increase in empathy and compassion. Because the number one source of awe on the planet is nature and water is the biggest subcategory of nature, then it follows that water builds empathy and compassion.

It's very important that we take care of ourselves and work on our personal emotional health so that we remain strong, clear, and creative. But what's even more important is that we connect that wellness to the world around us to improve life on earth.

Find awe in your water, whatever your water is—whether it's the pond down the street, the creek running through your community, or an ocean that you visit during a vacation.

Another part of the lover age is falling in love with each other. It's about romance and the romantic connection that we have with each other. And there's something about the water that is incredibly romantic; it's almost a cliché that water and romance are intertwined.

THE FIGHTER

This age is when we fight for what we love. We can fight for our water. We can restore coral reefs and fight for the water and life within our oceans.

We can also fight on the court and on the field as athletes, and elite athletes are understanding that water helps them heal, reduce stress, and come back stronger.

Athletes use flotation therapy as a way to calm their minds and improve their performance, and using flotation pods is becoming more mainstream among elite athletes. Research shows that floating in water is good for the mind and body, and athlete performance is backing this up.

Sometimes we fight for what we believe in. All warriors need to know about humility, and nature—especially water—teaches us about humility. The ocean will knock you down; the river will sweep you away.

Water gives us the resilience we need to come back over and over and fight for what we love. When you fight for what you love, you will fall down and get hurt, and you will need to stand up and come back to fight again—whether it's fighting for the people you love, the ideas you care about, or the places that help make you whole.

THE JUSTICE

This is the widest and longest age of our lives, when we are in our productive years and are expected to be responsible, be creative, and solve problems on demand day after day. This occurs at work, in our household, in our place of worship, on our sports teams, and in our schools. This is the long, heavy age where we're carrying the weight of responsibility on our shoulders and doing our part for our communities and for society.

We need to find balance in this age. We need to understand that it isn't just about work; it's also about relaxing. And water can play an important role in helping us maintain our creativity, be responsible, and come back and be persistent, productive members of our team.

We need to be able to find a place to go where we can reset and relax, and the water provides a great opportunity to do this in many ways, whether we are near the water, on a boat, or even walking through an aquarium. Research shows that just standing in front of an aquarium tank puts you into a different state of mind. People's breathing and heart rates slow, and they report a higher level of wellness.

This blue-mind state also gives us a feeling of solitude. And in this increasingly connected world, where we're wired to each other all the time, solitude is at a premium. Being able to truly disconnect and be alone with your own thoughts is important to our mental health and wellness. Water provides an outlet for us to reclaim our solitude and leave our devices behind.

EBB AND FLOW

This is when we need to get in the water to heal our bodies. We need to get near the water to reduce the weight of the world. This typically happens later in life, but it can happen at any point when we need water therapeutically.

We tend to find that this is needed most acutely later in life, as our joints start to get sore and our body starts to fail, but this can also happen after any kind of accident at any age.

Hospitals are beginning to understand that pools can be used therapeutically for their patients, both for recovery of their bodies but also to help them relax and mitigate pain. Children that are hospitalized and dealing with the pain of their condition can receive some relief from that pain through water.

The research around the world on the health and well-being benefits of swimming is clear: Getting in the water is a tool that is underutilized and available to everyone. We just need to step in and prioritize it. When we get in the water and move our bodies, we reduce the chances of injury and increase the chances of healing and recovery.

> Even virtual water can help us mitigate pain and promote a path of healing. Research has shown that virtual ocean experiences via virtual reality goggles help reduce pain in children in intensive care.

Health-care professionals have begun to prescribe water as medicine. It's becoming more and more common for doctors, nurses, and medical practitioners to encourage their patients to get in the water.

Water is also a source of nostalgia. If we form memories of the water we love in the places we play during childhood, we can rely on those memories when it's harder to get to those places later in life. And these places can produce feelings of wellness, joy, happiness, and connection.

DEATH

Water and death have always gone together. There are various kinds of ceremonies involving rivers and water. Around the world, there are burials at sea. And it's increasingly common for families to gather by the water to remember lost loved ones.

Water helps us reconnect with our families and with each other. It also helps us reconcile some of the differences that occur at the end of lives. Reconnection and reconciliation are facilitated by being near and in the water with those we love, even in the face of death.

ACCESS TO WATER

If water is medicine for our bodies and minds—if it's a path to mindfulness and relaxation—then we should all have access to it. But we often don't.

There are three main reasons why we may not have access to water: the physical barriers that separate us from the water; the pollution that can preclude spending time in the water; and the perception (either in your mind or as a result of your culture telling you) that the water is not available to you.

GO DEEPER: THE SEVEN AGES OF WATER

LESSON 20 TRANSCRIPT

In the previous section, we described how blue mind works and how our brains are hardwired to respond positively to water in ways that improve our emotional health. In this section, we want to take those ideas and that definition and apply it to our lives in what I call the seven ages of water. We want to look at how blue mind can be carried through our entire life history from birth through death.

So, let's begin with birth. We all spent nine months in the womb, underwater in the dark, in a saline environment, just swimming around relaxing without a care in the world. There was no gravity. It was entirely an aquatic experience. We have very few clear conscious memories of that. But there are scientists who believe that we do carry the memory, deep memory, of that experience. So, we emerge into the world, and boom, its gravity, its bright lights, its air. Some people do something called a water birth or at least a water labor that transitions from one watery environment to the next to make it a little bit less harsh. But our birth story is probably one of the most important stories that we carry with us. So, when our birth involves water, that may actually set us up for a lifelong love of water, when that story gets repeated over and over.

So, it's important to consider the role of water in conception, in gestation, in birth, but also in our early lives. People are realizing that getting our children, getting our babies, into the water at an early age is really good for our cognitive development. Moving in the water safely together, supervised, is something referred to as water parenting.

And it's starting to catch on all over the world. So, that's the first age of water is birth, starting out our lives in a water-full way is setting ourselves on a positive path towards loving the water, but also being happy and healthy in it.

The next age I referred to as play. So now we become mobile. We're walking around. We begin to engage with the world around us and what scientists have shown is that play is not just for fun. It helps our brain and our body develop properly. Playing in three dimensions, interacting with the world, trying things, sometimes failing, trying again until we succeed. Learning new skills in the context of water for play is one that allows us to fall and fail less painfully, throwing water, splashing in water, moving water from one container to the next. Eventually learning to swim, learning to dive, learning to jump into water, and interacting with water in all of the many ways, shapes, and forms that it allows is part and parcel to play.

Water helps us build hope. It helps us to connect with the world around us in a hopeful way. It can also help us to deepen our trust in ourselves, in others, those around us, and trust the water itself. Now this is no small deal considering that most of the planet is covered with water. We will all interact with water on purpose or otherwise throughout our lives, so building a trust and a respect for water is incredibly important.

Programs across the nation and around the world are introducing kids to water and helping them work through many of the disorders and dilemmas that may plague their young lives. Programs for at risk youth, such as Northwest Passage in Wisconsin, invite the kids to put on wetsuits, masks, and snorkels and dive into the rivers of Wisconsin and the kids describe that experience as one where they felt freedom for the first time. Now think about that. Playing in the river with a camera, a wet suit, a mask, and snorkel allows a young person to experience freedom for the first time. That's profound and that's also available to all of us, to all of our kids.

Programs like Soul River, run by my friend Chad Brown in Oregon, he gets inner city youth out to the rivers of Oregon and they play at the river, they fish. They learn to fly fish. They interact with the water; they interact with each other. It's joyful, it's fun. They build skills and they feel good. They get to escape from the stressors the red mind of the city and just put their minds at ease out on the river. So, for Chad and Soul River rivers are in fact medicine.

Now this is a conversation about kids and nature that is completely nonpartisan. Melania Trump, our First Lady, she has been a powerful advocate for kids and nature. She said on numerous occasions that nature is medicine for our kids. So, this is a conversation that crosses all political boundaries, crosses all socio-economic limitations. All of our kids should know that water is medicine.

Our kids build confidence when they learn a new skill and the water can be the vehicle that allows that building of confidence. My daughter Julia, when she learned to surf, I can remember how full of herself she was that evening.

She already had a lot of confidence, but she had even more confidence after she acquired that new skill and was able to surf some waves in Waikiki, Hawaii.

There are programs like the Wahine Project that get kids from agricultural communities in California, who have never even stepped into the ocean, and they get out on surfboards, they learn to surf, they learn to swim, they learn basic safety skills. They do beach clean-ups and they leave those programs feeling empowered, feeling stronger, more connected, more connected to each other and more connected to the planet we live on.

There's a sense of freedom that comes from being in the water that is hard to find anywhere else and probably the best way to depict that is to describe the life and work of a young man named Naoki Higashida. He at 13 years old wrote a book called *The Reason I Jump* about his experience with autism. He couldn't find any books that adequately described the way it felt to be him. And so, he wrote his own book. In one passage in that book describes how in the water it's so quiet and he feels so free and happy. But outside on land, there's distraction and stimulation and red mind and it's all more difficult. But back in the water he feels normal. He feels like the rest of us, he says.

And that's really amazing for Naoki Higashida, water is his medicine. It's his best medicine.

Now it's very important that we continue to play throughout our entire lives. Play isn't just for kids. Playing around in the water is something we can do throughout our lives. I like I like to say, balloons are fun but water balloons are way more fun. Slides are great, but water slides are a serious party. Parks are nice, but waterparks, you know bring it, you know it's really, that's where the fun in the play really happens, when you add water to any situation and this is something we need to remember throughout our lives.

My friend, musician Alexi Murdoch, wrote a song called "Blue Mind" and right at the end he sings, "Remember when you were only a child and start to see with your blue mind. Don't be afraid of what you find." Don't be afraid of what you find and I think as adults we have a fear of letting go and playing and really just splashing around and finding that part of ourselves that is more open and more creative. And so, what Alexi says, don't be afraid of that.

Continue to get into the water and play, splash around, and let your mind open.

The next and third age of water I call the lover. This period called the lover is when we fall in love with ourselves, when we fall in love with big ideas. We decide what we're passionate for and we fall in love with each other. There's a romantic piece, but there's also the love of ideas and love of special places. It's the age when we begin to dream big dreams that become our future, become our lives, become our careers and our hobbies and we connect to the things we care most about. And what we know from research is that mind wandering and daydreaming are incredibly important to creativity and solving problems.

Now removing opportunities to let your mind wander will reduce creativity. So, it seems kind of counterintuitive, that you know, kids who aren't paying attention, looking out the window, are just mucking around and, quote-unquote, wasting time may in fact be having creative breakthrough, aha moment. So, it's really important that we understand that time disconnected, time to let your mind wander, is when you begin to dream and those dreams become the ideas that will dictate our lives in many cases.

Taking time away from others, from screens, from traffic, from technology, and just walking on the beach, either alone or with someone you love, perhaps with your dog, with your spouse or your child, with a friend and having that moment of privacy to just kind of connect to each other is really what falling in love is all about.

We have a sense of awe that overcomes us, a sense of awe and wonder when we experience nature, when we experience the big ocean, lake, river, sunset. That sense of awe, in fact, is increasingly understood by scientists and we're learning that awe and wonder sets us up for an increase in empathy and compassion. In fact, it's a vehicle to achieve empathy and compassion.

So, connect the dots on that one. Think about that. The number one source of awe on planet earth is nature, and within that category water is the biggest subcategory, and awe and wonder is a pathway to empathy and compassion.

So, water builds empathy and compassion for ourselves, for our fellow-humans, and for nature around us. So, that's a positive feedback loop that's also regenerative. That sense awe switches us from a me perspective to a we perspective. It takes us out of ourselves. It's very important that we take care of ourselves and we work on our personal emotional health, that we remain strong and clear and creative. But what's even more important is that we connect that wellness to the world around us, to the people we care about, to our communities and to improving life here on this little blue marble we call our home.

I like to encourage people to find awe in their water. Whatever your water is, whatever you answered to that question—what's your water? — you can find awe in it, whether it's the pond down the street, the creek running through your community, an ocean that you visit during a vacation. Whatever your water is, find the awe in it.

Now another part of the lover age is falling in love with each other, romance, the romantic connection that we have to each other. So, this one scene in *From Here to Eternity* where the couple is on the beach, smooching in their swim suits, and it was actually a scandalous scene. But I like I like to consider that scene without the water. The water is rushing up and covering them and they're embracing and rolling around and kissing. Imagine that same scene without the ocean and its very strange people rolling around in their underwear, in the dirt, would not be included in the film. But you bring the ocean back to the scene and it makes perfect sense. So, there's something about the water that is incredibly romantic and very sexy, but it doesn't make sense. The scene doesn't play without the water. So, it's almost a cliché that water and romance go together.

The next stage, the fourth age of water, I refer to as the fighter, and that is when we fight for what we love. People like Sylvia Earle is a great advocate, lifelong advocate for the ocean. People like Manna Jo Greene, fighting for the Hudson River and Alice Brown Otter, she's an advocate for her water, her indigenous waterways. We can fight for our water.

We can also fight on the court and on the field as athletes and elite athletes are understanding that water helps them heal, helps them reduce their stress and come back stronger. Athletes like Steph Curry who plays for the Golden State Warriors. The Chicago Cubs, they installed a float tank in their locker room the year that they won the World Series. And the New England Patriots also are known to use flotation therapy, floating in hyper saline water, as a way to calm their minds and improve performance. So, getting in these flotation pods, as it turns out is becoming more mainstream among elite athletes. They know that floating in water is good for their minds and their bodies and research is backing that up, but also their performance and the result on the court and on the field, is backing it up.

So, we fight for what we believe in. We fight through sport and all warriors need to know about humility. Nature teaches us about humility. If you lose humility, you will crash and you will fail. That's lesson number one is to remain humble. It's another gift that water brings us. The ocean will knock you down, the river will sweep you away. It gives you lessons related to humility.

Sometimes we fight for what we believe in. Like my friend Martin Pollack, who fought, he is a British military man, he fought in Afghanistan and came home with neither of his legs and only one of his arms. And what Martin learned was that the ocean was his medicine. So, he became a surfer and quite a good surfer and now he teaches others to get on their surfboards or overcome their fears and use water as a way to heal and feel stronger. And he's an ambassador, not only for fellow veterans, but also for the ocean and he would tell you that he's a trained warrior and we're lucky to have him on our team, on behalf of the ocean. So, people like Martin Pollack who fought for what he believed in and came back injured, but knows that water will help him be more resilient.

Groups like Heroes on the Water have chapters across the nation connecting veterans to their lakes and their rivers and their oceans through kayak fishing. And what we know is when you're on a kayak fishing mostly what you're doing is calmly sitting, quietly, looking at the water in a mildly meditative state. But if we called it kayak meditation maybe fewer people would show up. So, it's called kayak fishing and involves a lot of downtime, a lot of waiting and thinking and just being calm while surrounded by water. Groups like Forest Blue recruit special operations veterans from all sectors of the armed forces. And not only are they healing themselves through scuba diving, they're also restoring coral reefs and fighting for our oceans.

Water gives us the resilience we need to come back over and over and over and fight for what we love. Because when you fight for what you love you will fall down, you will get clobbered, you will get hurt and you will need to stand up and come back and fight again, whether it's fighting for the people you love, the ideas you care about, or the places that help make you whole. You need to be resilient and be able to come back and do more over and over again.

The next age is one that I referred to as the justice and it is the widest and longest age of our lives. It's the one where we are in our productive years, where we're expected to be responsible. We're expected to be creative and solve problems on demand, day in and day out. And that occurs at work, it occurs in our household, it may occur in our place of worship, on our sports teams, in our schools. In this age, the justice, we are expected to perform and you get very few chances to not perform. So, this is the long heavy age where we're carrying the weight of responsibility on our shoulders and doing our part for our communities and for society.

And we do need to find certain kind of balance in this age and understand that it isn't just about work, but it's also about relaxing and that water can play an important role in helping us to maintain our creativity, to be responsible and to come back and be persistent and productive members of our team. We need to be able to find a place to go reset and chill out and maybe by the water, maybe on a boat, could be fishing, even walking through an aquarium and just meandering through and looking at the animals.

Aquariums around the world know that people go there to learn, but they also go there simply to walk around and relax. And there our recent research on this shows that just standing in front of an aquarium tank puts you into a different state of mind. Your breathing rate slows, your heart rate slows, and you report a higher level of wellness from that experience, just standing quietly in front of a tank full of water with fish swimming around in it.

This blue-mind state also gives us a feeling of solitude. And in this increasingly connected world where we're just wired to each other all the time, solitude is at a premium. Being able to truly disconnect and be alone with your own thoughts, knowing that they aren't recorded, they won't be played back to you, is incredibly important to our mental health and our wellness. There's a recent study that showed that young people are increasingly unable to do solitude, they find it painful to sit for six to

15 minutes quietly with their own thoughts. That will play out and will change the way society works. I think water provides an outlet for us to reclaim our solitude, leave our devices behind.

It's also a place where we achieve creativity, getting near and on and even underwater can boost our creativity. The late, great Oliver Sacks, the neurologist, said he got his best ideas in the water and he was a good idea factory. He had so many world changing, insightful brilliant ideas throughout his career. And he said he got his best ideas while in the water while swimming laps or swimming across lakes. The great musician Pharrell Williams also said something similar, that his creativity is based in water and he took that creativity and turned it into music that makes a lot of people happy.

The next age, the second to last age, I call ebb and flow and this is when gravity starts to weigh on us, later in life typically, but it can happen at any point, where we need water therapeutically. We need to get in the water to heal our bodies. We need to get near the water to reduce the weight of the world. Now we tend to find this needed most acutely later in life as our joints start to get sore and our body starts to fail, but really can happen after any kind of accident at any age.

People just really enjoy taking time out and going and spending some time by the water. Hospitals are beginning to understand that pools can be used therapeutically for their patients both for recovery of their bodies, but also to help them relax and mitigate pain.

Our friend Jamila, who spent 10 years in a nursing home suffering from Alzheimer's, when asked, "Jamila, what do you want to do?" She said I want to see the ocean one more time and she was able to stand up from her wheelchair, shuffle forward grab the rail at the Santa Monica Pier and spend a few last moments with the ocean she loved. Later in life it was therapy for her.

But even kids that are hospitalized and dealing with the pain of their condition can receive some relief from that pain through water and that water can even be virtual water. There's a study at UCSF that shows that virtual ocean experiences using VR goggles helps reduce pain of children in intensive care. Even virtual water can help us mitigate pain and promote a path of healing. The research around the world on the health and well-being benefits of swimming is clear, that getting in the water, especially when gravity is taking its toll on us, is a tool that is underutilized and available to everyone. We just need to step in and prioritize it. Get in the water, move your body, and you reduce the chances of injury, you increase the chances of healing and recovery.

If you could put water in a pill, if you could put blue mind in a pill like this, it might look like a little blue and green pill, it would it would not have any side effects, it would promote health and healing and wellness and doctors would prescribe it all over the world. You can't put it in a pill, but you still can prescribe it. And that's beginning to happen. Health care practitioners and professionals have begun to prescribe water as medicine: as surf therapy; as fishing and paddling therapy; aquatic therapies.

It's becoming more and more common to hear that doctors, nurses and medical practitioners are encouraging their patients to get in the water, especially important for those who need it most. And it works best when we believe that it works. This idea of the placebo effect is powerful. Placebo means only that we are making the neurochemistry happen internally, rather than taking a medication externally. So, when we believe that something is working and we align our thoughts with that that potential, it works better and there's plenty of research that shows how that is true.

Now water also is a source of nostalgia later in life, and if we have formed memories of the water we love in our childhood, in the places we play, we can rely on those memories when it's harder to get to those places and they can produce feelings of wellness, feelings of joy, feelings of happiness and connection.

Now the last and least popular of the seven ages is death. Water and death have always gone together: The River Styx, various kinds of ceremonies involving rivers and water around the world, burials at sea. But also, memorialization that occur remembering lost loved ones at the edge of the water is increasingly common; families gather by the water to remember lost loved ones.

In my case when both of my fathers— my biological and adoptive fathers— passed away we celebrated their lives by the water. And I recall one moment standing up on a mountaintop with my mother, overlooking the lake in the community where my parents lived, and she smiled and it was the first time I had seen her smile since the passing of my dad. Something about being out there in nature and reflecting on the lake that they loved. That helped her with her grief.

Now there are memorial benches all over the world often facing waterways. Plaques are put on those benches that depict the name of the person who loved to sit there. So, going and visiting those places allows us to think about the people we miss and look out on the water. Water helps us to reconnect with our families, reconnect with each other and reconcile perhaps some of the differences that occur at the end of lives. So, reconnection and reconciliation are facilitated by being near and in the water with those we care about and those we love, even in the face of death.

Now, this is really not a new idea at all, that water can soothe our red minds. In fact, if you go back 3,000 years and read what King David wrote in the 23rd Psalm, he said that if things are really rough, if red mind is all around you, if you're walking through the valley of the shadow of death, find yourself a meadow by the water and sit down and relax. That's a paraphrase of an ancient passage, but 3,000 years ago there it was, that water is medicine for a bright red mind when things are bad. Find your calm by the water. Not a new idea at all.

Now the last piece of this conversation is the one about access. If all of this is true, if water is medicine for our bodies and our minds, if water is a path to mindfulness and relaxation, then we should all have access to it. And we often don't. And there are there are three main reasons why we may not have access. First is the physical barriers that separate us from the water. Second is the pollution that can preclude spending time in the water. And the third is the perception that may just be your mind telling you, or your culture telling you, that the water is not available to you.

So sometimes you go to the water and there are signs that say "No, you can't come here, go away." The gate may be closed. It may be locked. It may be private property and maybe after hours. Sometimes you arrive at a pool and you've missed the window of time to actually get in the pool. Sometimes the water quality is not sufficient to actually get into the water safely. And we see that around the world in different ways, whether it's the tap water being polluted or things like oil spills that can really take away the possibility of enjoying the ocean, enjoying the beach, after the water is polluted.

It can also be plastic pollution on the beach that will remove us from our blue mind. If you go to the beach to relax and to restore, but you spend your time cleaning up trash, you may come home satisfied that you contributed, but you will not have achieved the mindfulness benefits of spending time in and near the water. And research shows that is true: that the psychological benefits of time spent at the beach are reduced when there is pollution and trash in those places. We literally have a war on plastic under way right now to try to remove the plastic pollution from places where it shouldn't be.

Now there are perceptual barriers as well. Throughout our history people have been excluded from pools, from lakes, from beaches, from rivers because of the color of their skin, because of their race. And in many places, we've overcome that, but there's a great example in Carbondale, Illinois where my friend Harvey Welch who grew up there at a time when he wasn't allowed to swim in the pool and therefore didn't learn to swim. But as an 86-year-old he and his community have fought, worked, and opened the first public pool in Carbondale.

And when I first met Harvey he said, I did not become the man I could have become because I didn't have access to the water. And when he served in the Air Force, around the world, while his friends and colleagues swam, he waited it out and he said also I'm still angry about that. But he turned his anger into action and opened the Carbondale's public swimming pool.

In other parts of the world, young women are not allowed to surf because of their gender. And there are groups that are working to break down those perceptual barriers.

And even in places where the gate is open, where the water is clean, and where everybody is allowed to go enjoy it, we have this other problem, perceptual problem, which is people have their noses in their screens and they don't even notice that they're at the beach. They don't even notice that there's a whale swimming by or that there's just beauty surrounding them, because we are tethered to our devices. So, technology can take us right out of our blue minds.

I prefer that we replace sometimes those smartphones with baby sea turtles at the beach, leave the technology at home or in the glove box, and go out there and put a baby sea turtle in your hand and help it get into the ocean.

So, the summary here of these two parts of our conversation that water is life and it also makes our lives worth living. And when we undervalue water, in fact, when we undervalue anyone, anything, bad things happen. We lose what we love. We remember that water is the first medicine, our first medicine both for physical and mental health. And we need to remember to always include the emotional benefits of healthy waterways in our conversations, because water provides a universal tool for achieving mindfulness. All people, whether it's the water in your home, the water at a public pool, in a lake, a river, or an ocean, and that access to water should be for all people throughout all seven ages of our lives and that we need to have this conversation. We need to take this conversation forward and communicate it in our schools, in our in our meetings, in our organizations, and in our households.

So, let's take this conversation out of the bathroom, out of the aquariums, out of the lake house, and let's take it to the boardrooms, and let's take it to the state house and the White House and deliver this blue mind conversation to the people who need it most.

If you have ever received a blue marble as a as a token of gratitude, please pass it on to someone. Please pass these ideas along to someone that you think needs to understand their water better, who can really benefit from their water. Share your blue mind with those in your community and your family who need it most. Pass this message on because the water will help us be more mindful and being mindful will help us be unstoppable in the things we care about most in fixing what's broken here on this little water planet.

I want to end with a question and that is, what if? What if schools taught blue mindfulness? What if we learned about how water can boost our creativity, help us relax, and connect us to each other at every step of our education?

What if our medical system embraced blue mindfulness and we prescribed spending time near, in, on, and underwater? If we could share a blue mindfulness across all sectors of our society we would create a positive regenerative feedback loop that would connect us to ourselves, to each other, and to our little water planet.

MINDSIGHT: UNDERSTANDING YOUR INNER LIFE

LESSON 21

This lesson is about the mind and mindsight, which is the ability to see the mind. Strangely, the word "mind" is rarely defined in the many fields that explore it, such as psychiatry and philosophy of mind. But this lesson attempts to determine what the mind actually is and to use research to explore the nature of our mental lives.

EXPLORING THE MIND

One of the ways of exploring the mind is to say that it includes our feelings and thoughts, called subjective experience. It's the first facet of the mind, and it's profoundly important. It's present in relationships of all sorts, including parent-child relationships, friendships, and romantic relationships. In fact, it's present in every kind of relationship where two people are interacting in society.

The first facet of subjective experience is known by us because we have the second facet—consciousness, which can simply be defined as the quality of knowing. Consciousness plays a crucial role in our development—in how we help people grow through life, whether it's in the process of helping children grow in families or in the process of psychotherapy. Consciousness is needed for intentional change.

Another facet of the mind, which you may be experiencing at this moment, is information processing. As you're reading this text, you're using an extension of the body's experience to have cognition. Information processing doesn't necessarily involve consciousness; it can happen when you're sleeping or when you're focusing on one thing but your mind is processing something else. This is why information processing, or cognition, is said to have four E's to it.

Embodied. We experience this type of information processing not just in our head but throughout our whole body. There are processers of information in our head, of course, but there are also processors in our heart and even in our intestines.

Enacted. Our body and its movements, or its enactments, allow us to experience different ways that information flows.

Extended. Through books, computers, and phones, we can extend the information processing we do inside the body to outside the body.

Embedded. This is the way we culturally have shared meaning and symbols. For example, we have words that we use with each other, and linguistics embeds meaning in our relationships in our culture.

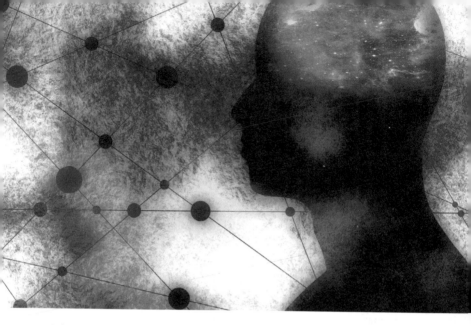

These three facets of the mind—subjective experience, consciousness, and information processing—are wonderful descriptions. But if someone asked what exactly a subjective experience is, or how consciousness emerges, or what exactly information is, these descriptions don't help us move to a level of considering, for example, where the mind is in all of that or what a healthy mind is. There is a fourth facet of the mind that helps us address these important questions.

ENERGY AND INFORMATION FLOW

Consider that the word "mind" for many people is the origin of the self. It is often thought of as coming from the brain. The field of modern psychology has based a lot of research on the notion that whatever we think the mind is, it is roughly equal to brain fire, and the mind is what the brain does from that perspective.

Subjective experience is not the same as brain firing, even if the mind is totally dependent on the brain. What exactly is this mind that has subjective experience that isn't exactly the same as the brain, even if it's dependent on brain activity?

What are subjective experience and consciousness? What are they arising from? What is information processing? And why is it that various fields, such as psychiatry and neuroscience, emphasize the head brain but other fields, such as sociology and linguistics, emphasize the relational aspect of mind? What could be both within your brain and also within your relationships with other people and the larger culture in which you live?

What is the essence of the substance that happens inside your brain in your head, maybe even throughout your whole body, but that also happens between you and your friends and family? That essence is something that completely changes how we understand the first three facets of the mind and helps us define a fourth facet that takes us to the next level of asking, What is the mind and what is a healthy mind?

That substance is energy and information. And because energy and information changes, or flows, we can use the phrase "energy and information flow." But where is this energy and information flow?

The location of the system of the mind is both within your skin-encased body, including the skull-encased brain, and it's between what goes on inside your body and what happens between your body and other people. Energy is shared in our relationships with other people, and even with the planet as a whole.

Energy is streaming through the body. And if we focused on the brain, we could see that energy is what the brain is all about. It is a transformational organ of energy and information flow.

But if this is the system from which the mind emerges, what actually is the mind? It could be subjective experience, consciousness, and information processing. Maybe those processes are simply emerging from energy and information flow.

But there's a fourth facet of the mind that not only helps us answer the question of what the mind might be—something about energy and information flow—but also asks the question, What is a healthy mind?

This system of energy and information flow that goes within you and between you has several qualities that from a mathematical perspective meet the criteria for a complex system: being open, or influenced from outside of itself; capable of being chaotic, which roughly means random in what's going on; and nonlinear, which means that when something small happens, large and difficult-to-predict results unfold.

If a system is a nonlinear, capable, open system, then in mathematical terms it is a complex system. And in this complex system in our universe, mathematics shows it has emergent properties, which means the stuff of the system is interacting with itself and giving rise to something that is more than just its elements. In other words, the whole is greater than the sum of its parts.

Maybe subjective experience, consciousness, and information processing are simply emergent properties of a complex system of inner and outer energy and information flow. And that could be, but a second aspect of complex systems is that they have one particular emergent property called self-organization, which illuminates many properties of the human mind.

It's a proven outcome of complex systems that they have emerging from them a self-organizing regulatory process that regulates the very essence from which the system then continues to arise.

SELF-ORGANIZATION AND INTEGRATION

Self-organization is the fourth facet of the mind. And with that, we now have a definition of "mind": An aspect of the mind can be defined as the embodied, relational, emergent, self-organizing process that is regulating energy and information flow.

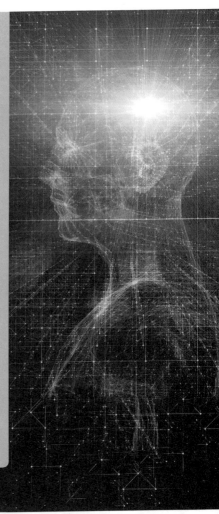

Embodied means that this energy and information flow is not limited by the hard case of the skull. To make the mind—that is, this self-organizing aspect of the mind—reside only in the head makes no sense. And many researchers concur that looking deeply at the whole body is a natural way to understand the mind and not limit it to just the head.

Relational means that energy and information flow happens between two people. In that view, an idea is a piece of information that is being shared between one body and another.

Emergent, a deeply scientific term that comes from mathematics, suggests that the mind is an emergent phenomenon, a property of energy and information flow that is embodied and relational.

Beyond just the possibility of the other three facets, this fourth one actually is one particular property, called self-organization, which is the self-organizing process that regulates the flow of energy and information.

From this definition, we can ask what optimal self-organization looks like, how we develop it, and what happens when we repair it. And does that give us any insight into the mind?

Optimal self-organization is predicted by the mathematics of complex systems when the system is differentiating aspects of itself and then linking them together. The linking of differentiated parts of a complex system is called integration.

When integration is occurring, the system moves with harmony. It has five qualities, which spell the acronym FACES: flexible, adaptive, coherent, energized, and stable.

Integration can explain almost all the listed symptoms of the various syndromes of mental disorders in the American Psychiatric Association's *Diagnostic and Statistical Manual of Mental Disorders.* In fact, we can reinterpret every one of the syndromes as chaos and/or rigidity. For example, there is the chaos of mania and the rigidity of depression.

What support do we have for the mind having this fourth facet that we've defined as a self-organizing, emergent process? Every study done of the brains of individuals with various psychiatric conditions so far, without exception, has found impaired integration in the brain. In various disorders, the structures of the brain are not well developed.

A new set of studies called the Human Connectome Project show how the differentiated areas in the brain are linked. So far, major psychiatric disorders also have impairments in the connectome, the map of neural connections in the brain.

In the practice of mindfulness, you go from states of chaos and rigidity to states of harmony. Brain studies show that areas of the brain that are integrative grow and the connectome becomes more interconnected. Therefore, it's reasonable to state that a practice like mindfulness or mindful awareness training or any reflective practice that integrates your mind is also integrating the brain.

In studies of the connectome, when researchers analyze every measure of mental well-being and try to determine the brain feature that goes along with it, one brain feature has been found to predict well-being in every measure that researchers could assess. That is how integrated our brain is.

MINDSIGHT:
UNDERSTANDING YOUR INNER LIFE

[Introduction by Shauna Shapiro]

Dr. Dan Siegel is a clinical professor of psychiatry at the UCLA School of Medicine and the founding co-director of the Mindful Awareness Research Center at UCLA. He's also the executive director of the Mindsight Institute, which teaches individuals, families, and communities about the interface between human relationships and basic biological processes. Dan Siegel is one of the great integrationist thinkers of our time and I'm delighted he's joining us on this journey into mindfulness.

[End of introduction]

It's an honor to speak to you about something very close to your life experience, which is the mind and how we see the mind, how we have what I call mindsight. Now you may think it's strange, but the word mind actually is rarely defined in the many fields that explore the mind, like my own field in psychiatry or in my training in psychology. Even fields like the philosophy of mind say we shouldn't define the mind. But what you're about to experience is actually an effort to say what the mind is and to use research to explore the nature of our mental lives.

So, what is this thing that we have, a mind, and yet we rarely define it? One of the ways of exploring the mind is to say that it includes our feelings and our thoughts. So, we're not using the word mind to distinguish it from, let's say, what your heart is doing. So, the mind includes the first facet which is called subjective experience.

So, when I was in medical school often the professors would rarely focus on the subjective experience, the felt sense of life of their patients. They would rarely even focus on the subjective experience of their students. And so, this experience for me as a medical student was very strange, because I had learned in college that when you focus on the subjective experience of another person, and this was through a suicide prevention service I was trained to work on, you could actually make the difference between life and death. And so, subjective experience, our first facet of the mind, is extremely important.

In fact, when we look at relationships of all sorts, not just between someone in a crisis calling a suicide prevention service caller, reaching out to them and saying, "Hey, I need help," and the listener focuses on that subjective experience with what we can say is empathy and that saves the person's life. We also see it in parent-child relationships, in friendships, in romance, in every kind of relationship where we're looking at two people getting along at work and school and society, we see that subjective experience is profoundly important.

The first facet of subjective experience is known by us because we have the second facet and this is called consciousness. Consciousness can simply be defined as the quality of knowing. So, if I say hello to you, you know I said hello, but you also have the knowns, so you have the word hello. Now this may sound very simple that consciousness is knowing and the knowns, but remarkably it's rarely clarified how consciousness plays a crucial role in our development, in how we help people grow through life, whether it's in school and the process of helping children grow in families or even in the process of psychotherapy.

So, consciousness is needed for intentional change. That's our second facet of the mind, but another aspect of the mind that you may be experiencing right at this very moment is that we have what's called information processing.

So, in whatever recording form you're hearing me or seeing me you're actually using an extension of the body's experience and even that brain in the head's experience and we have this cognition or information processing, the third facet of the mind.

Now, information processing does not have to be in consciousness. Of course, right now, you and I are connecting with your conscious mind. But in all sorts of ways we have information processing that doesn't necessarily involve consciousness. And this way that information flows through us can happen when we're sleeping. It can happen even when you're focusing on one thing, but your mind is processing something else. And so, information processing is said to have four "E's" to it.

The first E is that it can be fully embodied and you experience this information processing, not just in your head, but throughout your whole body. We actually have processers of information, of course in our head, but also in our heart and even in our intestines. We have at least three brains.

You also have information processing that's enacted and this enactment is something that you may be familiar with but never had recognized before when you say something like, I'm understanding something, standing under or I'm grasping something. And in these many ways what we have then is that your body and its movements, its enactments, actually allows us to experience different ways that information flows.

A third E is that we have extended information processing and what this means is that you have information processing that goes through books, it goes through computers, it's on your phone these days, and we extend what we do with inside the body out of the body. And so, that's called extended cognition or extended information processing.

And then finally, we have something that we rarely think about, but that is embedded cognition and that is the way culturally we have shared meaning and symbols. For example, we have words that we use with each other and linguistics embeds meaning in our relationships in a culture.

So, in all these ways we have information processing that can be embodied, enacted, extended and embedded. Now those three facets are wonderful descriptions and they're readily available many different disciplines. But while their descriptions, if I said to you, what exactly is subjective experience all about or how does consciousness emerge or what exactly is information? These descriptions don't help us move to a level of saying something, for example, like where's the mind in all of that or what is a healthy mind?

So, the fourth facet of mind I'm going to present to you now helps us actually address those important questions. And what I'm asking to do is to consider that the word mind, which for many people is the origin of the self, is often thought of as actually coming from your head, coming from the brain in your head. Now you may say, "Well, Dan, that is so obvious, why would you even question it?" After all Hippocrates said this 2,500 years ago and modern medicine has assumed it to be true? And the field of modern psychology is based a lot of research on that notion that whatever we think the mind is it's somehow is roughly equal to brain firing. The mind is what the brain does from that perspective.

Now even if you take that view of mind being totally dependent on the brain, what I want to suggest to you is that subjective experience is not the same as brain firing, even if it's totally dependent on it. And the reason I'm saying this is that there are a number of studies that show if you're in a crisis let's say, or you're having a medical problem, like even a common cold, and you go to your medical doctor, research shows that a physician who focuses on your subjective experience and makes a comment about it, like if you were a student class with a cold and they said, "Oh, this must feel so frustrating for you to have a cold when you're studying for exams. Here do A, B, and C," versus a physician who tells you to do A, B, and C, but never makes the empathic comment, and empathic comment meaning they've felt in empathy—path is to feel, em is in— they felt inside you, they've made this empathic comment identifying your subjective experience and those people who get a subjective comment made about their inner experience actually get over their cold a day sooner and their immune system functions in a more robust way. So, it's a fundamental part of a healthy relationship, even a healing one, when you come with a common cold to have someone identify your subjective experience.

And so, we can ask the question, what exactly is this mind that has subjective experience that isn't exactly the same as the brain even if it's dependent on brain activity? So, if you were to go to a physician who said, "Oh, I think the amygdala part of your brain is a little active right now with the frustration you might be feeling," and only identified the brain parts and not the feeling tone of your experience it likely wouldn't have the same effect. So, what is subjective experience in consciousness? What are they arising from? What is information processing? And why is it that the various fields for example, like psychiatry and psychology and neuroscience, emphasize the head brain, but other fields, like anthropology and sociology and linguistics, actually emphasize the relational aspect of mind? The question then arises, what could be both within your brain and also within your relationships with other people and the larger culture in which you live?

Now this exercise I'm going to ask you to do is difficult, but it begins by saying what would be the essence of the thing, the substance, the stuff, the process, that was happening inside your brain, in your head, maybe even throughout your whole body, but also happening right now between you and me, between you and your friends and family? And what I want to suggest to you is that essence, while it's rarely talked about, is something that changes completely how we come to understand the first three facets of the mind, but also help us define a fourth facet that takes us to the next level of asking, what is the mind and what is a healthy mind? That substance, I'll suggest to you, is energy and information and because energy and information changes it flows. We have a phrase we can use energy and information flow. For many scientists, energy is the fundamental essence of the universe. Other scientists actually think information is. Either way what we see is that a pattern of energy, like the sound you're hearing from my voice right now, embeds a symbolic value in it. So, if I say the word ocean, the phrase ocean, that word the sound ocean, it isn't just the sound, it is standing for something other than the sound, it's standing for the huge body of water that rests right outside where I'm sitting right now.

Now that ocean as a symbol we call energy in formation. So, we can just simply call it information. And because it changes, I can say ocean and waves and I can say tides and all sorts of related informational processes that come up.

You can see that there is information processing. Ultimately then, for our third facet of the mind information processing is a flow of patterns of energy. It can be enacted, embodied, extended, and embedded and we can start to understand that the relational side and the embodied side share energy flow. Sometimes if I go "blah-blah-blah" that's just pure energy. That sound pattern of "blah-blah-blah" has no symbolic value and so it's just pure energy. It's changing so we call it flow and it's a form of energy, in this case sound, and so we can say that we also have a kind of conduit like a hose where energy isn't in a formation symbolizing something, it's just pure flowing of energy. But we also have energy that's constructed into a symbol like ocean or tide or moon. Those constructed patterns of energy we're simply going to call information. When we combine it all together we have this phrase energy and information flow.

Now, the next part of our response to this question, what in the world is this stuff of the mind? We say, where is this energy information flow? And this is probably the most challenging aspect of our discussion so far. The location of the system of mind is actually both within your skin encased body, including the skull encased head brain, and it's between what goes on inside your body and what happens between your body and other people and even your body and the planet as a whole.

What could be happening between yourself and the planet or people? Energy flow. Energy is shared in our relationships with other people on the planet. And energy is actually streaming through the body. And if we focus on the brain right now we could see that energy is actually what the brain is all about. It is a transformational organ of energy and information flow. So, we've answered our question: What could be both within and between energy and information flow?

But if that's the system from which the mind emerges, what actually is the mind? What could it be? Well, we've already said subjective experience, consciousness, information processing. So, would we just leave it at that and say maybe those processes of having subjective felt texture of life, having consciousness, even having information processing like thoughts and memories, maybe that is just simply emerging from energy and information flow? That could be. But there's a fourth facet of mind that helps us take the question of not only what the mind might be, something about energy and information flow, but asking the question, what is a healthy mind? And that is this: The system of energy and information flow, that goes within you and between you, has several qualities that in a mathematical point of view of looking at systems meets the criteria for what's called a complex system.

Now this is not going to get super complex, it's actually quite simple, amazingly. But when you have a system that has the three qualities of being open influences from outside of itself and think about your own life. Do you feel that stuff from outside of what you might call you affects you? If so, you are part of an open system. The second criteria is: Are you as a system capable of being chaotic, which roughly means random in what's going on? And if you feel your chaos capable then you're both an open and a chaos capable system. And the third criteria is if you are what's called nonlinear. Now that term simply means something happens, that say, in the morning, a small thing that happens, your bicycle tire is flat, and because of that small thing, large and very difficult to predict results unfold.

That means you are a nonlinear system.

If you're a nonlinear, chaos capable, open system then in mathematical terms you are a complex system. And in this complex system, in our universe, mathematics shows that you have what are called emergent properties.

Emergent properties sound like it's a fancy name, but it actually just means the stuff of the system is interacting with itself and giving rise to something that is more than just its elements. It's how the whole is greater than the sum of its parts. That's called emergence.

Maybe subjective experience, consciousness, and information processing are simply emergent properties of a complex system of inner and inter energy and information flow. And that could be. But a second aspect of complex systems is that they have one particular emergent property and that is called self-organization. And self-organization, a math term, actually illuminates many properties of the human mind and what self-organization is, basically, a system as an emergent process of unfolding interacts with its elements so the energy and information flow is unfolding. It then turns back and regulates its own becoming.

Now this sounds completely ridiculous. It sounds counter-intuitive, but it's a proven outcome of complex systems. They have emerging from them a self-organizing regulatory process that regulates the very essence from which it then continues to arise.

Self-organization, I'm going to suggest to you, may be our fourth facet of the mind. Now if this is true we would then have beyond a description of subjective experience, consciousness, and information processing now a definition. The definition of mind I'm going to offer to you that we use in our mindsight approach is the following: An aspect of the mind can be defined as the embodied and relational, emergent, self-organizing process that is regulating energy and information flow. Now let's take that definition, step by step, so we can really embrace it and see what its implications are.

Embodied means that this energy flow is not limited to the skull, because after all, energy and information flow is not limited by the hard case of the skull. So, to make the mind, at least this self-organizing aspect of the mind, only in the head, makes no sense. And many researchers, like Antonio Damasio, would concur that looking deeply at the whole body is a natural way to understand mind and not limit it to just the head. So, we talk about the embodied aspect of this definition.

The second part of the definition is relational. What this means is that energy and information flow is happening right now between you and me. And as Oliver Wendell Holmes once said, "A mind stretched to a new idea does not return to its original dimension." Now in that view, an idea is a piece of information and we are sharing it now between this body and your body. That's what we mean by relational. The mind happens between as much as within.

So, we have embodied in relational, we have the next term of our definition emergent. Now it sounds like a soft term, but it's a really, really deeply scientific term that comes from mathematics and what we're suggesting is that the mind is an emergent phenomena, a property of energy and information flow, that's embodied and relational, and beyond just the possibility of the other three facets are emergent properties, we're saying this fourth one actually is one particular property and that's called self-organization; the self-organizing process that regulates the flow of energy and information.

Now with this definition we can now say, okay, we've offered a definition of mind, who cares? The reason to care is this: From that definition, you can say, what does optimal self-organization look like? How do you develop it? What happens when you repair it? Does that give us any insight into the mind? And here's where the absolutely fabulous set of implications can predict research outcomes.

Here is how it looks. Optimal self-organization is predicted by the mathematics of complex systems when the system is differentiating aspects of itself and then linking them together. We're just going to use a term integration and define it very clearly as the linking of differentiated parts of a complex system. Now, when that is occurring, when integration is occurring, the system moves with harmony. It has five qualities which spell the acronym FACES: It's flexible, F; it's adaptive A; it's coherent, C, which really means resilient over time; in mathematical terms, it's energized, E, which means having a sense of vitality; and it's stable, S. This FACES flow, if you can picture a river, is like a central flow of harmony when integration is arising.

If you block integration, blocking differentiation or linkage or both, you then move the system to two banks outside of the river; one bank is the bank of chaos, the other bank the bank of rigidity. Now this map of a river of integration actually can explain almost all the listed symptoms of the various syndromes of mental disorders in the book the *Diagnostic and Statistical Manual of Mental Disorders*. So, you can reinterpret that as symptoms that are all either chaos, rigidity, or both.

For example, in post-traumatic states, we have chaotic symptoms of being flooded with emotions or memories, or we have rigid ones of removing yourself from social interaction or avoiding things like things that remind you of your trauma. Or in a disorder called manic-depressive illness, we have the chaos of mania and the rigidity of depression. On and on, you can go through every one of the syndromes and reinterpret it as the chaos and rigidity that, what I'm going to suggest to you, comes from impaired integration.

Well, what support do we have for the mind having this fourth facet that we've defined as a self-organizing emergent process? Well, what we have is, number one, every study done so far of the brains of individuals with various psychiatric conditions, so far without exception, has found impaired integration in the brain. And you can see this if you imagine in a hand model of the brain, just imagine putting your thumb in the middle of your palm, and folding your fingers over the top. (My daughter says don't call this a handy model of the brain, so please don't tell her, but it's a useful model.) And it goes like this, where if you lift-up your fingers and lift-up your thumb, the palm represents the deepest part of the brain called the brain stem. This brain stem is about 300 million years old. On top of it if you put your thumb back over the limbic area, and this limbic area is about 200 million years old.

And then, an even newer part of the brain is the cortex. If you put your fingers over the top, this cortex helps us do all sorts of things, but most importantly it makes maps of things like imagining the future or deciding to take a course on the mind or mindfulness and this part of the brain, this higher part with your fingers folded over, actually plays an important role in integrating the differentiated areas. So, you have the area behind your forehead that plays a major integrative role, connecting various parts to each other. You lift-up your fingers, for example, the limbic area also has a very integrative area called the hippocampus. And if you look at the left and right side of this brain, you have in your hand model, if you can picture fibers linking the differentiated left to the differentiated right, that's called the corpus callosum.

So, one thing to say, for example, is in various disorders, these structures I just mentioned— the cortical prefrontal cortex, the limbic areas, hippocampus, and the corpus callosum—are not well developed. The linking fibers are not functionally and structurally working. And there's a new set of studies called the connectome which show how the differentiated areas, and not just these big cities linked by big highways, but how little towns in the brain essentially are linked by little roads, country roads. We can now study that and that's called the connectome. So, so far, major psychiatric disorders have impairments in the connectome as well.

Now it may not be surprising to you, if you've ever been doing the practice of mindfulness, to know that you go from states of chaos and rigidity to actually states of harmony with the practice. Well, brain studies show that areas of the brain that are integrative grow. Which ones? The corpus callosum linking the left and the right; the hippocampus in your limbic region, linking widely separate areas to each other; the prefrontal cortex and the connectome becomes more interconnected.

So, it's reasonable to state that a practice like mindfulness or mindful awareness training or any reflective practice that I think integrates your mind actually is also integrating the brain. Studies of the connectome even suggest if you look at every measure of mental wellbeing and try to assess what's the brain feature that goes along with it, one brain feature was found to predict wellbeing in every measure they could assess and that was how integrated your brain is.

So, what we're going to do in our next section is to take these four facets of the mind and ask the question, if we've defined the mind and even define mental health as integration, what can you do to create more integration in your life? And fortunately, we know enough from science to say, in a practical way, what you can do to integrate your mind and likely grow these integrative fibers in the brain, which are the basis of optimal regulation in your life. And that we will do next.

THE WHEEL OF AWARENESS: A MODEL FOR WELL-BEING
LESSON 22

Mindsight, the ability to see the mind, has three components: insight into your inner life, empathy for the inner life of someone else, and integration. We've defined integration as things being differentiated, or allowed to be special and unique, and then becoming linked together, or connected. The important aspect of integration is that it maintains the differences yet creates the linkages to one another. And integration creates a harmonious flow of the FACES—flexible, adaptive, coherent, energized, and stable—which we're defining as mental health. What can you do to create more integration, and therefore more well-being, in your life?

HOW TO CULTIVATE INTEGRATION

We know enough from science and with this framework of the mind to determine what you need to do to cultivate integration. It builds on insights and empathy—the first two parts of mindsight—and teaches you how to create the third part of mindsight, which is to promote integration in your life.

One scientific notion is that consciousness is needed for intentional change. To intentionally create more well-being in your life, you want to use the experience of being aware.

Another scientific notion is that integration is health. That's what we're suggesting comes from seeing the mind as a self-organizing process.

If integration is health and consciousness is needed for any change, what would happen if we integrated consciousness?

Picture a wheel with an outer circle, which is the rim, and an inner circle, which is the hub, and a singular spoke connecting the central hub to the outer rim. Now picture your rim and divide it into four sections, each of which represents the knowns of your life.

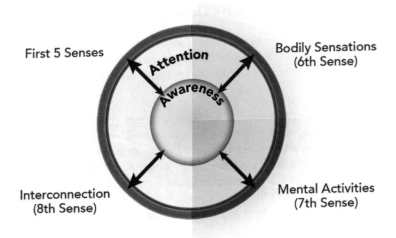

First 5 Senses

Attention

Awareness

Bodily Sensations
(6th Sense)

Interconnection
(8th Sense)

Mental Activities
(7th Sense)

On the first segment, we place the first five senses, which basically involves bringing energy in from the outside world through sound for hearing, light for seeing, chemical energy for smelling and tasting, and tactile energy for touch.

We then move the spoke over from the first segment to the second segment of the rim, which represents the energy patterns from the inside of the body. This is known in science as the sixth sense—interoception—which means perception of the interior. For example, it is the sensations of muscles and bones and the feelings of each of your organs, which you can review one by one and differentiate each from the other.

We then move the spoke over to the third segment of the rim. Imagine what else can be unknown in your conscious experience, such as thoughts, feelings, and memories. These are all considered mental activities, and they can be considered out seventh sense.

We then move the spoke over to the fourth and final segment of the rim. This is the segment that represents our sense of interconnection—our sense of relationship with other people, nature, and the world around us. This can be considered our eighth sense.

HOW TO USE THE WHEEL OF AWARENESS

There are three aspects to the wheel of awareness: focused attention, open awareness, and kind intention or compassionate care. These three pillars of mind training have been identified by researchers as cultivating well-being in many ways.

When you have this three-pillar mind training, you cultivate a more integrated brain, which it turns out is necessary for having a nimble, resilient brain—a brain that regulates with more efficacy attention, mood, emotion, thought, memory, behavior, relationships with others, and morality. All of these functions are part of self-regulation, or executive function, and they all come from integrative fibers in the brain, many of which have been shown in preliminary studies to grow after mind training.

By doing the wheel-of-awareness practice, you get in a single practice the three pillars of training focused attention in the mind. In the first segment of the rim, you're focusing on the energy flow coming from the outside world. Moving over to the second segment, you're focusing attention one by one on the different signals of the body.

Then, you move the spoke of attention over to the third segment, shifting from building the first pillar of mind training—focused attention—to developing open awareness. With focused attention, you're focusing on something and then get distracted and then return to your focus again, and so on, like building up a muscle.

With open awareness, you're sitting in the hub of being aware and inviting anything to come in—in this case, from the third segment of mental activities, our seventh sense. You're distinguishing the hub of knowing from the knowns. This is very different from choosing what you're paying attention to and thus makes a clear distinction between being in the hub versus being on the rim.

Then, after open awareness, we move the spoke around to the fourth and final segment, where we cultivate an awareness of our interconnections with other people, such as our family and friends, people in our neighborhood, and people with whom we work.

Based on a study conducted in Richard Davidson's neuroscience lab, in which verbal statements of care and kindness produced positive changes in the brain and even in behavior, the third pillar of the mind, kind intention or compassionate training, was incorporated into the wheel practice.

> In many people, the hub becomes a very special place of simply being aware.

This mind-training pillar can be cultivated, like all of the other pillars, with repeated practice. This brings up a principle of neuroscience: Where attention goes, neural firing flows and neural connection grows. In other words, where you aim your attention—that's the spoke of your wheel—neural firing gets the brain to fire in particular patterns, and with repeated firing, a stronger, more interconnected brain results.

Studies suggest that with this kind of training, you're growing changes in the molecular basis of health and enhancing your physiology.

There is one more step in the wheel practice that is often done as you move along the practice and get used to the wheel: You explore the hub itself by imagining bending the spoke around, or leaving the spoke in the hub, or retracting the spoke—or just being in the hub—and in this awareness of awareness, amazing things happen.

By doing the wheel-of-awareness practice on a regular basis, you can cultivate an integrated state so that you create the traits of integration—the FACES flow. Do this practice daily for a minimum of 12 minutes a day, but typically anywhere from 20 to 30 minutes a day, depending on how you do it.

With practice, you intentionally create a state, and when that state is repeatedly created, you make changes in the structure and function of the brain so that your baseline way of being becomes a trait. And in this way, without effort, you develop the integrative capacities of the FACES: flexibility, adaptability, coherence, energy, and stability.

Research of thousands of people from all around the world has shown that when people go into the hub, they have a universal set of experiences. They feel a spaciousness, an odd sensation of things being empty and full, a sense of tranquility, a sense of God, a sense of love and peace and joy, a feeling of gratitude, a feeling of interconnection.

If our proposal that the mind is an emergent property of energy is accurate, then it's natural from both a scientific and a practical perspective to ask, What exactly is energy? If the brain is really an organ that's allowing energy to flow through it, then what actually is energy?

Physicists say that energy is the movement from possibility to actuality. Based on this notion, we could map out the research findings from people across the globe with what the hub may actually be in energy terms and propose that energy is a movement from possibility to actuality.

What may be going on is that when we have a thought or an emotion or a memory, it's actually an actualization of all the possible thoughts we could have.

Picture a graph where the top of the graph has a 100 percent line on the vertical *y*-axis. That will be called a peak.

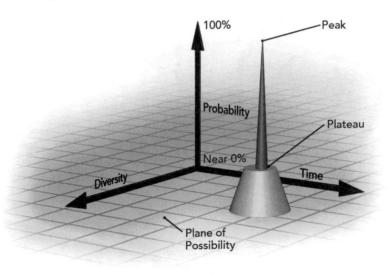

You add a thought, such as "I'm hungry for dinner." That thought is a peak. As you come down below the peak, which is 100 percent, maybe you want to only think about restaurants you're going to choose and maybe you only want a certain kind of food. Maybe there's only 10 of those restaurants nearby. When you drop down to the choice of 10, that is a plateau. When you go to the actual restaurant, that's a peak.

But let's say before you ever got to that plateau or peak you were in what quantum physics calls the sea of potential, a quantum vacuum. It's the mathematical space where all possible things rest. In that space, probability is called near zero, so it's very uncertain, but possibility is maximal.

What this means from a mathematical point of view—that energy emerges from this sea of potential, the bottom of our y-axis, near-zero-possibility place—is that when people say "I was in a place that was empty and full at the same time" and "I felt interconnected," what may be going on is that awareness of the hub comes from what we can call the plane of possibility.

This graph, made three dimensional, turns into a plane, and when you look at this plane, it maps out on exactly what people have been describing all around the planet about what the hub feels like.

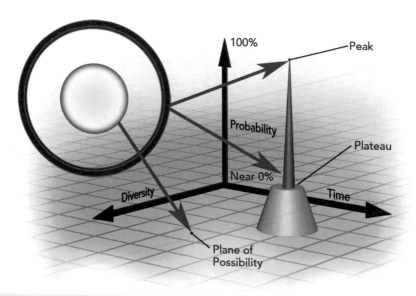

If this is true, then we have an entire model for understanding what your mental life is and that integrating your mind would mean learning to access this plane of possibility, where not only awareness arises, but you can put a pause between the different plateaus and peaks that might arise so that you can think about what to do before you have an action.

You also have the experience where you drop into the plane of pure awareness. You come to realize how deeply interconnected we all are.

Finally, if this proposal is true, it means that when we learn to do the wheel-of-awareness practice and cultivate a differentiation of the hub from the rim, we're not only enhancing our experience of being aware, but we're actually dropping into the source of other options. So, instead of getting lost in the plateaus or peaks that could be imprisoning us, such as anxiety, depression, and post-traumatic states, when you do the wheel-of-awareness practice, the reason it may work so well for so many people is that you're dropping into this plane of possibility where other options rest. And then you are free.

And that is how the wheel of awareness can cultivate integration of consciousness in your life and set the stage for a healthier, more enriched life for you and everyone that you relate to.

THE WHEEL OF AWARENESS:
A MODEL FOR WELL-BEING

We've looked at the four facets of mind: of subjective experience, consciousness, information processing, and self-organization. And we've come to not only this view of what the mind is, but actually a proposal about what a healthy mind is, and a healthy mind then would be a mind that's optimizing self-organization by creating integration. Where? Within your body, including your head brain, but also within your relationships with other people and the planet.

Now integration we've defined as things being different or differentiated or allowed to be special and unique and then becoming linked together, to be connected. The important aspect of integration to keep in mind is that integration is really more like a fruit salad than a smoothie. Integration is not the same as blending something up and just grinding it all together, it's homogenous. Instead it honors the differences, maintains the differences, and yet creates the linkages to one another. So, in a state for example, if you had different cities, you wouldn't need the different cities to become the same. They would just be linked by communication cables, by all sorts of highways, or bike ways, and you would be linking the differentiated cities in your state.

So, integration creates this harmonious flow of the FACES: flexible, adaptive, coherent, energized, and stable flow which we're defining as mental health. Now how can you create that in your life? Well, we said that mindsight is the ability to see the mind and it has three components. Mindsight has insight into your inner life. Empathy for the inner life of someone else and a third process called integration, which we're going to dive into deeply now.

When you ask the question, how do I create more well-being in my life? How can I take a course, let's say on mindful awareness, and learn how to create more well-being in my own journey through life? You want to have something very practical, that's science informed, and that can be something you can do on a regular basis and in many ways kind of like brushing your teeth which you do every day to keep dental hygiene going well. You can also have a regular practice, that's like mental hygiene, almost like mental floss where you're cleaning out some of the aspects of the way the mind functions.

Now fortunately we know enough now from science and now with this framework of the mind to actually say what you need to do to cultivate integration. And it builds on insights and empathy. these first two parts of mindsight and teaches you how to create the third part of mindsight, which is to promote integration in your life.

So, let me walk you through this very practical way of cultivating integration. The first notion is that consciousness is needed for intentional change. So, if you say well I want to intentionally create more wellbeing in my life, what can I do? Well, that's consciousness, you want to use the experience of being aware and that which you're aware of.

And the second scientific notion is that integration is health. That's what we're suggesting comes from seeing the mind as a self-organizing process. Well, what happened with me was, as a treating physician, as a psychiatrist, I had people coming to me with all sorts of difficulties, facing traumas from the past, dealing with challenges in the present, having anxiety or various degrees of depression. And for my work with them I wanted to help them reduce that chaos and rigidity of their mental suffering by offering them some way to integrate their lives.

In our office, there is a table and the table has a glass center and an outer wooden rim. So, I would bring my patients up from the couch or the chair and say, "Look, if integration is health and consciousness is needed for a change, what would happen if we integrated consciousness?" Now they looked at me, maybe like you're looking at me now, like going, "What? What are you talking about?"

And I'd say, "Well, let's try this. If consciousness is the experience of knowing and it's also the knowns, what if we metaphorically place around this table, in the hub the knowing, and on the rim the knowns? And they would go, "Okay, then what?" I say, well, then what is we're going to take this spoke which looked like a part of the table holding the table up a singular spoke and move it around the rim, so we differentiate the different knowns from each other and from the hub itself and then link them to each other. Well, what can be on the knowns on this rim of …no one wanted to call it a table of awareness, so we call it a wheel, a wheel of awareness? What can be on that rim? Well, picture a wheel with an outer circle, that's the rim; an inner circle, that's the hub; and a singular spoke connecting the central hub to the outer rim.

Now picture your rim and divide it into four sections and each of these sections represents the knowns of your life. On the first segment, we place the first five senses, which is basically bringing energy in from the outside world through sound for hearing, through light for seeing, through chemical energy for smelling and tasting, and tactile energy for touch—our first five senses.

We're then going to move the spoke over from the first segment to the second segment of the rim and this represents the energy patterns from the inside of the body, what in science we called the sixth sense, interoception, which means perception of the interior. This would be the sensations of muscles and bones; the feelings of your organs, for example, your heart, your lungs, your intestines. And after you review that, differentiating each from the other, one by one, we then move the spoke over to the third segment of the rim. And imagine what else can be unknown in your conscious experience. And you may be thinking, "Oh, thinking!" And yes, thinking would be one or feelings like emotions, memories, hopes, dreams, longings, desires, beliefs, attitudes. All of that, we're going to call mental activities. Of course, they're influenced by the body. Yes, but we'll put these distinct experiences of consciousness— our thoughts or feelings or memories— right there in the third segment of the rim.

We then move the spoke over to the fourth and final segment of the rim. And this is the segment that represents a sense that we rarely discuss, but is extremely important. It's our sense of interconnection, our sense of relationship with other people and nature in the world around us.

Now just to keep these numbers going, we have the first five senses on the first segment, bring in the outside world; we have in the second segment what's called the sixth sense, right? We have mental activities. We'll just keep the numbers going, call that our seventh sense. And we have this final segment of our relationality, we'll just call it our eighth sense. just to keep those numbers. We have eight senses.

Now when I was doing with my patients, this wheel, this wheel of awareness, they started getting better. They dealt with the stressors of everyday life in a more effective way. They stopped having the chaos and rigidity of various anxious conditions they had or depressive conditions they had, mild to moderate depression. They dealt with trauma in a much more effective way. This became so clear in the patients I was working with, I started teaching it to my students, who were therapists.

They in turn started finding their own lives improved. They started teaching it to their clients, their patients. they got better. So, then I started having the courage to say maybe I'll try teaching this in workshops. And because I'm trained as a scientist, I started recording all the proceedings which would include knowing doing the wheel of awareness as a practice, but then people taking the microphone and saying what the experience was like. And I did this systematically with 10,000 individuals. I accumulated that data and then what I did was ask the question—what in the world is going on? — because people all around this planet have very, very similar reactions to the wheel. Everyone's unique of course. But when you look for the patterns people describe very similar processes.

Then what I did was say, well could we turn to the basic statement we made earlier, that the mind might be an emergent property of energy and information flow. So, whether it's subjective experience and consciousness or naturally information processing or even self-organization, if that was true we would want to really turn not only to brain science, but also to the science of energy.

And so, what I did was I had the opportunity to work with the major field of science, physics and the physicists that work in that field, to dive deeply into what energy flow really means. And what I want to describe to you now is how the wheel of awareness practice can be used by you; what a possible view of the nature of consciousness itself might be; and then how you can use these findings to create wellbeing and enhanced health in your life.

So, let's begin with what the research tells us. For the wheel of awareness, it turns out that there are three aspects to this one practice, that in other ways of studying mindfulness and compassion training, were built into the wheel almost serendipitously or by accident, if you will. And those three pillars of mind training that researchers have shown are the foundation for training the mind with mindfulness and compassion that have been shown to promote wellbeing in various ways. Of course, we need more science and of course the details will be fascinating as they come out and likely we'll find even more pillar's than these three.

But the research is very clear that when you train the mind to focus attention, open awareness, and cultivate what I call kind intention or compassionate care; those are the three pillars that have been identified of mind training that cultivate wellbeing in the following ways. When you have this three-pillar mind training you cultivate a more integrated brain, which it turns out is necessary for having a nimble brain, a brain that's resilient, the brain that regulates with more efficacy, regulates attention, mood, emotion, thought, memory, behavior, relationships with others, and morality.

All of those functions are part of what's called self-regulation or executive functions. They all come from integrative fibers in the brain, many of which have been shown in preliminary studies to grow after mind training and include these three pillars. What other studies show, in an amazing way, and I sent the book *Aware* which describes the wheel of awareness and these three pillars out to the researchers themselves to get feedback, to make sure I wasn't overstating the case, and one of them even wrote to me and said, everything you're saying is accurate but you left one thing out. Has it gone to the printer yet? And I said no it hasn't, what did I leave out? She said, you also have to add that doing these practices slows the aging process.

So, let me go over with you what these findings are because I said to her, can I really say slows aging? She goes absolutely. This is Elissa Epel, the world's expert in aging. And Elissa Epel, with her colleague Elizabeth Blackburn wrote a beautiful book called *The Telomere Effect*, and Elizabeth Blackburn won the Nobel Prize for discovering the system in ourselves that governs the health of our chromosomes, these are the caps on the chromosomes called the telomeres and the enzyme that is optimized with this three-pillar practice is called telomerase, pronounced telomerase.

In addition to optimizing telomerase, you actually change the molecules that sit on top of genes called epigenetic regulators that control inflammation and so you actually can reduce inflammation with these three pillar practices. Mind training also reduces stress, reducing the hormone cortisol, the stress hormone. It optimizes cardiovascular risk factors like optimizing cholesterol levels, heart rate functioning, blood pressure. And you also improve the immune systems functioning, so you can fight off infectious illnesses with more efficacy.

Now if you told me these things 20 years ago, I would say you're dreaming. But now it's a dream come true that we have a wide array of studies that in various ways show when you train the mind you're actually improving the molecules of health.

Now ultimately you may say, "Okay how do I do it?" And I'm going to describe to you how to do the wheel of awareness because in this one singular practice you get the three pillars of training focused attention with your first two segments of the rim, focusing on the energy flow coming from the outside world in the first segment, moving over focusing attention one by one on the different signals of the body.

Then you move the spoke of attention over to the third segment and now you're going to shift from building the first pillar of mind training, that is focused attention, to actually developing open awareness. Now open awareness is different from focused attention. Focused attention is, let's say, we're working on sound. You focus on sound, you get distracted. you returned to the sound, you get distracted again, return to the sound; kind of like building up a muscle. You know when you're focused attention, your pull, you tighten the muscle, pull your arms together. When you are getting distracted, the muscles relaxing then you redirect attention, that's great, focused attention first pillar.

But open awareness is different. Now you're sitting in the hub of knowing, of being aware, and just inviting anything to come in. In this case from the third segment of mental activities, our seventh sense, and you're inviting anything in and you're distinguishing the hub of knowing from the knowns. And this is very different from saying let me choose what I'm paying attention to. And in a way, it makes a clear distinction between you being in the hub versus being on the rim.

And I'll just give you a little story here, just while we're on this one point. You know, we teach this actually to kids in kindergarten, not so much as a reflective practice that you might like to do, but just as a drawing. And let me tell you about Billy, who was kicked out of one kindergarten for beating up a child on the playground, was transferred to a new school, entered Mrs. Smith's kindergarten, and this is the story she tells me through an e-mail.

She says she taught Billy and the other students the wheel of awareness and on the next day Billy came to her during recess and said, "Mrs. Smith, Mrs. Smith, you need to give me a break. I'm out on the yard. And Joey took my blocks and are about to hit him. I'm lost on my rim. I got to get back to my hub." And she said in her follow up emails that he learned to use the wheel and the spaciousness of the hub of knowing even just as a drawing to give him the opportunity to put a pause between impulse and action and then to choose more useful responses with his peers.

Now we'll get into the hub in just a moment. But this finding for Billy has been found in many of the people I work with, whether it's in therapy or in workshop settings, where the hub becomes this very special place of what you could call simply being aware. So, it isn't just what you're aware of, but you're actually being aware and as one mother said to me after I taught this to her young son, her face looked wide, wide awake and she said, "Oh my gosh!" and I said, "What? What?" She said, "I never knew I was more than my thinking and my emotions." I said, "Oh, yeah." She goes, "Now I know I have the hub of awareness, so I don't have to be a slave to those emotions and thoughts." I said, "Right." And that was a clear articulation of the power of the wheel. It distinguishes components we have right there but that are rarely differentiated and linked.

So, what we do then after open awareness is we move this spoke around to the fourth and final segment where we cultivate an awareness of our interconnections with people sitting close to us, with our family and friends, of the people of our neighborhood, people with whom we work. And then after I presented this to Richie Davidson's neuroscience lab, where they study meditation and the brain, they said that they had just completed a study using verbal statements of care and kindness that showed they produced positive changes in the brain and even positive changes in behaviors, so I incorporated that also into the wheel practice, to develop kind intention or compassionate training, the third pillar of the mind.

Now, this mind training pillar can be cultivated, of course, like all of them can, with repeated practice. And it brings up a general statement we should just say, that the principle of neuroscience that we build on of neuroplasticity, that you're aware, of goes like this: Where attention goes, neural firing flows, and neural connection grows. Let me repeat that. Where attention goes, where you aim your attention, that's the spoke of your wheel; neural firing flows, it gets the brain to fire in particular patterns; and then with repeated firing, like Shauna's Shapiro said, what you practice gets stronger. This is the mechanism with which that happens. When you repeatedly fire neurons it actually activates the genes, gets all sorts of things that happen to grow a stronger, more interconnected brain. Where attention goes, neural firing flows, neural connection grows, and you do this with the three pillars training, each of them train a different aspect of the brain, but you're basically building a more integrated brain. Studies suggest you're growing all these changes of the molecular basis of health in your physiology is enhanced with this kind of training.

Now what I'd like to talk to you about is something that is absolutely thrilling, that I've been discussing with various scientists in various fields, which is we have one more step in the wheel practice and you can go to my web site and do this and you know try it out for yourself. So not in this moment when you're just hearing my voice, but in your own time, when you're taking time to sit quietly and just do a practice. Because when you do a regular practice and Amishi Jha has powerfully shown that probably the minimum would be about a dozen minutes a day.

When you do the wheel practice, which can take anywhere from 20 to 30 minutes, depending on how you do it, you can have your daily dozen, that's the minimum amount we need do, just like brushing your teeth every day, you want to try as best you can on a regular basis to cultivate this integrated state, so that you create the traits of integration. The faces flow.

So, let me repeat that: With a practice you intentionally create a state, and when that state is repeatedly created, you make changes in the structure and function of the brain so that your baseline way of being becomes a trait. So, that without effort you develop these integrative capacities of flexibility, adaptability, coherence, which is resilience, vitality, energy, and stability.

So now, one extra step we do and this is often done, you know, as you move along the practice you get used to the wheel, you do it, it's fine, you're getting all three pillars in one practice, you're of getting your daily dozen in, it's great, you don't have to buy any gadgets, it's just you working with your mind. Here's the extra step. We decided, my patients and I, to have them explore the hub itself by imagining bending the spoke around or leaving the spoke in the hub or just retracting the spoke or just being in the hub, so that they had a hub-in-hub experience and in this awareness of awareness amazing things started emerging.

I remember once doing this in Seattle at a workshop and when we did the practice, bent the spoke around, took a break and then people went in and took a little time off, came back after half an hour, one of the people who took the microphone came up to the microphone said you know, "I'm a software engineer, I'm 70 years old, I've never meditated before in my life, I've never been to therapy. My wife's a therapist and she took me to this workshop you're doing and I didn't want to come. But then I did the wheel."

And then he started speaking very slowly and says and then he bent the spoke around and something shifted in him and then we went and had a break, he went out in the park where we were doing the workshop. and he slowly said, "I saw basically said I saw gardener watering the roses and there were butterflies, there were birds," and then he gets very teary and he says, "I realize we're all interconnected. We're all interconnected." And you could hear a pin drop in the room and I share this with you because here's someone who has never meditated before, first time trying, a meditation simply means a mind training practice or a reflective practice where you look inward at the nature of the mind, the wheel of awareness that he did is simply an integration of consciousness practice. That's all it is.

For Billy, the five-year-old, it's just a drawing that integrates his idea about the mind, but here's what's happened now that I've done this with 10,000 people and now a lot more in the systematic study, here's what people say. When they go into the hub, they feel this spaciousness, this odd sensation of things being empty and full; this sense of tranquility. For some, a sense of God; for others, a sense of love and peace and joy; for others, still, a sense of awe.

This feeling of gratitude that emerges, this feeling of interconnection that arises, has happened over and over and over again, all around the planet that it made me ask the question: What in the world is the hub that has this universal set of experiences that people, after saying it's so hard to describe, ultimately describe?

So, what I'm going to offer to you is a proposal that's built on science, but will need future scientific studies to affirm its validity. But it's completely consistent with the reports of the 10,000-person study and the science of energy. And it goes like this. If our proposal that the mind is an emergent property of energy is accurate, then it's natural from a scientific point of view and a practical point of view, to say, well what exactly is energy? So yes, we can look at the brain and say the brain becomes more integrated and studies of consciousness and just being aware suggests integration in the brain is the basis of awareness for some reason. And that's what those studies generally show.

But what about energy. If the brain is really an organ that's allowing energy to flow through it, what actually is energy? And what physicists say energy is the movement from possibility to actuality. And when I heard this at a meeting we were gathered at where we're spending a week together, 150 physicists, mostly quantum physicists looking into questions about the nature of reality, and I would ask them, "What is energy? What is energy?" And they said this.

I realized you could map out that 10,000-person study findings with what the hub may actually be in energy terms.

And here's the proposal. Energy is a movement from possibility to actuality. And what may be going on is that when we have a thought or an emotion or a memory, it's actually what's called an actualization of all the possible thoughts you could have, you're now having this one thought. It's like if you pictured a graph where the top of the graph has a 100 percent line on this vertical Y-axis, that would be called a peak. You add a thought, "I'm hungry for dinner. I want to go to the beach." Whatever you thought would be, there it is, it is a peak.

As you come down below the peak, which is 100 percent, maybe you want to only think about different restaurants you're going to choose and maybe you only want a certain kind of food. Maybe there's just 10 of those restaurants nearby. So, that would be a plateau of one out of 10 restaurants you could choose to go to. So, when you go to the actual restaurant that's a peak, but when you drop down to the choice of the 10 that will be a plateau.

But let's say before you ever got to that plateau or peak you were in, what quantum physics call the sea of potential, a quantum vacuum. It's the mathematical space where all possible things rest. Now in that space probability is called near zero. So, it's very uncertain, but possibility is maximal.

Now, when you take this step by step, what I want to suggest to you is when you really analyze what that means from a mathematical point of view that energy emerges from this sea of potential the bottom of our y-axis, this near zero possibility place, then what that means is that when people say, "I was in a place which was empty and full at the same time. Time disappeared, it was expansive. I felt interconnected." I think what may be going on is that awareness of the hub actually comes from what we can call the plane of possibility.

This graph made three dimensional turns into a plane and when you look at this plane it maps out on exactly what people have been describing all around the planet about what the hub feels like. Now if this is true then we have an entire model for understanding what your mental life is and that integrating your mind would mean learning to access this plane of possibility, where not only for whatever reason awareness arises, but actually you can put a pause between the different plateaus and peaks that might arise so you can think about what to do before you have an action like Billy. You also had the experience, like that software engineer did, where you drop into the plane of pure awareness. You come to realize how deeply interconnected we all are.

And then finally if this proposal is true, what it means is that when we learn to do the wheel of awareness practice and cultivate a differentiation of the hub from the rim, we're not only enhancing our experience of being aware, we're actually dropping into the source of other options.

So instead of being lost, let's say and plateaus or peaks that could be imprisoning us, like anxiety, depression, post-traumatic states, instead of getting lost in those, imprisoned by them, when you do the wheel of awareness practice the reason it may be working so well is that you're actually dropping into this plane of possibility where other options rest. Then you are free. And that is how the wheel of awareness can cultivate integration of consciousness in your life and set the stage for a healthier more enriched life for you and everyone that you relate to.

Thank you so much for being with me on this journey into integration.

IMAGE CREDITS